THE WORLD OF FLOWERS

Edited by
DR HERBERT REISIGL

A Studio Book
The Viking Press · New York

THE FRONTISPIECE SHOWS THE MYRTACEA 'OHIA LEHUA' (METROSIDEROS POLYMORPHA), WHICH GROWS TO TEN YARDS HIGH AND IS FOUND IN THE TROPICAL PACIFIC

COMPILED AND EDITED BY
DR HERBERT REISIGL,
BOTANICAL INSTITUTE OF THE UNIVERSITY OF INNSBRUCK

NOTE: READERS WISHING TO VISIT THE BOTANICAL GARDENS LISTED IN THIS BOOK ARE URGED TO CHECK CAREFULLY ON THE OPENING TIMES AND CURRENT REGULATIONS

BLUMENPARADIESE DER WELT

THE WORLD OF FLOWERS

PUBLISHED IN 1965 BY THE VIKING PRESS, INC.
625 MADISON AVENUE, NEW YORK, N. Y. 10022
LIBRARY OF CONGRESS CATALOG CARD NUMBER: 65-10265
PRINTED IN AUSTRIA BY
WAGNER'SCHE UNIV.-BUCHDRUCKEREI BUCHROITHNER & CO., INNSBRUCK

This book could not have been compiled without the co-operation of botanists and flower-lovers all over the world. Particular gratitude is due to:

COUNT LENNART BERNADOTTE, PRÄSIDENT DER DEUTSCHEN GARTENBAU-GESELLSCHAFT, INSEL MAINAU-BODENSEE

FRITZ ENCKE, DIREKTOR DES PALMENGARTENS, FRANKFURT AM MAIN

PROF. DR. FRIEDRICH EHRENDORFER, VIENNA

DR. WOLFGANG ENGELHARDT, WISSENSCHAFTLICHER GESCHÄFTSFÜHRER DES DEUTSCHEN NATURSCHUTZRINGES, MUNICH

OTTO FAUSER, BENTLEIGH-EAST, VICTORIA, AUSTRALIA

PROF. DR. GERHARD FOLLMANN, SANTIAGO, CHILE

PROF. DR. HELMUT GAMS, INNSBRUCK

DR. J. GERLOFF, BOTANISCHER GARTEN, BERLIN-DAHLEM

STEFAN A. GROHS, JOHANNESBURG

H. HERRE, BOTANICAL GARDEN, STELLENBOSCH

WERNER HARRO KÖNIG, LÜNEBURG

PROF. DR. HANS KRIEG, PRÄSIDENT DES DEUTSCHEN NATURSCHUTZRINGES, WOLFRATSHAUSEN-WALDRAM

DR. WALTER LARCHER, INNSBRUCK

PROF. DR. W. LÖTSCHERT, HAMBURG

JOSEF AND JOYCE MUENCH, SANTA BARBARA, CALIFORNIA

PROF. DR. I. ORMOS, BUDAPEST

FRED M. PACKARD, NATIONAL PARKS ASSOCIATION, WASHINGTON, D.C.

NINA PAVLOVNA NIKOLAYENKO, MOSCOW

PROF. DR. WERNER RAUH, HEIDELBERG

PROF. H. B. RYCROFT, KIRSTENBOSCH

WILHELM SCHACHT, BOTANISCHER GARTEN, MÜNCHEN-NYMPHENBURG

MOTOO SHIMIZU, OFUNA BOTANICAL GARDEN, JAPAN

DR. MONA LISA STEINER, MANILA

PROF. DR. HERMANN ULLRICH, BONN

PROF. DR. HEINRICH WALTER, STUTTGART

PROF. DR. HANS WEBER, MAINZ

PROF. DR. GUSTAV WENDELBERGER, VIENNA

F. E. WIELGOLASKI, OSLO

P. ZÜLLI, BOTANISCHER GARTEN, ST. GALLEN

THE BRITISH TRAVEL AND HOLIDAYS ASSOCIATION, LONDON

CAPE PENINSULA PUBLICITY ASSOCIATION, CAPE TOWN

DEUTSCHER NATURSCHUTZRING, WOLFRATSHAUSEN-WALDRAM

INSTITUT FÜR NATURSCHUTZ, VIENNA

THE ROYAL HORTICULTURAL SOCIETY, LONDON

SATOUR, PRETORIA

UNITED STATES NATIONAL PARKS SERVICE, WASHINGTON, D.C.

CONTENTS

Botanical Gardens, Parks, and Floral Regions

What would life be worth without flowers?

PROFESSOR HANS KRIEG, PRESIDENT OF THE GERMAN COUNCIL FOR THE PROTECTION OF NATURE

The mountain snow is brittle under the spring sun and glitters like a thousand diamonds. At its edge a little reddish-purple flower bell dares to lift its head, the first tender blossom of the Soldanella. One of the skiers who swing and tumble and laugh on the nearby practice slope, looking for a sunny spot to rest, discovers it. He cries out in rapturous amazement, a flower, a flower in the snow! And they all come over and silently admire this tiny, modest creation of nature: a flower in the snow!

It is only a solitary tiny flower. Why are these young people, who are surely not particularly sentimental or gentle, suddenly so silent? Because they hear the first call of spring? But down in the valley it has long since made its entrance with blossoms and yellow butterflies above the green tint of the meadows. Yet they marvel at the bold Soldanella in the snow as if it were a rare gem. 'We mustn't pick it,' one of them says finally. 'No, no, of course not.'

In a few months' time, when summer has come, a small tent over there by the rock face will house two or three young people, the sons of artisans and farmers in the nearby valley. They render a rare voluntary service in guarding the last specimens of the protected edelweiss against the all too greedy hands of mountaineers. Such sentries are needed, for everywhere beautiful flowers are threatened with extinction by people who love to take a little bit of nature home with them and never stop to think that flowers are organs of propagation which must bear seeds if the species is to survive.

Why so much ado about a few flowers? We all know why: we love them because they are beautiful. But they are more than that. They are symbols, friendly signposts of a world without which our life would be overwhelmed by sheer materialism.

I once sailed with two Red Indians in a dug-out on a quiet arm of the River Paraguay which penetrates deep into the lush primeval forest. Big, vividly coloured kingfishers and other birds perched on dead branches protruding from the water and every now and then the head of a caiman would silently emerge at our approach. I paid little attention to these accustomed sights. Suddenly the river widened to a small lake and there I saw it, the Victoria regia. Between gigantic floating leaves like rimmed baking sheets stood a bursting bud, almost as large as a man's head. You may ask what all the fuss was about, as you can find them in nearly every big botanical garden. But this Victoria regia was more than just an enormous water lily. It was a regal greeting from a strange, oppressive, somewhat dangerous world. I could not and did not want to evade its fascination any more than I did that of the wonderful, often bizarre orchids which I have admired many times on journeys in South America, Africa and India. Unfortunately they are usually to be seen only when a decayed tree collapses under the weight of its epiphytic bromelias, orchids and ferns. But how wonderful are today's orchid houses in botanical gardens! It is only there that one realises the incredible diversity of orchid flowers.

Indeed, flowers, like butterflies in their fantastic variety, are exponents of nature and, quite apart from any scientific significance, form aesthetic and emotional bridges to this nature which seems to elude us more and more—whether they are daisies or dream-like shapes of exotic luxuriance.

What is nature? Sometimes the great mother, embracing the mountain, the forest and the deer; sometimes the violent destroyer of her own children by storms, by lightning, by floods. At one moment she is the cosmos, the incomprehensible law; at another, where man takes a hand in shaping her, she is the cornfield, the galloping horse. Now she is the clever elephant, emerging silently from the jungle, and now the little flower, modestly shimmering among blades of grass. We are her creatures, her parts, and we imagine that we are her masters. Just because we have grasped a few of her laws and make use of them for our own purposes, we feel entitled to abuse her at every step we take and so we have long since become her naughtiest children.

Of course it is wrong to see nature always as a mother or a fairy tale witch. Of course it is wrong to blame man for exploiting creation in order to live. We must look at these things realistically, but, just because we do, we must guard against the wanton and greedy destruction of nature and rejoice in the fact that all thoughtful and sincere people, for instance, love flowers.

Vast tulip fields in Holland, carnation fields in the South of France supply the world with plants and cut flowers; nurseries of world renown surprise us year by year with evidence of their skill; flower shops enchant us throughout the year with their displays; private and public gardens have never been more pleasing or richer in flowers than they are today. Certainly all this is to be welcomed. But what about the countryside, where the flowers should be children of freedom? We are obliged to create protected areas and to hedge them round with laws and we have to watch helplessly as one flower after another falls victim to so-called progress, overcrowding and ignorance.

Only a short time ago my house stood at the entrance to a beautiful national park, a fir-studded moor, the last oasis of its kind in the whole country. There were masses of native orchids; the pretty little rock rose, which is becoming rarer every year, formed hummocks of glowing red. In March the Pasque flower lifted its delicate, ivory with a hint of purple, above the still wintry heath, and soon afterwards the ground was speckled with blue gentians of many different kinds. The procession of colourful flowers would go on until the late autumn. How carefully I used to walk on that festive carpet! Today tractors and lorries are flattening out everything and hissing motor saws are felling century-old trees. Because the ground is cheaper here than elsewhere, horribly efficient contractors and authorities have chosen this place of all places to build rows and rows of houses. I fought in vain to preserve what is now lost for ever. It isn't the slightest use to hope, as I do, that the culprits will roast in hell. I am as sad as at the graveside of a friend to see the death of thousands upon thousands of flowers.

A Botanist on Expedition

PROFESSOR WERNER RAUH

No visitor to the hothouses of a botanical garden, no owner of a private plant collection has ever thought seriously how and under what circumstances these often bizarre plants have made their way to Europe from their native lands, the sun-parched deserts and semi-deserts, the steamy jungle, the mountain forests shrouded in mist, the tropical mountain ranges topped by icy giants. Only one who himself has travelled in distant countries and collected plants knows of the toil and privations a collector has to endure to secure rare plants which are of value not only to the amateur but to science. Dangerous expeditions lasting for weeks have sometimes been carried out for the sake of a single plant. It may interest the reader, therefore, to learn something about the work of a scientific collector.

A journey for the purpose of scientific studies, which may take several months, requires intensive preparation and planning. Existing literature about the area to be studied is often sparse, maps have to be assembled and contacts made in advance with local scientists, amateurs and farmers who may be able to advise and help. The equipment to be taken is another problem: there must be neither too much nor too little. Items omitted at the outset could wreck a whole journey. A botanist needs more equipment than, for instance, a geographer or geologist. Apart from a complete tent and photographic equipment, he must carry packing materials for transporting living plants, plant presses for the herbarium and containers to preserve parts of plants. On the other hand, the luggage must not be so cumbersome as to immobilise the expedition, particularly if it is a question of traversing unknown districts with the help of pack animals. Today one of the basic items of equipment for a botanical expedition is a spacious, tough vehicle with a four-wheel drive, for woe betide the man who gets bogged down in viscous laterite clay or desert sand. He may have to wait for days or even weeks before help comes. For expeditions in desert country the vehicle must be equipped with sufficiently large drinking water containers.

The equipment should further include a stock of essential drugs for curing tropical diseases and, most important, snake bite serums. In an emergency each member of the expedition must be able to be his own doctor and to protect himself against the many dangers to which he is exposed every day.

After many months of preparations the day has come at last to start the journey. The large luggage has been sent ahead by boat; today the members of the expedition usually follow by plane to save time. A few hours' flight takes them into the heart of the country they wish to explore and into a strange world with a climate to which they must gradually become accustomed. There are customs formalities to be dealt with, which in some countries takes days, and after stocking up with provisions, the expedition is ready to start for the 'unknown.' The members will have studied the appropriate literature and acquired a certain idea of the country, but reality always looks entirely different.

An expedition for the purpose of collecting plants usually consists of only two members; they are frequently obliged, however, to hire local guides and porters who also help with the collecting. Orchids and bromelias, for instance, are epiphytes and as such grow high up in tree tops. To secure them, trees have to be climbed, or if necessary, felled—labours which are better left to the natives. They are also better than Europeans at hacking out a trail through the pathless jungle.

At first the travellers are overwhelmed by the abundance of tropical vegetation and tend indiscriminately to take samples of every flowering plant they find. But after a few days they realise that they cannot possibly make use of the mass of collected material; more and more they concentrate their efforts on specific genera and soon learn to recognise the surroundings in which these are to be found. Gradually co-operation with the natives begins to function and a certain routine is established. If no special events intervene, one day looks much like another: rise at 5.30 a.m. while it is still dark. Daylight in the tropics begins at 6 a.m. After a substantial breakfast which has to last until the evening, tents are struck and the luggage loaded up. Now it is 8 a.m. Already the sun stands high in the heavens and burns down mercilessly. The heat rouses thousands of mosquitoes and other tormentors which make life a pure hell. Then work begins. Plants are assembled and provisionally packed, plant-geographical, -climatological and -ecological examinations are carried out. Not later than 4 p.m. search must be made for a camping place, for the tropical day ends at 6 p.m. In spite of the vast expanse of the country, it is not always easy to find a suitable site, because certain rules of safety have to be observed. When the tents have been erected and supper has been eaten, the real work begins. By candle, oil or gaslight, the day's harvest has to be examined and catalogued. Each plant is numbered and labelled with a short description of where it was found, for not all of them can be identified then and there. Particular care must be taken with plants which are to be shipped live to Europe. For every plant collected alive there must be a detailed botanical record. When the results of the expedition are evaluated later and it transpires that a new species has been found, no valid description of it can be made unless there is a record to refer to. When the live plants have been packed and those that are to be dried have been treated—they have to be placed between fresh sheets of newspaper every two days to prevent moulding—entries must still be made in diaries and the most important observations recorded. By then it is usually midnight. A short, deep sleep on a hard camp bed, and a new working day begins. So it goes on for week after week, month after month. Gradually the parcels of plants mount up. They will soon have to be shipped, for delicate and tender jungle plants cannot stand long transport. Therefore, from time to time the expedition has to call at larger towns, if possible those with flight connections. The difficulties of sending live plants begin at that point. To be imported into Europe or the United States, they need a health certificate to show that they are free from disease and pests. This is important because many of the pests attacking cultivated plants have been introduced in this way to Europe or America from overseas. Therefore, each plant must be shown to a botanical health inspector. Since in most countries these inspectors are available only in the capital, it is necessary to have an agent there who will undertake this job. When they have received a clean bill of health, the tropical plants can begin their long journey by sea or air to continue their lives in changed circumstances and to beautify our hothouses. When the expedition returns after months of travelling, the members can commence the evaluation of the results. The collected plants are identified, new species described, and this work may take years to complete. If the plants have survived the journey and can be easily propagated, they may then be distributed to botanical gardens and amateur gardeners.

Work and Pleasure in a Botanical Garden

WILHELM SCHACHT, BOTANICAL GARDENS,
MÜNCHEN-NYMPHENBURG

Botanical gardens exist in every country of the world. They are usually associated with the botanical faculty of universities and subsidised by the government; sometimes they are municipal institutions, for which the public parks department of the city council is responsible, and there are a few (especially in North America) which owe their foundation and maintenance to private trusts.

The first botanical gardens were created in the Middle Ages. Already in the sixteenth century, Padua, Pisa, Bologna and Leiden (Holland) had botanical gardens. All these early gardens contained only medicinal and aromatic herbs, which they displayed in orderly rows. In the course of centuries, the purposes and aspects of botanical gardens have undergone a change, like so many other things. A modern botanical garden not only serves scientific interests by breeding and tending plants for the purpose of research and teaching and as an object lesson for schools, it also wants to be of use to many garden lovers. In addition to wild plants, it increasingly displays cultivated, notably ornamental plants, such as annuals, shrubs, bulbs and trees, and their latest varieties, in particular areas set aside for them. A modern botanical garden is intended to acquaint the inhabitants of our growing cities, which become more and more remote from nature, with the abundance and beauty of the botanical world in an artistically satisfying manner.

As I have said, botanical gardens exist in every part of the world and under differing climatic conditions. The demands they make in regard to attention and maintenance differ accordingly. But the welfare of every one requires boundless devotion on the part of those who administer and care for them.

One of the most important tasks is to maintain and, if possible, increase the plant population. For decades botanical gardens and important amateur collectors have been in the habit of publishing an *index seminum,* a seed exchange list, which is sent to every botanical garden in the world. In it are listed the seeds that have been collected in the garden or in the open country and are available to other collectors. Thus every participant in the exchange has the opportunity of meeting his needs. The dispatch takes place in autumn and winter, when the harvest is over and the seeds (in large gardens there are many thousands of every kind) have been cleaned and sorted. To give some idea of the scope of this exchange it may be mentioned that, for instance, the Botanical Garden of München-Nymphenburg annually dispatches about 12,000 portions. The seeds received from other gardens are handed over to the gardeners responsible for the various sections, who sow them at the appropriate time in greenhouses or in the open ground. The great difficulty in growing and tending thousands of plants from every climate in the world lies in the fact that each of them makes different demands in regard to temperature, light, soil, humidity, feeding, etc. In the moderate climate of a Central European botanical garden, for instance, it is necessary to create appropriate conditions for the succulents of Africa and America, which require aridity and light, as well as for plants from the tropical jungle, demanding heat and humidity, for the exacting flora of heath and moor, which thrives only in particular kinds of soil, as well as for the alpines of high mountains in every part of the world, which are extremely fastidious as to the place where they will flourish.

Of the many plants which are grown annually from seed, I will mention only one: *Victoria amazonica (V. regia).* This enormous aquatic plant from the river basin of the Amazon, with its perfectly round leaves which under favourable conditions can reach a diameter of over six feet, has spherical black-green seeds about the size of a pea. Placed in water at a temperature of about 30—35° C. (86—95° F.) in February, these seeds germinate in about a fortnight. In May the seedlings, whose leaves have already reached the size of a bowl, are planted out in the hothouse for aquatic plants. In the spacious warm water basin and a moist sultry atmosphere the plants develop with amazing rapidity. In July they reach their full size and produce the first blossoms, which open only at night. In the autumn this regal water lily ends its life on the compost heap, for it is not worth while keeping it alive during the dark winter months. The hothouse is then used for the winter storage of azaleas, camellias and other non-hardy shrubs of Australia and New Zealand, which have spent the summer in tubs in the open.

In contrast to the extraordinary rapid development of *Victoria regia,* some other plants grow particularly slowly, for instance, orchids. Their seeds are like dust. The sowing on culture media in test-tubes is laboratory work which demands as much skill, experience, understanding and patience as the further cultivation of the minute seedlings, and the plants will not flower for years (in the case of Vanda, 15 years).

But whether it takes a short or long time, the gardener is pleased when the cultivation is successful, when he has safely brought his charges through all the dangers and hazards that await them, such as unfavourable weather, pests and diseases. But there may be unexpected incidents and much annoyance at a later stage. For instance, when the blackbirds, in their quest for food, destroy the most beautiful hummocks in the rock garden or, together with greenfinches and sparrows, wantonly peck at crocuses and primroses and strew the petals around. Even more annoying are ignorant and thoughtless visitors who pick flowers, or regard a botanical garden as a kind of self-service flower shop. But the bitterest sorrow comes to gardeners and botanists through unscrupulous collectors and experts who, with devilish certainty, discover even the best hidden rarities, of which there is often only a single irreplaceable specimen, and dig them up when they think themselves unobserved. Thus the 'botanical' gardener has many worries apart from the damage caused by acts of God, such as gales, cloudbursts, hail or exceptionally 'arctic' winters. But in the end there remains with him a sense of deep satisfaction at being able to give pleasure and edification to countless people. Every botanical garden is like a green flowering oasis, a little Garden of Eden, amid a stony city desert, which presents old and young with ever new happy experiences and makes them forget their daily worries.

The first flowers of spring in the mountains. Hungry for light and warmth, the delicately fringed little bells of *Soldanella pusilla, Primulaceae,* often break through the melting snow cover, as the picture shows

Christmas roses *(Helleborus niger, Ranunculaceae)*, in the Bavarian Alps

←

Crocus meadow in the Dolomites *(Crocus albiflorus, Iridaceae)*. Spring comes to the high mountains: thousands of delicate chalices cover the wintry brown of the meadow like newly fallen snow

←

Spring Snowflake *(Leucojum vernum, Amaryllidaceae)*. Like its little sister *(Galanthus nivalis)*, it is popularly known as snowdrop, a typical flower of riverside woods

The large-flowered Gentian is one of the most brilliant flowers of Central Europe. Several species, closely related to each other, occur in the Alps. Especially beautiful and luxuriant is *Gentiana dinarica* of the Dinaric Alps and the Abruzzi. The photograph was taken in the Alpine Garden on the Schachen above Garmisch

→ Weather Thistle *(Carlina acaulis, Compositae)*. The flower nestles in the centre of a rosette of spiky leaves. The silvery, straw-like bracts close in cloudy weather (hydroscopic movement), so that the plant is regarded as a weather prophet

Edelweiss *Leontopodium alpinum, Compositae)*, the most sought-after but by no means the most characteristic of alpine flowers. From Central Asia, where the genus *Leontopodium* is represented by some 30–40 species, it invaded Europe during the ice ages

The Spring Gentian *(Gentiana verna, Gentianaceae)* climbs from the valleys up into the alpine region

Pulsatilla vernalis, *Ranunculaceae*, on the Seiser Alm, Dolomites. In the background is the Schlern Mountain

–

ilium
ulbi-
erum,
iliaceae

→

earded
ampa-
ula
Campa-
ula
arbata,
ampa-
ulaceae)

Spotted Gentian *(Gentiana punctata, Gentianaceae)* against Lake Sils, Upper Engadine

→

Yellow Foxglove *(Digitalis grandiflora, Scrophulariaceae)*. In the background is the Dachstein Mountain

29

→

Cotton Grass *(Eriophorum scheuchzeri, Cyperaceae)* by Lake Märjelen, with the Great Aletsch Glacier in the background (Wallis, Switzerland)

Rust-red Rose Bay *(Rhododendron ferrugineum, Ericaceae),* the most beautiful ornament of the sub-alpine stone-pine forests, in often unmixed colonies it climbs to altitudes far above today's tree line

Lady's Slipper *(Cypripedium calceolus, Orchidaceae).* A most stately orchid. In some places it has become almost extinct and is only rarely to be found in its wild state

32

live grove
ith Poppies
apaver
oeas), near
mone on
ke Garda,
ith Monte
ldo in the
ckground

→

aquis of
e Medi-
ranean
gions. Tree
ather *(Erica*
borea) and
rse *(Calyco-*
ne spinosa)
ar Casa-
cciola,
hia

←

Cytinus hypocistis, Rafflesiaceae, a parasite of the Mediterranean regions, growing on Cistus

→

Worm Killer *(Aristolochia grandiflora, Aristolochiaceae)* from Guatemala

Island of Mainau in Lake Constance (in the foreground the rose garden). The mild climate of the lake allows tender sub-tropical plants, such as palm and banana trees, to grow in the open during the summer months

Scenery in the exotic park of the Principality of Monaco *(Jardin Exotique)*. The picture show *Neobuxbaumia polylopha, Leuraireocereus marginatus* and *Trichocereus pasacana;* in the foreground a Cape Aloe *(Aloe africana, Liliaceae)*

37

Inflorescence
of the Banana Tree
(Musa paradisiaca, Musaceae)

The large-flowered tropical water lily 'Director George T. Moore,' in the Botanical Garden, München-Nymphenburg

←

La Mortola near Ventimiglia is one of the most famous Riviera gardens. The picture shows a section of its rich collection of succulents. In the centre spine cacti *(Echinocactus grusonii)* and the pillars of *Neobuxbaumia polylopha* on the left, several species of Aloe

Scenery in a garden paradise in the midst of a city: the heather garden in München-Nymphenburg. From the soft carpet of Erica grow the greyish green columns of the Swedish juniper *(Juniperus communis 'Suecica')*. Above them the swaying branches of silver birch trees

→

Flowering rhododendrons at Kew Gardens near London, the largest and most famous of England's botanical garden

In Central Europe roses and carnations are the flowers most given as presents. They are often grown in large fields. (Left) Rose fields near Bad Nauheim, Germany. (Top right) Carnation 'Simm.' The largest carnation plantations are found on the French (Mentone and Nice) and Italian Riviera (Bordighera and San Remo). (Bottom right) Tea hybrid 'Crimson Glory,' one of the most beautiful dark red garden roses with a delicious scent

→

Flowering giant water lily *(Victoria amazonica, Nymphaeaceae)* at Kew Gardens, London

←

The Palm House in the Palm Garden, Frankfurt/Main

Victoria amazonica (Victoria regia), the giant water lily of the Amazon, in the large heated outdoor basin of the Wilhelma, Stuttgart. In the foreground, right, *Hydrocleis nymphoides*, the water poppy, a flowering rush species *(Butomaceae)* of tropical South America

Tulips, Narcissi and Hyacinths in the Keukenhof, Holland. Holland leads the world in the cultivation of tulips. The genus *Tulipa,* with numerous species, is to be found from Central Asia to Southern Europe (Mediterranean regions). The garden tulip was introduced into Central Europe in 1554 by Ghiselenius Busbequius, an ambassador of the German Emperor Ferdinand I, who found it near Constantinople

←

'The Pride of the Table Mountain' *(Disa uniflora),* the most popular orchid of South Africa, in the Botanical Gardens, Göteborg, Sweden

Flowering date palms *(Phoenix dactylifera),* in Morocco

←

Characteristic plants of the high mountains of East Africa:

a) *Lobelia deckenii*, grows as tall as 6½ feet. Photographed on Mount Kilimanjaro at 13,123 feet

→

b) Arboreal Dogwort *(Senecio spec.)*. Photographed at over 8,202 feet

←

The red alpine Snake Flower *(Echium bourgaeanum WEBB)*. It is endemic in a small area on Pico de Teide, Teneriffe

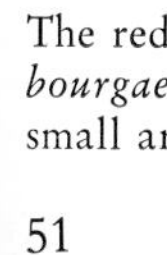

'Red-Hot-Poker' *(Kniphofia uvaria, Liliaceae)*, a colourful perennial of our gardens, in its native South Africa

←

Travellers' Tree' *(Ravenala madagascariensis, Musaceae)*, a banana tree of Madagascar

←

Globe Euphorbia: *Euphorbia obesa* (above left); *Euphorbia symmetrica* (above right). These plants have a diameter of about 3¼ inches

Euphorbia esculenta, somewhat enlarged. *Euphorbiaceae.* All three species are natives of South Africa. Photographed at the Botanical Gardens, Heidelberg

Bread Palm Fern *(Encephalartos spec., Cycadaceae),* with flower cones. This interesting genus with 14 species is endemic in Africa (especially East Africa)

'Pin-cushion Shrub' *(Leucospermum bolusii, Proteaceae).* An evergreen shrub, about 6½ feet tall, one of the most popular ornamental plants in its native South Africa

→

Giant Protea *(Protea cynaroides, Proteaceae).* About natural size. This magnificent plant grows on the south coast of Cape Province

Candelabra Flowers of the family of *Asclepiadaceae.*

a) (right) *Ceropegia stapeliaeformis*
b) (left) *Ceropegia ampliata*

The flowers are about 1¹/₄ inches tall. Photographed at the Botanical Gardens, Heidelberg

→

(Top) *Ceropegia elegans.* This plant is a native of East India. Its flowers are about 2¹/₂ inches long

(Bottom) 'Living Stones' (Pebble Plant) *(Lithops kuibensis, Mesembryanthemaceae)*, a steppe plant of the Cape Province. The single plant has a diameter of ³/₄–1¹/₄ inches. Photographed at the Botanical Gardens, Heidelberg

(Top) *Caralluma dummeri.*
Enlarged three times

(Bottom) *Heurnia zebrina.*
Enlarged twice

Zantedeschia aethiopica (Araceae) near Cape Town. In South Africa it grows in vast colonies on marshy meadows which dry up in summer

'Bird of Paradise Flower' *(Strelitzia reginae, Musaceae)*, South Africa. Slightly reduced. The colourful, bizarre flower is pollinated by flower birds

Adenium obesum var. multiflorum (Apocynaceae), a native of South-east Africa, grows abundantly in Kruger National Park. A succulent shrub some 10 feet tall. Also known as Impala Lily or Sabie Star

Nama(qua)land daisies *(Ursinia anethoides, Compositae)*, one of the many species of the genus which in South Africa replace our daisy

→

(Above) Mesembryanthemums *(Herrea spec.)* with flowers 2½–3¼ inches in diameter, in the Mesembryanthemum steppe of Nama(qua)land, South Africa
(Below) *Welwitschia mirabilis, Welwitschiaceae,* one of the strangest of known plants. It grows in the misty Namib Desert in South-west Africa. The leaves reach a length of over 10 feet

(Above) *Aloe dichotoma* vegetation in South-west Africa. (Below) *Pachypodium namaquanum* vegetation *(Apocynaceae)* in Nama(qua)land

Livistonia spec. This palm species grows in Asia and Australia

Flower Shapes of Exotic Orchids:

←

(Top left) *Aërangis stylosa.* About natural size (Top right) *Mormodes wendlandii.* Somewhat enlarged

←

Bottom left) *.aelia anceps.* Natural size Bottom right) *'hragmo- edilum audatum.* omewhat educed

→

ider Orchid *'artholina ctinata).* ılarged ree times

uropean
round
rchids:

←

Top left)
phrys
nsectifera.
nlarged
hree times
Top right)
pipogium
phyllum.
nlarged
hree times

←

Bottom left)
phrys ten-
hredinifera.
nlarged
our times
Bottom right)
phrys
peculum.
nlarged
ive times

→

tropical
enus's
lipper
Paphio-
edilum
lauco-
hyllum).
wice
nlarged

Orchids *(Vanda* and *Euanthe*, hybrids) in Floraleigh Garden, Hilo, Hawaii

←

Even the simplest Philippine nipa-house is decorated with orchids; this one shows the white Malaya flower in the wide open windows

Flowering orchids (*Grammatophyllum scriptum*) being sold in the street

→

Top left)
ycaste
eppei
om
lexico
Top
ght)
endro-
um
ardia-
um from
urma and
ssam

→

entre
ft)
asso-
ttleya
entre
ht)
phio-
dilum
brid

→

ottom
t)
phio-
dilum
brid
ottom
ht)
elogyne
rfor-
nse

Cirrhopetalum ornatissimum, an epiphytic orchid from Assam and Sikkim, greatly enlarged, in the Botanical Gardens, Heidelberg

(Above) Kangaroo Flower *(Anigozanthos humilis),* an *Amaryl-lidaceae* of the Cannington swamp near Perth (West Australia) (Below) *Banksia coccinea (Proteaceae).* Photographed north of Albany (West Australia) →

→

The giant flower ($3^1/_4$ feet in diameter!) of *Rafflesia tuan-mudae (Rafflesiaceae)*, a parasite on the roots of jungle trees in Indonesia. Photographed at the Botanical Gardens, Bogor

←

Kangaroo Flower *(Anigozanthos manglesii)*. About natural size.
Photographed in Perth (West Australia)

'Bottle Brush' *(Callistemon citrinus)*, a *Myrtacea* of Australia. About natural size. Photographed at the Botanical Gardens, Munich

→

Giant ferns in the Botanical Gardens of Tjibodas, Indonesia

Australian 'Grass Tree" *(Xanthorroea spec. Liliaceae)* in Tjibodas, Indonesia

→

(Above) Mariposa del Campo (Span. 'Field Butterfly') flowers above the remains of some cacti. It is a typical plant of the 'flowering Atacama' *(Alstroemeria violacea)*. Somewhat enlarged
(Below) *Anthurium andreanum*, a rare flower in its habitat at the foot of the Columbian West Cordilleras

(Top left) Native village in the jungle of South Ecuador
(Bottom right) Mist forest in the Andes, South Ecuador. The constant high humidity (hence mist forest) is indicated by the abundant growth of lichens and mosses, as by other epiphytes (orchids, bromelias, ferns, etc.)

Espeletia gigantea, a rosette-forming Composita, typical of the cold and damp Paramos of Northern Ecuador. Photographed at 13,123 feet

→

The Andes are rich in various gentian species, the largest and most beautiful being *Gentianella (Gentiana) weberbaueri.* The plant is some 16 inches tall and climbs to the edge of the glacier. The white background is snow. The flowers are enlarged about three times

←

ledge Cactus,
*spostoa
elanostele,*
notographed
the Rimac
alley, Peru.
me 6 feet tall.
he white
owers are
me $1^1/_4$ inches
diameter

*oraimondia
antea*
ctus),
racteristic
nt of the
remely dry
k deserts
Peru. Up to
feet tall,
urs in
tudes of
02 feet

←
Hedge Cactus *(Browningia candelaris)* near Arequipa in South Peru, in the background the Misti volcano. The stem may be as much as 20 inches in diameter and grows to 10 feet before branching out

Puya raimondii (Bromeliaceae-pineapple family), one of the strangest plants of the High Andes (occurs at altitudes of 13,123 feet). Characteristic plant of the 'tufted rosette puna' with stems of over 20 inches in diameter and up to 13 feet tall

Globe Cactus *(Horridocactus curvispinus)*. Shaped like a bird's nest, it nestles among rubble. From the edge of the desert towards the Andes. One third natural size

←

The characteristic Chilian hedge cactus *(Trichocereus chiloensis)*, popularly known as Quisco. One third natural size

Old Man Cactus *(Cephalocereus senilis)* on the Cordillera side of the Atacama border, reaches heights of up to 5 feet

→

Cola de Zorro (Span. 'fox tail'), pampas grass *(Cortaderia atacamensis)* in a dry valley on the Cordillera side of the Atacama desert. One tenth natural size

A plant of the pineapple family *(Puya beteroniana)* on the southern edge of the Atacama. Reaches a height of about 8 feet

Passion Flower, giant Grenadilla *(Passiflora quadrangularis)* of South America. Natural size. Photographed in the Botanical Gardens, Munich →

→

'Barrel' palm
(*Colpothrina*
wrightii) in
West Cuba

Tree-like
Thorn App
(*Datura*
arborea), n
of the And
Peru and C
Photograph
at 11,027 f
in Central

←
Aroid *(Lysichitum americanum)* with leaves as long as 39 inches. Occurs in Kamchatka, Japan and North-west America

The cactus *Hylocereus undatus* climbs shrubs and trees. Widely cultivated in subtropical and tropical regions, where it often escapes and grows wild. Photographed in the Caribbean

Bear Grass *(Xerophyllum tenax, Liliaceae)*. Photographed at Lolo National Park in Montana, where a great many flower in summer

Palm Lily *(Yucca brevifolia, Agavaceae)*, 'Joshua Tree,' may grow as high as 33 feet. The genus occurs with some 30 species fr the Southern States of North America and Mexico to Central America. Also verbenas, yellow compositae and others flowering in the desert

Echinocereus polyacanthus (Cactaceae) forms large colonies in the dry bush of the North American deserts from Arizona to East Texas and in adjoining Mexico

→

Arizona's cactus desert in spring: Giant cactus *(Carnegiea gigantea)*, flowering yuccas *(Yucca thornberi, Agavaceae)* and *Senecio lemmonii, Asteraceae.* Bare and stony in the dry season, in spring the ground is covered with countless annual species

Spring in Virginia. Large woodlands turn into flowering gardens. Rhododendrons form a dense undergrowth in these forests

Annual spring flowers among the sand dunes of the Colorado desert of South California. Sand verbenas *(Abronia villosa, Nyctaginaceae)* and evening primroses *(Oenothera spec., Onagraceae)*

Yucca elata (Agavaceae) in the Sierra Madre (Rocky Mountains)

Cowboys in the flowering desert of Arizona.
Sand verbenas *(Abronia spec., Nyctaginaceae)*

←

[S]pring flowers along the Apache Trails in Arizona.
[C]alifornian Poppy *(Eschscholtzia spec.,*
[P]apaveraceae) unfolds its petals on slopes decorated
[w]ith Saguaros and other members of the cactus
[f]amily *(Cylindropuntia spec.,* etc.)

Page 112: *Poinciana regia (Caesalpiniaceae)*, 'Flamboyant' or 'Flame Tree,' is one of the most beautiful tropical trees. A native of Madagascar, it is grown anywhere in the tropics, especially in Florida and in the West Indies

Heralds of spring in the higher regions of the Glacier National Park in Montana, the 'Glacier lilies' *(Erythronium parviflorum, Liliaceae)*

→

Castilleja miniata (Scrophulariaceae), 'Indian Paint Brush' grows up to 8,858 feet on Mt. Rainier (Washington)

Notes to the Illustrations

DR HERBERT REISIGL

Because the captions to most of the illustrations offer no opportunity for the fuller descriptions some flower lovers may expect, the following section is intended to give rather more information about the plants illustrated or to mention some generally interesting facts from the wonder world of botany. It is not the purpose of this book to go into greater detail and, in view of the limited space, that would be impossible.

Alpine Plants (pp. 17—31)
See article on page 126.

Hellebores *(Helleborus niger, Ranunculaceae)* (p. 19)

In light beech woods and among dwarf pines, the Christmas rose often flowers before Christmas. The flowers, at first pure white, later turn a brilliant red; the large palmate leaves remain green during the winter.

Spring Snowflake *(Leucojum vernum, Amaryllidaceae)* (p. 20)

Together with hepatica and wood anemone, wild leek and wake robin, it is one of the characteristic spring flowers of moist deciduous forests (beech forests).

Edelweiss *(Leontopodium alpinum, Compositae)* (p. 22)

Where man has pursued it too greedily, it has retired to steep rock faces and ridges. Its natural habitat is dry heaths on lime-stone. The little stars are densely felted hypsophylls, in the centre of which there are several capitula, each with a hundred or more minute flowers.

Pulsatilla *(Pulsatilla vernalis, Ranunculaceae)* (pp. 24—25)

At Whitsuntide countless masses of these flowers with their silky fur, people the Seiser Alm. The plant is poisonous. It flowers earlier than *Pulsatilla sulphurea,* with which it often associates, and is more widely distributed; it is by no means confined to the mountains, not even to the Alps, where it reaches altitudes of 11,811 feet. It may be found, for instance, in the north German plain in light pine forests and on sandy heathland. In the north it occurs in Scandinavia, in the east, in the Ural Mountains.

Lilium bulbiferum *(Liliaceae)* (p. 26)

This magnificent flowering bulb prefers a warm soil, sunny forest clearings, mountain meadows and rocks from the valleys up to 6,590 feet. Of the more than 50 species in the Alps, only *Lilium carniolicum* and *L. martagon* (Wake Robin) still grow wild. It is interesting to note that the plant is capable of propagating itself asexually by means of axillary gemmae.

Bearded Campanula *(Campanula barbata, Campanulaceae)* (p. 27)

Like arnica, it decorates lean mountain pastures; on lime-free humus in the Central Alps it climbs to 9,515 feet.

Spotted Gentian *(Gentiana punctata, Gentianaceae)* (p. 28)

This stately, magnificently flowering perennial occurs on lime-free soil in alpine and sub-alpine regions from the Alps to the Northern Balkans. It is to be found on dwarf shrub heaths, among dwarf-pines and on mountain meadows up to 11,484 feet. In contrast to the pure yellow, deeply slashed flowers of the taller yellow gentian *(Gentiana lutea),* its petals bear brown spots. The roots of both species are used for the distillation of schnapps.

Yellow Foxglove *(Digitalis grandiflora, Scrophulariaceae)* (p. 29)

Grows in clearings and at the edge of forests in South and Central European mountains (as far east as Western Siberia). All *digitalis* species contain the most effective of known substances for the treatment of heart disorders, but only the red foxglove *(Digitalis purpurea)* is used medicinally.

Rust-red Rose Bay *(Rhododendron ferrugineum, Ericaceae)* (p. 30)

Above the tree line it is considered to be the remaining undergrowth of former woods. The shrub is strictly dependent on very acid humus. On the southern edge of the Alps it occurs low down in the valleys (Lake Maggiore, Lake Como, even in association with Mediterranean tree heather *[Erica arborea]),* but it may also be found at altitudes of up to 9,843 feet. In winter the rose bay depends on sufficient snow cover; where this is lacking, the frost does not kill it, but the leaves dry up because the plant is unable to extract moisture from the frozen ground. Of more than 1,000 species occurring chiefly in Asia and North America, only two, with red flowers, are natives of Europe—the rust-red and the hairy rose bay *(Rhododendron hirsutum*—on limy soil).

Lady's Slipper *(Cypripedium calceolus, Orchidaceae)* (p. 30)

Grows on limy soil in shady mountain woods and among dwarf pines in most of the European and Asian mountains to above 5,234 feet. The flower is a trap for insects which enter easily through the large opening but are prevented from returning the same way by the inward turning edges of the petals. They are forced to squeeze through one of the tiny exits at the base of the flower and in so doing are dusted with pollen.

Cotton Grass *(Eriophorum scheuchzeri, Cyperaceae)* (p. 31)

The silvery-white cottonwool tufts of the cotton grass make a lively contrast to the monotonous yellowish-brown of alpine heathland. The plants produce runners in the direction of water and thus help to silt up alpine ponds and lakes. Cotton grass (the 'cotton' is attached to the seed vessels) is widely distributed over the mountains of Europe (in the Alps up to 9,515 feet), Asia and North America, as well as in the Arctic (Arctic-alpine species).

Olive Grove with Poppies *(Papaver rhoeas, Papaveraceae)* (p. 32)

Surrounded by mountains, open only towards the south, Lake Garda lies embedded in the massif of the Alps. Climatically speaking the situation is a very favourable one and permits a rich flora to grow in gardens and wild. From the shores of the lake, with evergreen oaks and olive trees, to the summit of Monte Baldo (6,562 feet) almost any level of vegetation is represented up to alpine hummock plants.

Maquis (p. 33). See also the article on page 130.

The maquis, bushy vegetation of the Mediterranean countries, is characterised by evergreen oaks, cistus and acid-loving tree heather *(Erica arborea, Ericaceae)*, with northern outposts near Lake Como and a second pocket in the tropical mountains of Africa, where it occurs at altitudes of up to 13,122 feet. On stony ground the prickly gorse with its rigid spikes *(Calycotome spinosa, Papilionaceae)* forms impenetrable thickets.

Cytinus hypocistis *(Rafflesiaceae)* (p. 34)

As this plant does not possess any chlorophyll, it is entirely dependent on the juices of the host plant; it needs no roots, no stalks, no green leaves: the yellow inflorescence, surrounded by fiery-red involucral leaves, breaks directly from the host root.

Large-flowered Worm Killer *(Aristolochia grandiflora, Aristolochiaceae)* (p. 35)

This tropical liana is often grown in greenhouses of botanical gardens for the sake of its giant flowers. Its colour and repulsive smell of decaying meat attract carrion flies. On entering the flower, the insects are trapped by hairs until the anthers open up, when the hairs wither and leave the entrance free.

Island of Mainau, Lake Constance (p. 36). See article on page 196.

Inflorescence of the Banana Tree *(Musa paradisiaca, Musaceae)* (p. 39)

The 'Banana Tree' is really a shrub, the bases of the leaves growing closely together so as to form a pseudo-stem. The enormous leaves are not reinforced at the edges, so that they soon tear to the midrib and thus appear like palm branches. The mighty inflorescence carries female flowers at the base and male flowers at the tip, standing in the axils of scarlet-red leaves. The cultivated banana, whose fruits have no seeds, is probably a native of tropical Asia. Of the many species of *Musa*, several are cultivated in the tropics as vegetable plants on account of the starchy contents of their rhizomes, and some as fibre plants *(Musa textilis*, 'Manila hemp' of the Philippines.)

Botanical Gardens, München-Nymphenburg (p. 40). See article on page 13.

Water Lilies *(Nymphaeaceae)* (pp. 39, 43, 45)

The tropical representatives of this family are often distinguished not only by magnificent blue or red flowers, but also by their enormous size. In addition to the lesser known *Euryale ferox* of East Asia, the *Victoria* species of the New World, especially *Victoria amazonica* (discovered in 1832 in the Amazon region), are cultivated as a particular attraction in botanical gardens. The floating leaves of these water lilies may reach a diameter of 6½ feet. They are reinforced by ribs on the underside and have upturned edges, so that they can easily support a child. Growth is so rapid that the *Victoria* can annually be grown from seed. Other wellknown tropical water lilies are lotus, the yellow-flowering *Nelumbo lutea* of America and especially the pink *Nelumbo nucifera* of Asia, with leaves carried above the surface of the water on long steams. In some places they are cultivated for their most decorative flowers (e.g. in Lake Mantua).

Roses (p. 42)

There is probably no plant with a firmer hold on man's affections throughout thousands of years of history than the rose. (Pliny already knew of 11 different garden roses!) Today the number of wild species is generally estimated to be 200. The garden rose is descended from Middle Eastern and Chinese ancestors, such as *Rosa centifolia*, perhaps the oldest cultivated rose, which crusaders brought to Central Europe in 1100, together with *Rosa damascena*. Already about the year 1800, 116 varieties were offered for sale in Germany, among them cultivars of *Rosa chinensis*. The introduction of the Indian rose *(Rosa odorata)* in 1809 and the yellow tea rose *(Rosa thea)* in 1824 from East Asia gave new impetus to rose cultivation, at that time almost entirely concentrated in France. Today the number of varieties is incalculable. They have, therefore, been divided into 20 'classes' and four main groups: large-flowered garden roses (e.g. remontant roses, perpetual flowering roses, tea roses), floribundae, climbing roses, park roses. The garden lover who wishes to devote himself to the cultivation of roses would be well advised to consult the lists published by rose research institutes which describe objectively the most valuable and suitable varieties.

Carnations (p. 42)

Representatives of the genus *Dianthus (Caryophyllaceae)* with 300 species, are to be found chiefly in the Mediterranean regions but also in Central and Northern Europe and East Asia. They have been known for at least 2,000 years *(Theophrastus)* as garden and medicinal plants. Also introduced by crusaders, the large-flowered cultivated forms of *Dianthus caryophyllus* came from the East Mediterranean region to Central Europe and became the ancestors of our present-day carnation strains. From the 'cottage carnations', flowering once a year in summer only, French breeders evolved the remontant garden carnations, probably by cross-breeding with the shrubby *Dianthus fruticosus*, which in the north are cultivated under glass only but in the Riviera grow in the open.

The Palm House in the Palm Garden in Frankfurt/Main (p. 44). See article on page 192.

Tulips, Narcissi, Hyacinths (pp. 46, 47)

The genus *Tulipa*, with about 150 species, occurs anywhere from Central and Southern Europe to Japan but chiefly in Central Asia. The yellow-flowering *T. silvestris* has become naturalised here and there in vineyards and at the edge of fields in Southern Central Europe. The individual bulb flowers only once, in its third year, and then dies. Our garden hyacinths probably stem from the dark-blue wild species, *H. orientalis* (from eastern Mediterranean regions), which has but a few flowers. Altogether there are about 25 species, some of which are listed today as separate genera from *Hyacinthus* in the strictest sense of the world. The genus *Narcissus* (Fam. *Amaryllidaceae)* radiates out from the western Mediterranean, where there are about 40 different species, to the Alps, as shown by the great numbers to be found in the Upper Austrian and West Swiss foothills of the Alps *(Narcissus biflorus, exsertus, pseudonarcissus.)*

Date Palm with Fruit *(Phoenix dactylifera)* (p. 49)

A grove of tall slender stems, branching out at the top into tufts of giant feathery leaves, and between them bunches of fruit. Play of light and shade on the ground, irrigated by countless rivulets of water. Does not the date palm always conjure up a picture of the oasis, the orchard of the desert? The great date palm oasis of Elche (Southern Spain) shows us 'a piece of Africa in Europe' (Rikli). Most oases are artificial orchards, depending on the availability of underground water supplies but there are also natural oases, especially in the Sudan.

Palms (pp. 67, 97)

Often extremely tall trees with one stem (ramification occurs very infrequently), at the top of which there is a head of radiate ('fan palms') or feathery leaves ('feather palms'). The main root ceases to grow very early and the tree forms numerous adventitious roots which act as prop-roots and thus carry the stem as if it were on stilts. The flowers are generally unisexual, great numbers of them forming a spike or panicle, initially enveloped by a sheath (spathe), which grows from the axils, rarely terminal. For rapid development of the large spikes of fruit, the tree requires a great deal of sugary sap which can be tapped and after fermentation provides the palm wine of the tropics. The fruits, usually cherrysized berries or drupes with often a very hard stone ('vegetable ivory' of *Phytelephas*), in some species grow to a surprising size. *Lodoicea seychellarum*, a palm endemic on the islands of the same name, has 'twin nuts' 20 inches across, probably the world's largest tree fruits, which take ten years to mature. The palm tree, with more than 1,000 species, is found in the tropical regions of the Old and the New World, especially in equatorial America and India to the tenth degree of latitude, less in the sub-tropics. The dwarf palm *Chamaerops humilis*, is the only species to be found in Western Mediterranean regions. The enormous industrial importance of the palm may be illustrated by the following examples: the fruits of date and cocos palms: Indian sago (the marrow of a single *Metroxylon rumphii* tree provides 661½ lb. of starch): oil from the fruits of the oil palm *(Elaeis):* fibre (especially *Cocos*), cane *(Calamus)*, wax, a coating on the stem of *Ceroxylon* and *Copernicia cerifera:* timber, vegetables, etc. The palm also boasts what are probably the largest leaves in nature *(Raphia*, with feathery leaves 49 feet long).

Echium bourgaeanum *(Boraginaceae)* (p. 50). The red alpine snake flower—in Spanish, *'Taginaste de las Cañadas'*. The inflorescence reaches a height of 6½—13 feet.

The flower spike, closely covered with flowers, rises from a rosette of lanceolate leaves, 12 feet long or longer. The plant, which takes several years to flower and then dies away, grows wild in Teneriffe and there only within a very small area of 120—240 square yards between altitudes of 6,462 feet and 7,446 feet in the giant ring mountains (Cañadas) around Pico de Teide. It is one of the largest, rarest and most beautiful flowering plants of the Canaries. The picture shows several plants and in the foreground right some flowering specimens of *Cheiranthus scoparius Brouss. (Cruciferae);* in the background, climbing up the walls of the ring mountains, the more than man-sized globular bushes of white Retama *(Spartocytisus nubigenus W.B., Papilionaceae.)*

Giant Crucifers and Giant Lobelias of the East African Mountains (p. 51)

In 1921 the Swedish botanists Robert and Thore Fries went to East Africa to study the famous giant *Compositae* of Mount Kenya. At that time only two species were known: today we already know 11 different species of the giant crucifers which, together with the *Bromeliacea Puya raimondii* of the Peruvian Andes, are probably the most impressive plants of the tropical mountains. They are characteristic inhabitants of the ever damp 'Paramos', as these high plains are called in South America, where temperatures daily drop below freezing point. The following altitude levels can be distinguished on Mount Kenya:
The level of *mountain forests:* 6,562 to 8,058 feet. Alpine rain forest with conifers *(Juniperus procera* —'Cedar', *Podocarpus* species);
7,875 to 10,500 feet Bamboo region *(Arundinaria alpina);*
10,500 to 11,970 feet *Hagenia abyssinica—Hypericum leucoptychodes* forest;
Ericaceae level: 11,155 to 11,810 feet. *Erica arborea —Philippia keniensis,* at the lower limit up to 20 feet high, at greater altitudes only low shrubs;
Alpine level: 11,810 to 15,092 feet. *Festuca* grassy heaths with giant crucifers.
The fact that we are here dealing with giants of a genus, otherwise represented only by low herbaceous or slightly woody plants, is evidenced by the trees of *Senecio johnstonii,* some 48 feet high, of the Kilimanjaro region, and some of these species are to be found at the upper limit of flowering plants *(S. keniodendron* on Mount Kenya at 15,256 feet.)
In no way inferior to the giant crucifers are the giant lobelias, enormous shrubs of the *Campanulaceae* family, up to 25 feet tall and inhabitants of the rain forests. Smaller but still impressive species are to be found in the alpine regions. Varieties of the *Lobelia deckenii* group (see illustration p. 51) grow to an average height of seven feet and *Lobelia bequaertii,* 16 feet high, grows at altitudes of up to 14,108 feet (Ruwenzori Mountains.) The American counterpart to the African *Senecio* species are the *Espeletia* species of the High Andes *(Compositae)* (illustration p. 84.)

Traveller's Tree *(Ravenala madagascariensis)* (p. 52)

This tree cuts an imposing figure, its strictly two-rowed leaves forming an enormous fan (up to 82 feet tall.) It grows in the dry regions of Madagascar. Because of its enormous vitality it spreads much more rapidly than its competitors after the destruction of the primary forest vegetation. The quantity of water (not rainwater) secreted by the plant itself amounts to 2½ pints per leaf scale. Like most banana species *(Musaceae),* the *Ravenala* is pollinated by honey birds. As the flower opens, two of its white petals remain enclosed in a hard, boat-shaped bract; as soon as a bird touches the tip of the bract, stamen and pistil shoot out from the flower and the bird's breast is dusted with pollen ('explosion flowers'). See also illustration on p. 62: *Strelitzia,* where pollination occurs in the same manner.

Red-Hot-Poker *(Kniphofia uvaria, Liliaceae)* (p. 53)

It grows on damp meadows and alpine marshes of the Cape Province. The flower stalks, about 39 inches tall and of the thickness of a thumb, rise from a tuft of sword-shaped leaves. They carry a dense spike of flowers, at first scarlet, later yellow in colour, which are pollinated by birds. *Kniphofia* is hardy in our climate, if suitably protected against frost, and is a very decorative plant in late summer. It has been cultivated since 1707.

Euphorbia obesa and symmetrica (p. 54)

Both species are natives of the Cape Province. They are closely related to each other and bear a striking resemblance to certain Central American globe cacti. Only the rather inconspicuous flowers convince even the untrained eye that they are not in fact cacti. After pollination, the female flowers develop into a woody capsule from which the seeds are ejected with explosive force.

Euphorbia esculenta (p. 54)

An uncommon shape which does not occur in cacti. The side-shoots proceed very densely and in great numbers from a short, thick primary shoot. Because of its appearance it is sometimes called 'Gorgon-Euphorbia.'
Euphorbiaceae (spurge): a family rich in species (about 1,600) which range from insignificant annual weeds to stately trees (e.g. *Hevea brasiliensis,* the genuine caoutchouc tree, formerly of great industrial importance but today almost completely superseded by synthetic rubber). The cactus-like euphorbias are in a separate group and in Africa take the place of cacti. The milky juice is highly poisonous (arrow poison!).
Succulents: the generic name not only for cacti but for all 'fleshy' plants belonging to very different families (there are about 50 families with some succulent members). The resemblance in the vegetative appearance is frequently so startling that, in the absence of flowers, only the expert can

tell the family to which a particular specimen belongs. Most succulents are inhabitants of waterless, hot steppes. They are extremely well adapted to conditions caused by poor water supplies. The spherical shape reduces the evaporating surface to a minimum and stem and leaves have developed into reservoirs; in addition the plant must be capable of using its water supplies economically during the dry season. Therefore, many stem succulents have no leaves at all and the leaves of leaf succulents are often coated with wax or with a hairy felt to reduce evaporation. A naturally weak metabolism is the reason for the very slow growth of many succulents.
Among the best known stem succulents are cacti, many euphorbias, some species of Kangaroo vine *(Cissus)*, carrion flowers *(Stapelia* and relatives). Some striking examples are the so-called 'bottle trees' (e.g. of the families of *Bombacaceae* and *Sterculiaceae)*. The habits shown on page 66 also belong in this category. The commonest leaf succulents are the genera *Aloe* and *Agave*, the *Crassulaceae* (among them our native *Sedum* [see p. 65 top] and *Sempervivum* species), *Mesembryanthemum* species (and related species of *Aizoaceae)*, *Lithops*, *Conophytum*, and *Pleiospilos*—'living stones' (pebble plant), p. 59 bottom.

Bread Palm Fern *(Encephalartos sp., Cycadaceae)* with flower cones (p. 55)

Their striking outward resemblance to palms (generally a single stem with a tuft of feathery leaves at the top) has earned for the *Cycadeae* the name of fern palms, although they are not related to the palm family. Together with conifers and the Ginkgo tree, they belongs to the ancient group of gymnosperms. *Cycadeae* may be regarded as living fossils since some of their species have survived almost unchanged for millions of years to the present day. The bread palm ferns with about 14 species are endemic in Africa (especially East Africa), where they grow chiefly in the dry bush and on succulent steppes. In addition to tall species, e.g. *E. laurentianus* of the Congo with stems as high as 33 feet, and leaves of 23 feet in length, there are others with thick-set, almost spherical stems. All species of the genus are unisexual, i.e. the individual plants form either female or male cones. Better known than the representatives of the genus *Encephalartos* shown in the illustration, are *Cycas revoluta* from Japan (a further 15 species in tropical Asia, Australia and Polynesia), frequently grown in greenhouses and parks, especially in the Mediterranean regions, and *Dioon edule* of Mexico.

Proteaceae (p. 56/57)

Trees and shrubs, generally with leathery leaves, to be found chiefly in the southern hemisphere. Of almost 1,000 species of the family, 600 are natives of Australia (the genera *Banksia*, *Dryandra* and *Grevillea* are especially rich in species), 260 of South Africa, in addition to the illustrated genera *Leucospermum* and *Protea*, especially *Leucadendron* (silver tree) with many species.

Ceropegia stapeliaeformis *(Asclepiadaceae)* (pp. 58, 59)

This non-succulent 'candelabra flower' from the Cape Province grows on shrubs as a liana. The reddish-brown flower is a trap which functions similarly to that of *Aristolochia grandiflora* (p. 35).

Caralluma dummeri *(Asclepiadaceae)* (p. 60)

A native of East Africa (Kenya, Tanganyika). The genus has some 130 species and is closely related to *Stapelia*, although its flowers are much smaller and it has a procumbent shoot with expanding teeth.

Heurnia zebrina *(Asclepiadaceae)* (p. 60)

Representative of a wider genus (about 50 species) of the succulent carrion flower. The magnificent pale-yellow flowers, with reddish-brown cross bars and white hairs, spring from square, regularly dentate shoots.

Lithops kuibensis (p. 59)

The 'pebble plants' of the South African deserts are among the most interesting succulents. In colour and markings they could easily be taken for pebbles (mimicry), especially as they are generally buried in the ground and only the surface is visible. Two fleshy leaves, separated only by a narrow cleft, form a spherical little body. The chlorophyll is mostly hidden away in the centre, well protected from the all too intense rays of the sun.

Araceae (pp. 61, 98)

Many tropical lianas *(Philodendron, Monstera)* belong to this group, as well as some of the oldest of cultivated plants *(Colocasia antiquorum)* with corms containing starch. The giant *Amorphophallus titanum* from Western Sumatra is a curiosity of the first order: it consists of a single enormous leaf which may grow as much as 6 inches per day; a stem of some 13—16$^{1}/_{2}$ feet in height carries the inflorescence measuring 10 feet; the spadix rises from a funnel-shaped bract to a height of up to 10 feet.

Strelitzia reginae *(Musaceae)* (p. 62)

This bizarre bird flower, known to us as a precious cut flower, may reach a height of 6$^{1}/_{2}$ feet, in its native land. The green, boat-shaped bract envelopes five to eight single flowers which open in succession (see also *Ravenala*, p. 52).

Welwitschia mirabilis *(Gnetinae, Gymnospermae)* (p. 65)

The plant derives its name from the Austrian botanist Fr. Welwitsch who discovered it in 1860. One of the strangest of known plants. The stem consists of a carrotlike stump of considerable size, three-fifths of which are underground (up to 13 feet in circumference). The coarse, leathery leaves easily fray at the top and then wither away but are replaced from the bottom in endless succession. They are procumbent and reach a length of more than 10 feet. The *Welwitschia* is the most famous inhabitant of the misty Namib desert in South-West Africa, where it is established in a narrow strip some 31 miles inland from the Coast, with shallow, wide dry valleys. The root system consists of two parts: a tap root reaching down to a depth of about 5 feet, were the ground remains moist for a long time, and a second, ramified root system which spreads out about 4 inches below the surface, thus capable of making use of even small amounts of rainwater. In an extended drought the leaves may die down to the ground, though they may be replaced from the remaining tissue. The flowers form dense spikes which in turn produce perennial panicles; the plants are always unisexual.

Aloe dichotoma *(Liliaceae)* 'Dragon-tree' (p. 66)

The tree has a height of 33 feet and its ramified head bears a strong resemblance to certain *Dracaena* species, to which in fact it is related. The habit of the thorny *Pachypodium* species, aptly called 'spookmen' by the Hottentots, resembles that of the American hedge cactus. Their stems are about 6¹/₂ feet in height and always incline towards the sun.

Aërangis stylosa (p. 68)

A native of Madagascar. The flowers are white with a delicate aromatic scent (relatively rare in orchids).

Mormodes wendlandii (p. 68)

Costa Rica, flowers yellow with brown lines.
Both the above are epiphytic orchids of the tropical rain forest.

Laelia anceps (p. 68)

From Mexico, pink flowers, the lip has beautiful red markings.

Phragmopedilum caudatum (p. 68)

The photograph was taken in a mist forest of Southern Peru. One of the most peculiar South American orchids related to Lady's Slipper. The calyces are whitish with greenish-yellow markings; the lip ('shoe') green to purple, about 2–2¹/₂ inches long. The two calyces hanging down at the sides are twisted and elongated like a tail (caudatum). The 'tails' are over 20 inches long.

Bartholina pectinata (p. 69)

One of the daintiest and rarest of approximately 600 species of Cape ground orchids. Note the characteristic blue, deeply slashed lip ('lip of Medusa').

Cirrhopetalum ornatissimum (p. 76)

A bizarre, reddish-brown epiphytic orchid of Thailand, fringed with fine ciliary hairs which give it a fantastic appearance.

European Ground Orchids:

Ophrys insectifera (p. 70)

This dainty orchid generally grows in quite small colonies—not too rare—but exclusively on lime, up to an altitude of 4,920 feet. It is the only one of more than 200 species of the genus *Ophrys* (insect flowers) found in the Mediterranean regions to come as far north as southern Finland. The exceedingly pretty bizarre flowers of the group rival the most beautiful tropical orchids in shape and colour, if not in size. It has been suggested that the males of certain insects *(hymenoptera)* mistake the scentless flowers for females and approach them for that reason, but this is by no means certain. The fact that visits by insects are observed extremely rarely (sometimes less than one per 1,000) and very poor fruiting seem to argue against the theory, as does the observation that insects frequently appear to shun the flowers, apparently in the belief that they are already occupied. In O. *apifera* self-pollination is the rule.

Ophrys tenthredinifera and O. speculum (p. 70)

Two particularly pretty examples from a wide range. Hardly two individuals of the same species, not even all the flowers on one and the same plant, are exactly alike in markings and colour scheme. The two species inhabit stony, shallow, dry ground in the 'Garigue', the open, low bush of the southern Mediterranean regions. In autumn the corm produces two to three leaves and a flower stalk. By the beginning of the dry summer season the old corm has been consumed and a new one formed for the following year; leaves and flowers wither. As with all other orchids, there exists here a life partnership (symbiosis) between the plant and certain root fungi. That is one reason why most attempts to grow these pretty orchids in the garden are doomed to failure.

Epipogium aphyllum (p. 70)

A rare flower growing in shady beech and fir woods among decaying leaves, also on boggy soil near springs and streams, up to 5,250 feet. Like *Neottia nidus-avis, E. aphyllum* is a humus feeder (saprophyte) without chlorophyll. The plant propagates itself almost exclusively by runners from the root. After years of an underground existence it suddenly throws up the flowers.

Venus's Slipper *(Paphiopedilum glaucophyllum)* (p. 71)

The genus has about 40 species, all of which live on the ground from China to Java. Today a great many hybrids are sold as cut flowers; some are suitable for indoor cultivation.

Vanda Hybrids (pp. 72/73)

The orchid breeders' skill in selection and hybridisation is responsible for many spectacular varieties. There are about 20 wild species in East India and Malaysia, one in tropical Australia.

The Splendour of Philippine Flowers (p. 74.) See article on page 158.

Tropical Orchids (pp. 48, 68, 69, 71, 75, 76)

The great majority of members of this most varied of all plant families (about 20,000 species) are natives of the warmer regions of the world. They grow most luxuriantly in equatorial rain forests, where they exist as epiphytes on the top of jungle trees. Their holdfasts cling to the host tree. Their aerial roots, often intertwined, are coated with a spongy substance which greedily sucks up moisture and supplies the plant with nourishment. The tips of these roots support certain fungi as symbionts, which help to liberate chemicals, especially nitrogen, from the food supply. In their turn the fungi live on the by-products of their hosts' assimilation process. Terrestrial (rooting in the soil) orchids—every one of the 100 European species is in that category—are much less common in the tropics. Nature lavishes on orchids more inexhaustible imagination in varying a basically uniform pattern than on any other plant. Their habits cover a wide range from stately richly foliated shoots to minute rudimentary forms and frequently a tendency to succulence as adaptation to long dry spells. Their flowers present every possible variation from insignificant midgets to giant colourful 'butterflies' with incredibly bizarre shapes. Today we find it difficult to imagine the halo of exaggerated romanticism with which these precious flowers were surrounded in the past century, when adventurers risked their lives as 'orchid hunters' in tropical jungles. Whole shiploads of plants were sent to Europe. Few survived the journey and ignorance of suitable conditions for cultivation killed most of these. Many rare species were undoubtedly brought to extinction in this way before sensible governments issued bans on collection and export. It is understandable that in those days (especially in England) fantastic prices were paid for a single rare specimen. It was only at the turn of the century that orchid cultivation, by growing orchids from seeds, became independent of import from the tropics. In the course of barely a century careful breeding evolved hybrids from all the horticulturally important species, which surpass the wild varieties in size as well as quantity and colouring of the flowers. It is interesting to note that the minute seeds, devoid of endosperm, of which, for instance, the capsule of *Cattleya* may contain up to 2 million, require one to two years to mature. The only industrial plant in this giant family, *Vanilla planifolia,* is a creeper, cultivated everywhere in the tropics, with inconspicuous flowers but seedpods 8 inches long, from which vanilla is extracted.

Banksia coccinea *(Proteaceae)* (p. 77, bottom)

The large cylindrical inflorescence is composed of many individual flowers. The buds at the top appear to be covered with little grey caps. What look like red matches with yellow heads at the edge, are the styles of the open flowers. In the early stages the arched styles protrude from the buds. In stretching out later, they tear the petals apart and at the same time scatter the pollen from the anthers.

Anigozanthos manglesii (p. 78, top)

Inflorescence with woolly, vividly red flower stalks and sombre green flowers. The six petals are joined together in a tongue, the tip of which is inflexed. The six stamens range side by side on the underside. (See also p. 77, top, *Anigozanthos humilis.)*

Callistemon citrinus *(Myrtaceae)* (p. 78)

This genus (11 species) is endemic in Australia and on account of its beautiful flowers often cultivated in botanical gardens. The *Myrtaceae* are shrubs or trees, generally with hard, durable wood; the plants are known for their volatile oils, contained in the glands of the frequently opposite leaves *(Eucalyptus).* The striking appearance of *Callistemon* is due to numerous, beautifully red stamens which jut out from the inconspicuous flowers. The family consists of more than 3,000 species, especially well represented in tropical America and in Australia. The genuine myrtle *(Myrtus communis)* is a caracteristic shrub of the Mediterranean maquis. Some of the Australian eucalyptus species are among the world's mightiest tree giants (more than 328 feet high and up to 33 feet in diameter.)

Rafflesia tuan-mudae *(Rafflesiaceae)* (p. 79)

A tropical representative of this family of parasites without chlorophyll, with very rudimentary vegetative organs. As with the much smaller *Cytinus hypocistis* (p. 34) of the Mediterranean regions, the giant reddish-brown flowers, smelling of decaying flesh, are formed within the root or woody stem of the host plant (in this case chiefly species of Virginia creeper.)

Tree Ferns (p. 81)

In temperate zones ferns have relatively small, herbaceous habits (although some of them grow as tall as 6½ feet.) In the moist tropical and subtropical regions of the Old and the New World, especially in America and Asia, to a lesser degree in Africa, the tree ferns of the *Cyatheaceae* family reach a height of 33 feet. The most common representatives are: *Cyathea* with about 100 species, especially *C. arborea* in South America, frequently in colonies: *Alsophila* with more than 100 species of which *A. frigida* of the Colombian Cordilleras is to be found at altitudes of up to 13,123 feet:

Dicksonia antarctica from eastern Australia and New Zealand, sometimes as tall as 59 feet. Tree ferns depend on high degrees of humidity but are not readily affected by low temperatures, some even survive slight frost (in Tasmania in regions with snowfall, in New Zealand up to the glaciers.) In botanical gardens tree ferns are to be found under glass, in milder climates also in the open (Isola Madre, Villa Taranto, Lake Maggiore.)

Alstroemeria violacea (p. 83, top)

56 species flower in South America, half of them in Chile. See also article on page 163.

Anthurium andreanum *(Araceae)*
'Flamingo Flower' (p. 83, bottom)

This species, discovered in Colombia as recently as 1876, is often cultivated in our gardens as a decorative and long-lasting flower, as is also the smaller *A. scherzerianum* from Guatemala. The insignificant flowers congregate closely on a white or yellow spadix, protruding from a pale pink or vividly red spathe. Botanical gardens cultivate some 200 other species of the genus (all from tropical America) for their beautifully marked leaves (especially *A. crystallinum* and *magnificum.)*

Cacti *(Cactaceae)* (pp. 86—88, 90—92, 99, 102, 103, 109)

Succulent (fleshy) plants whose leaves, with very few exceptions (e.g. the shrubby genus *Peireskia)* remain rudimentary. The spines protruding from the so-called areolae (corresponding to axil shoots) are modified leaves. Ranging from the thornless flat and round shoots of *Zygocactus (Epiphyllum)* and *Rhipsalis* species to the flat shoots of the *Opuntiae,* with fine or coarse spines and the spherical or pillar-shaped, ramified and often tree-sized forms, there is a rich variety of shapes which still present the taxonomist with many a hard nut to crack. The great majority of cacti inhabit the dry deserts and semi-deserts of America (USA, Mexico, Brazil). Some species are relatively impervious to low temperatures. One *Opuntia* species, for instance, occurs in the Andes at an altitude of 15,420 feet. The genera *Phyllocactus, Zygocactus* and *Rhipsalis* grow as epiphytes in the moist-warm rain forests of Central America and Brazil. One species of the cactus family *(Rhipsalis cassytha),* otherwise endemic in the New World, has been found, apparently in its natural habitat, at certain places in Africa, where its seeds may have been dropped by birds, probably a long time ago. Several species of *Opuntia* certainly have been taken to the Old World by human agents. Today they have escaped in such quantities, e.g. in the Mediterranean regions, that the uninitiated often mistake them for native plants.

Bromeliaceae (pp. 89, 94)

Approximately 1,400 species of this family, which is endemic in America (especially in the tropical regions) are perennial shrubs, with the single exception of the annual *Pitcairnia pusilla.* The stems are generally very short, so that the stiff, often beautifully marked, leaves form characteristic funnel-shaped rosettes, which collect rainwater and contain real little 'aquaria' in the tree tops. Insects and even frogs live in these unusual 'ponds'. The spiky inflorescences grow from the axils of vividly coloured (especially red) hypsophylls. In one group the ovary is hypogynous, the fruit a capsule with several, generally very small seeds, equipped with a corona of hair to facilitate aerial flight *(Puya);* or the ovary is perigynous and the fruit in that case a berry. With *Ananas sativa,* a non-epiphytic species, the berries and the axis join together to form a collective fruit. Secondary shoots often grow from the axils of the main shoots and may be used for propagation. In the epiphytic species the roots are merely organs which enable them to cling to the plants on which they grow; water and mineral salts are absorbed through the scales on the sheaths of the leaves.
Genus *Puya* has some 80 species, which inhabit the higher regions of the South American Andes (up to and above 13,123 feet.) The stately *Puya raimondii* (see illustration p. 89) reaches a height of 33 feet. The stem is about 13 feet in height and 20 inches across. It carries the giant rosette of the leaves. The inflorescence, 16¹/₂ feet in height, crowns a stalk of 3¹/₄ feet. The giant *Puya* grows among dry quartz rubble and rocks in a few places in North and South Peru and Bolivia, generally at altitudes of between 13,123 feet and 14,436 feet. The largest single colony with about 10,000 specimens is to be found on Serro Cunsuch in the Black Cordilleras. In spite of the fact that shepherds regularly burn down *Puyas*—it is alleged that sheep get entangled in the barbed leaves and die—the vitality of the plant does not appear to suffer. The discoverer Raimondi counted about 8,000 flowers on a single plant and estimated the number of seeds to be 6¹/₂ million (according to Professor Kinzl.)

Giant Passion Flower *(Passiflora quadrangularis, Passifloraceae)* (p. 95)

Creepers with tendrils and generally palmately lobed leaves. Between the corolla and the raised stamens and stigma there is a circle of thread-like, often vividly striped, appendages which give rise to the comparison with Christ's crown of thorns. Some species have large edible fruit, sometimes beautifully coloured. Today we know about 400 different kinds of passion flowers, mostly in tropical, to a lesser degree in sub-tropical, America; others occur in Asia, Australia and Polynesia. Horticultural breeding has evolved many new varieties.

Datura arborea (p. 96)

from Peru and Chile and the related *D. suaveolens* from Mexico, with giant pendulous trumpet-shaped flowers are tree-like representatives of the family of nightshades *(Solanaceae)*, which in Europe occurs only in herbaceous forms and comprises such industrially important plants as the potato, tomato, paprika, as well as some poionous and medicinal plants like Belladonna *(Atropa belladonna)* and henbane *(Hyoscyamus)*, tobacco *(Nicotiana)* and mandrake *(Mandragora)*, which in mediaeval times was believed to possess magic powers.

Hylocereus undatus *(Cactaceae)* (p. 99)
(Mexican name 'Pitahaya')

This cactus climbs on shrubs and trees like a liana and flowers at night like some species of the genus *Selenicereus (S. grandiflorus*, 'Queen of the Night') and *Nyctocereus*. The flowers are up to 12 inches long and appear abundantly in July and August. This magnificent plant is a native of Hawaii and Jamaica but is cultivated for its fist-sized edible fruit anywhere in the sub-tropical and tropical regions; it is hardy in the Riviera.

Xerophyllum tenax *(Liliaceae)*, 'Bear Grass' (p. 100)

The man-sized stem rises from a rosette of grass-like, hard leaves, which Red Indians use for basket work. At the top it carries a dense tuft of small, yellowish-white flowers. Bear grass flowers in spring in great quantities in the northern part of the Rocky Mountains. The thick root corms have been known from ancient times to provide a nourishing meal for man and beast.

Yucca brevifolia *(Y. arborescens)* Palm Lily, Joshua Tree, Tree Yucca *(Agavaceae)* (p. 101)

The plant grows as high as 33 feet, and is of primeval appearance. It is related to the Dragon tree *(Dracaenoideae:* also arboreal, the genera *Dracaena, Nolina, Dasylirion, Cordyline)* and is the characteristic plant of the south-east Californian Mohave desert (also in Arizona, Nevada and Utah.) The genus *Yucca*, with about 20 species, is a native of the southern States of the U.S.A., Mexico and Central America. The smaller, non-arboreal *Y. filamentosa* and *angustifolia*, with sword-shaped leaves and very decorative inflorescence, over 3¹/₄ feet high, is hardy in Central Europe. In cultivation it fruits very rarely as its pollination depends on certain moths.

Rhododendron *(Ericaceae)*, Rose Bay, also the gardeners' 'Azalea' (pp. 30, 41, 104, 105)

There are about 1,000 wild species in the wooded mountainous regions of East and South Asia (Himalayas) and in North America. Only *Rh. ferrugineum* and *hirsutum* occur in the Alps, and the large-flowered *Rh. ponticum* today only in Southern Spain and on the coast of the Black Sea, although in the inter-glacial ages it was established in Central Europe. Today the large-flowered shrubs of our gardens with evergreen or summer-green foliage are available in almost countless numbers of varieties and every possible colour from white, pink, purple, dark red, dark purple to yellow and orange. 'Azaleas', the richly flowering pot plants which are among the most important winter flowerers, are all derived from *Rh. simsii ('Azalea indica')*, which in 1680 was introduced into Holland from Java. Almost all rhododendrons demand acid marshy soil; failures in cultivation are almost invariably due to hard, limy water.

Californian Poppy *(Eschscholtzia, Papaveraceae)* (p. 108)

The lack of milky juice in the yellow or orange flowers and the long, pod-like capsule distinguish this species from other Papaveraceae with similar habits. More than 120 species are characteristic plants of the steppes and deserts of North America. The best known species is *E. california*, Californian Poppy, the state emblem of California, which grows frequently as a summer flower in our gardens.
P. 109, see also the article on page 166.

Erythronium parviflorum *(Liliaceae)* (p. 110)

From the sub-alpine levels of the Rocky Mountains of California. Almost all 15 species of the genus are American, with the single exception of *E. denscanis* (dogtooth lily), which occurs in the southern Alps, Siberia and Japan.

Castilleja miniata *(Scrophulariaceae)* (p. 111)

'Indian Paint Brush.' On the edge of the forest region *(Tsuga pattoniana, Abies subalpina* and *Pinus albicaulis)* up to 9,858 feet, on Mount Rainier, Washington. A semi-parasite related to *Rhinantoideae*, which, like eyebright, is able to assimilate by means of chlorophyll but whose roots also tap other plants for nourishment.

Poinciana regia *(Caesalpiniaceae)* (p. 112)

There are three families in the large order of *Leguminosae;* more than 7,000 species. The tropical and sub-tropical *Mimosaceae* with radiate flowers and numerous stamens (among them the well known 'mimosa' with yellow capitula, botanically speaking classified as belonging to the genus *Acacia*, while our 'acacia' is really a *Robinia* and belongs to the third endemic European family of *Papilionaceae):* the second family *(Caesalpiniaceae)*, like the former, with dorsoventral flowers, but free stamens. They are shrubs and trees of the sub-tropical and tropical regions *(Ceratonia siliqua* and the Judas tree, *Cercis siliquastrum*, in the Mediterranean regions.) The genus *Poinciana*, with three species, belongs to this group and is a native of tropical Africa and Asia. With very few exceptions, *Leguminosae* have feathery leaves (often very regular and decorative.)

Plant Life in the Arctic Circle

ALWIN PEDERSEN

People generally imagine that the countries beyond the Arctic Circle are buried under snow and ice all the year round. They imagine vast icy deserts with only here and there some bare rock or steep mountain side, which for a short time in summer may clothe itself in sparse vegetation. But there are only a very few places in the Arctic Circle, and perhaps some rocky islands in the Arctic Sea, where those conditions prevail. Even the northernmost country of the world, the north coast of Greenland, knows a spring more tender and pure than anything we can imagine. True, the arctic spring is short and comes later than our spring. Not before the middle of May is the noon sun able to warm the air to above freezing point and the great thaw does not begin until a month later. But even before that moment has been reached, the sun now shining day and night, warms the dark soil through its blanket of snow, so that plants put forth green shoots while still thinly covered with snow. From now on spring makes giant strides. Around streams, ponds and lakes, as they emerge from the snow, there appear large hummocks of lush mosses and a carpet of many-coloured flowers. The valleys and damp low-lying meadows are clothed in green; creamy white heather flowers, berry shrubs, creeping sallow and arctic birch decorate the arid plateaux and gentle slopes. Plants and animals awake to new life. Musk-oxen and reindeer roam the green meadows, followed by white snow-hares, the prettiest, tamest little creatures imaginable, and from tiny holes in the only superficially thawed earth sound the whistles of the lemmings. Suddenly amid the burgeoning of spring, winged hosts of summer visitors return from milder parts. Gulls and petrels are fishing in the cracks of the ice; geese, divers and eider ducks bustle about and at the mossy edge of babbling brooks golden plovers and sand-pipers utter their clear flute-like calls by day and night.

To the arctic vegetation the short summer is of special importance because of the long, dark, very cold winter that follows. In the short period from May to August—higher up in the north, even from June to July—these plants must complete their life cycle of growing, flowering and bearing seeds. Only during these few summer months, when there is no snow, is the air warm enough for growth. Thus plant life is confined to the smallest and shortest round of time, but the summer compensates with almost uninterrupted sunshine, or at least continuous daylight. All arctic plants are small, low-growing and often scanty. Their leaves are small and closely bunched for mutual protection. However, their flowers are large and vividly coloured; thus they attract insects for pollination. All plants live several years and there are no annuals. Mosses and lichens prevail among approximately 1,000 species of arctic plants; flowering plants are represented by grasses, ranunculi, poppies, cruciferae, saxifragae, berry shrubs and low sallows and birches. The most resistant is the hummock-forming saxifraga, the northernmost flowering plant of this earth.

It is most important for the life of these plants that the sun should warm up the soil. On slopes facing south or west the surface of the ground thaws very rapidly and thus enables plants to grow. They nestle on the ground to benefit as much as possible from its warmth and for protection against the wind. On the northern coast of Greenland, I observed the strength of the sun in the pure dry air of the high North. In a shallow depression overgrown with heather I measured 35° C. (95° F.) while the air temperature about a foot and a half above ground was only 6° C. (about 41° F.). These comparatively high air temperatures near the ground account for the fact that chicks of snow-hens and golden plovers, when only a few days old, roam about quite happily, while we humans do not find the air temperature at all comfortable.

Water supply is no less important than ground temperature, especially in the arid climate of the high North. Almost all arctic plants are capable of growing with hardly any water and get sufficient moisture only in the summer and at the time of the thaw. On the very dry soil which is characteristic of large areas in the arctic proper, vegetation does not form a complete ground cover, but appears in the shape of hummocks, as is also the case on high mountains and in the desert. However, rich vegetation exists on the slopes and in the valleys which are irrigated for long periods at a time by melting snow and where water collects.
It is obvious from the habit of the plants that they seek to protect themselves against the drying winds. The more sheltered the area, the richer its vegetation, and the best plant cover is to be found at well-watered places inland and far from the gales of the coastal areas. A covering of snow also protects plants from frost and the drying effect of the wind. The first snow falls on green vegetation and covers the warm soil with a non-conducting air chamber. Gradually the plants stiffen but they retain their mineral salts and are thus preserved for the benefit of herbivorous animals which scratch them out of the snow in the winter time.
A feature of the arctic zone is the tundra, a dense cover of moss and lichen interspersed with grasses and herbs. In the plains it adjoins the forest, ranging from the transitional tundra, chiefly of dwarf shrubs, to the genuine tundra in which mosses, lichens, herbs and grasses prevail. Still further north and at great altitudes the arctic desert is to be found, which does not have a complete plant cover and, on account of its arid character, allows only primitive lichens and mosses to exist.
There are no erect trees in the Arctic Circle; the inhabitants have to make do with drift wood carried north by rivers which flow into the Arctic Sea, and this drift wood makes it possible for man to exist permanently in these areas. In spring and summer the North Russian, Siberian and North American rivers carry drift wood into the Arctic Sea, where currents take hold of it until it is washed ashore.

The Lüneburg Heath

WERNER HARRO KÖNIG

It is surprising how few people know the quiet, austere beauty of the countryside of North Germany between the rivers Elbe and Aller. The same applies to the rare art treasures of the old cities of Lüneburg, Celle, Verden and others. No one in the South of Germany or elsewhere knows about the treasures of their mediaeval monasteries. But whenever a visitor finds his way to the inhospitable north, perhaps because he has read books by the poet of the Heath, Hermann Löns, or a call has reached him from Lower Germany, his sincere admiration knows no bounds. Descriptions of the Lüneburg Heath in old school books abound in uncomplimentary expressions, such as arid, poor, monotonous, as bare and flat as a table top, unattractive and completely uninteresting. But a little research reveals that since 1650 authors have been more or less copying each other and that none of them has seen the heath with his own eyes. It was only at the beginning of the twentieth century, when Hermann Löns wrote his books and coined the phrase of the 'rose-red distance,' that people began to take notice. Incredulously at first, they read what the hunter poet had to say about rare plants and animals, great lonely farmhouses where one and the same family had resided for generations, mighty forests, delightful valleys and the wide sweep of the landscape. True, modern progress has left its mark on the Lüneburg Heath and inevitably the countryside has changed, but its essential character remains. Its in-

timate charm reveals itself only to him who goes out to look for it. The phrase 'The Heath has a hundred faces and more' is still valid, although cultivation and afforestation have turned the rose-red distance into park land.
Let me give a brief description of the characteristic features of the landscape. The contours of the area between the rivers Elbe and Aller were formed in the ice ages and in parts it is very diverse in its structure. During the milder periods between the ice ages vast amounts of water from the melting glaciers washed away the soil, cutting deep valleys in one place, piling up moraines to hilly ranges in others. Only the approximate centre of the area, the high moor around Soltau and the plateau of the southern heath, remained almost untouched. To this day it is possible to discern the effect of the pressure exercised by the three main glaciers from the north-west, the north and the north-east. In addition to some ranges of moraine running in different directions, they piled up the main range running from east to west, which serves as the water and weather divide and bi-sects the whole area from the Puglatz (387 feet) to the Wilseder Mountains (555 feet). From its ridge, on average about 328 feet high, streams flow in a northerly direction to join the Elbe and in a southerly to join the Aller. The third ice age overwhelmed the whole area with its dust storms; erosion completed the process and gave the landscape its final shape. Climatologically speaking, the northern part of the Heath has a maritime and the southern part a continental climate.
The botanist will deliver his sober judgement: lacking in variety. Compared with richer countrysides, the Heath is just that, for the variety of the flora depends on the nature of soil and climate. But throughout the four seasons of the year, there are many different species to be found, and the Heath has tender and intimate moods to touch the heart of the spectator. The vegetation presents a constantly changing picture.
It begins in early spring, when the pollen of hazel catkins floats in the rays of the sun like a golden cloud. The first snowdrops peep out from under last year's dry leaves. You can almost hear a thin, silvery tinkle when the gentle breeze moves them. Blackbirds, mistle and song thrushes whistle, the robin sings its rippling song, the tits chime, the finches warble, and from the dark pines sounds the low call of the wood pigeon. Soon the woods lay down a carpet of pink and white windflowers, of which there is also the yellow variety. Figwort covers the marshy ground and there is even some blue hepatica, though that is rare and protected by law. Around Easter there are primroses and scented yellow cowslips. Slowly the water meadows are getting green and the white blossoms of the cuckooflower hang over them like a delicate veil. The marsh marigold makes a great show in the ditches, where one may find an occasional *Fritillaria.*
The moor is also astir. Early on at its edges the wax-myrtle swings its catkins and the bushes are aflame in the sun. *Ledum palustre* with its pungent smell and white flowers is rare. Among trees the birch prevails and, where the ground is not so moist, holly bushes *(Ilex aquifolium)* form the undergrowth, but do not often grow to the height and thickness of a tree. Early in May cotton-grass speckless the heath and the leathery scent of young birch leaves fills the air. Then the curlew whistles and the heath cocks utter their love-calls at first light. The green plovers call from everywhere and wing in giddy flight over heath and fields. At the end of May, *Andromeda* flowers like a little miracle in hidden corners.
The forest, too, is not to be outdone, with the swelling leaf buds of the oak trees and the tender young green of the beeches, with tall bushes of the bird-cherry, dusted with white blossoms, and the light green tips of the pines. The hawthorn flowers at the edge of the woods and there are many rarities to be found. Wood violet, speedwell, lungwort, yellow dead-nettle, follow the invitation of the rising sun and on dry ground *Trientalis europaea* and May lily. Later the leaf

mould of the open deciduous forest bears Herb Paris, Solomon's seal, *Polygonatum multiflorum* and lilies of the valley amid a large expanse of flowering woodruff. In the half-shade you may find beautiful orchids, such as *Platanthera bifolia,* which emits its scent only at night, and, very rarely, *Cephalanthera* and the most splendid orchid of them all, lady's slipper *(Cypripedium calceolus).*

In the uplands the heath as yet knows nothing of spring. It still bears its brownish-grey coat of mid-winter. The blue chalice of the Pasque flower appears here and there in the few places where it does grow on the gentle hill slopes, but the upland does not really wake up until the pines have lit their candles and the weeping birch along the country road waves its light-green veil. That is also the time for the tall junipers to show the first green tips, for the mountain ash to blossom and the broom to clothe the sandy slopes in mantles of gold. The Scotch heather shows its first green very late, at the end of May, and at the same time spearwort flowers appear in the stream and yellow iris on the banks.

Early summer passes into high summer. No sooner do the ears appear on the rye than clouds of pollen blow over the fields. The water meadows await the mower. Their flora is scanty compared with that of the rich pasture, where hart's tongue and water avens vie with buttercups, orchids, ox-eye and lamp flower and, rarely, Star of Bethlehem. Above the moor the air vibrates in hot waves. The treacherous ground is covered with crowberry and bogberry and the rare sundew grows here. In the quiet ponds the beautiful stars of the water lily *(Nymphaea alba)* open up, and here and there *Nymphaea candida.* Blueberries and cranberries ripen in the woods. In July the golden fields of rye dominate the landscape. The warm summer wind is laden with the scent of ripening bread corn. Slowly the rowanberries begin to blush along the country roads and the bell heather flowers where the ground is moist. Herds of grey-fleeced sheep roam in the fields and on the slopes.

At the beginning of August the erica comes into its own. The first blush appears on the slopes and in the valleys. It spreads and grows until, in the last week of August, the country is wrapped in a festive dress. A wonderful sight reveals itself to the spectator from the hills, a fervent blossoming below the blue silk of the heavens. White clouds drift slowly with the gentle wind. There is a rushing and buzzing in the air like the sound of an organ—millions of bees gathering nectar.

As the heather fades, it assumes a warm bronze tint, which is particularly attractive. Slowly the birch leaves turn to gold. The blackberries ripen. The rowan trees are wrapped in the dark red of their berries and the silvery threads of the Indian summer drift over the wide fields. Early night frosts paint the woods with a multitude of colours and awaken the cries of the stags. Mid-October and the magic days of the 'crane summer': the cranes are flying south. These grey wanderers of the skies come down from the north in long chains of wedge-like formations and their raucous cries fill the sunlit vault of the October sky. The leaves drop, autumn has come. These weeks are a little sad and yet they bestow the gift of a peculiar joy and much beauty to the wanderer who surrenders to their charm. November comes in with the first autumn gales. Winter is not far away. One morning snow covers the countryside and with it comes the great silence, the stillness of waiting for new life. The year has turned full circle.

The Flora of South Tyrol and the Dolomites

DR H. REISIGL

South Tyrol has two merits which make it especially attractive to the naturalist: the mild climate of the valleys favours a vegetation unfamiliar to those from the north; and the beauty and vitality of the alpine flora is nowhere more impressive than among the mighty rock towers of the Dolomites. And what contrasts there are within so small a space! In the gardens of Merano palms grow and cypresses, figs ripen, fruit trees and vine bear their heavy burden and the cool shade of Spanish chestnut trees invites the wanderer to rest. About 9 miles north, as the crow flies, there tower the dark gneiss rocks of the Ötztal Alps to heights of over 12,139 feet. Thus nature offers a wide range, and in endless variety and fascinating contrasts bridges the gap between the southern vegetation of the Vintschgau to the last flowers on the edge of the eternal snows.

Characteristic of the lowest 'sub-Mediterranean' level of vegetation is a varied bush forest with *Quercus pubescens, Ostrya carpinifolia, Fraxinus ornus, Celtis australis, Ulmus campestris, Prunus mahaleb, Amelanchier ovalis, Colutea arborescens, Cornus mas, Cotinus coggygria, Pistacia terebinthus* and other shrubs.

As associated plants of a southern distribution may be mentioned the orchids *Ophrys fuciflora* and *apifera, Orchis coriophora, tridentata* and *latifolia, Anacamptis pyramidalis, Himantoglossum hircinum* and *Limodorum abortivum; Clematis recta, Dorycnium herbaceum, Tamus communis, Orlaya grandiflora, Lithospermum purpureo-coeruleum, Globularia willkommii, Galium rubrum, Campanula spicata* and *bononiensis* and *Aster linosyris.*

Decreasing in richness towards the north, the bush forest extends in the Adige valley to Silandro, in the Isarco valley to Bressanone and to a height of about 3,953 feet at the most. Where *Quercus pubescens* grows, there also vine and Spanish chestnuts are to be found.

On the hot rocky slopes facing south there is no water at all; here the bush forest gives way to pines and steppe. The Vintschgau, in particular, has wide stretches of brownish-white arid ground. On the sandy parched ground every sign of life seems to have withered between the solitary sparse shrubs of barberry, fire thorn, juniper and the poisonous *Juniperus sabina* with its unpleasant smell; however, a closer look reveals a few excellently adapted plants. Between the slate-blue tufts of *Festuca vallesiaca* and the silvery grey of the genuine wormwood *(Artemisia absinthium)* there flutter the white whisps of *Stipa pulcherrima* and the silky *Melica ciliata.* The brown arid slopes are enlivened by the beautiful *Andropogon gryllus, Tragus racemosus, Diplachne serotina, Carex supina* and *liparocarpus, Notholaena marantae* and *Asplenium ceterach, Linum tenuifolium, Helianthemum apenninum* and *Fumana procumbens* and *ericoides.* A special treasure of a landscape so splendid and impressive despite its apparent bareness are the various tragacanthae, some beautiful and rare papilionaceous plants which, like many of their neighbours, migrated from the inner-Asian steppes during the ice age (the purple flowering *Astragalus onobrychis* and silky-haired *Oxytropis halleri,* the yellow *Oxytropis camgestris, Astragalus exscapus* and *pastellianus),* as also *Ephedra distachya,* an old-fashioned little shrub which is to be found as a great rarity near Silandro.

Twice a year the woods of *Quercus pubescens* enchant even the hastiest tourist: in early spring when the bare wintry slopes are speckled all over with the yellow blossoms of the Cornelian cherry; a little later when the golden flowers of *Coronilla emerus* appear among the first tender green of *Ostrya carpinifolia,* and again in the autumn when the fiery colours of *Cotinus coggygria* gleam among the brown leaves.

More striking to the layman than the natural vegetation and more representative of the 'south' are the exotic strangers—some of them introduced only recently—to be found in gardens and parks. Particularly rich in trees and shrubs and well worth visiting because of their picturesque situation are the gardens in Merano (Gilfpromenade in the Passer Glen; Tappeiner Road to Dorf Tirol) and in Bolzano (Oswaldpromenade, Talferpromenade).
The most beautiful feature in a country as rich in beauty as South Tyrol, are the flowery larch meadows in the mountain regions, whose forests largely resemble those of the northern Alps. They were artificially created by the felling of pines. Especially in the late autumn, when the larch trees stand like golden flames in the gentle sunshine, a walk on the wide lonely plateau of the Salten, the long ridge between the Sarentino and the Adige, reveals the magic of this country. Walking from the Vintschgau through the Schnalser Valley towards the border ridge of the Ötztal Alps, we experience within a few hours' ascent to 9,843 feet a change of vegetation which takes us about 750 miles nearer to the North Pole. The plant types we might find on this mental journey to the north in successive zones, each measuring perhaps 100 miles, here change with altitude and within a relatively small space—the botanist calls them 'altitude levels of vegetation.' The main reason for this phenomenon is to be found in the deterioration of the climate or, in other words, in the diminishing period of vegetation. The more exacting the requirements of a plant in regard to temperature, the longer the period it requires for its life cycle, and the less its capacity to penetrate into cooler regions. Thus our journey takes us from the mountain forests of pine and larch, interspersed with a few deciduous trees, such as mountain maple, mountain elm, aspen and mountain ash, to the highest and last forests of stone-pine *(Pinus cembra)* and larch until at about 6,562 to 7,212 feet we reach the woodless 'alpine' region.
Where avalanches and falling rocks have scarred the woodland, dwarf mountain pine often fills the gap. In damp grooves but also on naturally woodless damp northfacing scree slopes with alkaline soil, *Alnus viridis* grows in vast, impenetrable thickets, often interspersed with sallows and shrubby birches, which not uncommonly become predominant; a lush undergrowth of tall plants *(Athyrium alpestre, Adenostyles alliariae* and *Mulgedium alpinum)* offers good pasture to the deer. On acid soil the dwarf pine, which is characteristic of lime-stone, in places covers larger areas.
Immediately above the tree line woody plants still prevail at first, even though they are small and finally dwarfish. *Rhododendron ferrugineum* and *Vaccinium myrtillus* not only provide the larger part of the undergrowth in stone-pine forests, together with *Juniperus sibirica,* they form the mosaic of the 'dwarf shrub heath' at that altitude. In the higher regions *Vaccinium vitis-idaea* and *Vaccinium uliginosum* are prevalent, the dark red leaves of the latter in autumn being visible from afar as coloured patches with clean-cut edges. On very acid soil Scotch heather *(Calluna vulgaris)* dominates; on wind-swept ridges the dwarf espaliers of *Loiseleuria procumbens* defy the gales and in shady moist runnels *Salix helvetica* collects in fairly large clumps. Where pasture has been intensive, heather has often been ousted by *Nardus stricta* which suppresses the growth of tenderer grasses. But the mountaineer finds pleasure in *Campanula barbata* and *Arnica montana, Potentilla aurea, Gentiana punctata* and, in the valleys of Schnals and Ötz particularly, the orange-coloured *Senecio abrotanifolius, sub-species tirolienses,* weave a carpet of flowers. At well manured places where cattle rest, they are accompanied by the splendid flowers of the blue *Aconitum napellus,* the yellowish-white *Cirsium spinosissimum* and *Senecio alpinus.*
In the adjoining 'upper-alpine' region dwarf shrubs disappear altogether and we approach the brownish-yellow fields of 'alpine grass moors,' the highest plant societies of the Central Alps. In the early summer vivid flowers enliven the monotonous grey of *Carex curvula.* Beside the

blackish-red *Nigritella nigra* and a deep blue gentian *(Gentiana rotundifolia),* there are scented alpine clover *(Trifolium alpinum),* the red throats of *Pedicularis kerneri,* above the white down of the leaves the dark yellow flowers of *Senecio carniolicus,* the highly valued aromatic *Achillea moschata, Erigeron uniflorus,* the yellow ears of *Luzula lutea* and *spicata* and blue grass *(Sesleria disticha).*

The grass moors of *Carex sempervirens* and *Elyna myosuroides* flourish on less acid soil and are particularly rich in flowers. Next to the elegant *Lloydia serotina* glow the crimson flowers of *Hedysarum obscurum,* the blue and white of some tragacantha groups *(Astragalus alpinus, montanus* and *campestris),* the purple stars of the alpine aster *(Aster alpinus)* and the shaggy edelweiss *(Leontopodium alpinum).* Between them nestle a great variety of lichens: *Thamnolia vermicularis, Cladonia rangiferina* and *Cetraria islandica.*

In warm rocky fissures *Juncus trifidus* together with *Sempervivum arachnoideum* and *Primula hirsuta* sometimes take the place of the sedges; the yellow *Sieversia reptans* creeps along moist rills with long reddish runners between the golden stars of *Doronicum clusii.* Where the snow lies for six months or more the moors give way to the so-called 'snow-floors' with their characteristic vegetation, in particular the dense dark brownish-green hummocks of *Polytrichum norvegicum* and whitish-grey *Anthelia juratzkana* covering small ridges on the ground. Among them—at least in the alpine region—flowering plants are still to be found. Beside the blue *Primula glutinosa, Cerastium trigynum* and *pedunculatum* and *Gnaphalium supinum* there creeps *Arenaria biflora.* The pretty little *Soldanella pusilla* and two valuable fodder plants, *Ligusticum mutellina* and *Luzula spadicea,* share the short summer season with the deciduous tree that climbs higher than any other (9,843 feet), *Salix herbacea,* which Linnaeus already called 'the smallest of all trees.' Where the snow lies even longer, only mosses and the beautiful *Solorina crocea,* whose leaves are saffron yellow on the underside, can survive.

Flower gardens under the Icy Wind of the Glacier

Above 9,843 feet the grass cover breaks up increasingly and the room-sized carpets of *Carex curvula* and with them many of the above mentioned plants climb on especially sunny and sheltered ridges into the snow region (up to 10,827 feet on Hinterer Spiegelkogel); above begins the region of hummock plants. Already in the grass moors, but even more so at these altitudes, the plants undergo a striking change. They are strong but compact, nestling low on the ground; the colours are more vivid, the leaves covered with long hair or thick felt. The close proximity of many individual stalks in dense hummocks protects the plants against wind and evaporation. At the same time many seeds find their first seed beds here. A tendency towards small, dwarfish growth is generally to be observed at the vegetation line. The dwarf form finds it easier to shelter among the rocks and no plant would be able to produce a great deal of matter in the short period of three or four months. A little leaf, another one, then flower, fruit and seed: this is only possible in the tiniest dimensions. Thus the tiniest forms of any plant genus are commonly found on the highest peaks at the edge of the ice and the arid desert.

Silene acaulis, Minuartia sedoides, Aretia alpina and several saxifrages *(Saxifraga bryoides, moschata* and *oppositifolia), Poa laxa, Cerastium uniflorum,* a minute crucifera *(Draba fladnizensis)* and above all the king of our alpines, *Ranunculus glacialis,* in many places approach close to the peaks. This most hardy flowering plant of the Alps which penetrates furthest into the icy waste, of all plants has no obvious protection, no fur, no hummock, no dwarf habit. It apparently has no need of any outward protection. Its innate structure enables it to perform its unique task, and science remains mystified.

Another fact strikes us: in these regions the greatest changes take place within the smallest space. At this altitude the smallest alteration of contour, the slightest change in exposure to sun or wind, corresponds to such enormous changes in the micro-climate (fluctuations in soil temperature of 122° F. between day and night are not uncommon) that the conditions necessary for plant life are actually not infrequently confined to a space measuring only a few square inches; immediately adjoining lies the desert: cold, lifeless rock, but even this only apparently so. That red patch is not a path marker, those yellow specks are not a mineral. They are lichens, the most undemanding creatures of the vegetable world still visible to the naked eye. They live on even the highest snowless peaks of the Alps and perhaps the world.

Observations to date have shown that in the Ötztal Alps 74 flowering plants grow above the 9,843 feet limit. On the Hinterer Spiegelkogel no fewer than 29 genera flower and seed in a tiny flower garden at an altitude of 11,255 feet, and the dwarf shrubs of *Vaccinimum uliginosum* defy the gales at 10,827 feet.

When after a long and exhausting journey over scree and ice we set our feet on firm rock and suddenly discover a big red ball, a living plant hummock, adorned with countless little pink-like flowers *(Silene acaulis)*, it strikes us in a strange way as symbolic: this plant must possess a vitality which passes human understanding. Here at life's uttermost limit, existence appears a miracle.

Descending after a rest on the summit of Similaun or Weisskugel, elated by the overwhelming view over mountains and valleys and returning to the realm of men as befits us, we follow the roaring waters towards Vent and the narrow path over steep mountain meadows where at an altitude of 8,874 feet the farmer gathers the precious sweet smelling hay, a difficult and dangerous task. Somewhat lower down the meadows are ripe for mowing in mid-July; the grass is knee-high below the splendid Turk's cap *(Lilium martagon)* and the shiny blackish-blue flowers of *Phyteuma halleri.* Stalk by stalk the sulphur-yellow anemones *(Anemone sulphurea)* tremble in the slightest breeze, and on black hairy stems the fiery red heads of *Hieracium aurantiacum* grow among the slashed leaves of *Laserpitium panax.* (The meadows of Heiligkreuz and Rofen at blossom time are an unforgettable experience.)

The South Tyrolean Dolomites have always been famous for the splendour of their flowers, although there are very few endemic plants and these are mostly so insignificant as to be known to, and appreciated by, only the expert. I would mention *Primula tirolensis, Rhizobotrya alpina, Sempervivum dolomiticum, Saxifraga facchinii* and *depressa* and *Campanula morettiana.* Although here in the heartland of the Alps western, eastern, northern and southern genera converge, the most beautiful and striking plants are to be found throughout or in the greater part of the Southern Alps, some of them as far westwards as the Maritime Alps and as far southwards as the Karst and the mountains of Northern Yugoslavia. Apart from these main areas in the south, some of them have smaller areas of distribution in the Northern Alps. As examples of such wide-spread 'Dolomite plants' I could mention *Asplenium seelosii,* some grasses such as *Festuca sieberi, Trisetum argenteum,* and *Sesleria sphaerocephala, Paradisia liliastrum, Aquilegia einseleana, Aconitum ranunculifolium, Soldanella minima, Androsace hausmannii, Douglasia vitaliana,* the peach-flowered, silver-leafed *Potentilla nitida, Saxifraga hostii, crustata* and *burseriana, Lamium orvala, Horminum pyrenaicum, Pedicularis rosea, Geranium argenteum,* the blue *Veronica bonarota, Rhodothamnus chamaecistus, Phyteuma comosum, Artemisia nitida,* and the feathery *Centaurea nervosa.*

The reason for the small number of endemic genera is to be found in the past. During the ice ages the Dolomites (with the exception of the southern spurs) were covered by glaciers up to heights of 8,874 and 9,202 feet, as were the Alps in general. Only the highest peaks and ridges were free from ice. In these unfavourable circumstances only the most hardy plants were able to survive, many were pushed out into the ice-free foothills of the Alps and only some of these returned later. Formerly continuous areas of distribution were divided into smaller separate pockets and not a few genera were probably completely annihilated. On the other hand, many plants which did not formerly grow in these parts migrated during the ice ages, some from the north (e.g. *Loiseleuria procumbens* and White Dryas), some from Siberia, like *Elyna myosuroides*, Stone-pine, *Aster alpinus* and edelweiss. Old, pre-ice-age 'relic' plants, living fossils so to speak, remain in greater numbers, particularly at the edges of the Southern Alps between Lake Garda and Lake Como, which were never covered with glaciers, and in the east in the Julian Alps.

The reputation of the Dolomites as a flowering Garden of Eden is due not so much to endemic plants as to the abundance of flowers on the alpine meadows surrounded by majestic mountains. There is no point in listing particular places; those that can only be reached on foot are decidedly richer in flowers than the more accessible mountain passes. To the botanist, it seems to me, the famous Seiser Alm is still the finest place. Although it is easily accessible by road from Völs or by funicular from St. Ulrich in Gröden, it is still possible on weekdays to roam for hours on this 'greatest Alm of Europe' without meeting too many people. What is the best season? You should see it at Whitsun, when a vast sea of white golden-furred and sulphurous-yellow anemones ring in the spring, and in July before the grass is mown, when flowers of every colour adorn the lush meadows. Hardly less beautiful are the Alms on the other side of the Grödner Valley, round the Regensburg hut, or on Raschötz at the foot of the Geislerspitzen. In summer you should stand below a majestic rock face and marvel at the miracle of a bouquet of *Campanula morettiana* apparently growing on bare rock, or admire the splendid *Phyteuma comosum.* You should walk the vast bone-white lime-scree slopes before the magnificent back-drop of the Drei Zinnen, where the big golden keys, as thin as tissue paper, of the yellow mountain poppy *(Papaver rhaeticum),* dance in their thousands to the music of the fresh mountain breeze. Even fleeting experiences may leave deep impressions; anyone who has ever seen this magnificent country will be enthralled and unable to forget it. How many have journeyed to Venice 'through the Dolomites' and not been seized by a longing to renew this first acquaintance. It takes patience to let the acquaintance ripen into friendship, the friendship into a firm bond. In our case it demands the almost unthinkable renunciation of the motor car; but if you have the will to leave the highroad of motorised mass tourism, you will find in the lonely valleys, on the unspoilt peaks of the Dolomites, a wild, yet tender beauty in the harmony of mountain and flower.

The Plant World of the Mediterranean Countries

DR H. REISIGL

Who, in snow and wintry cold, has never felt a longing for a little warmth, for the south? Every year hosts of people, hungering after the sun, journey to France, to Italy, to Spain and Greece. The edges of the Mediterranean are ancient cultural ground; Egyptians, Phoenicians, Greeks and Romans lived on these coasts, colonised, waged wars and traded. What has that to do with the world of plants? If you want to understand the modern aspect of a country, so largely determined by its vegetation, you must know its past. When we remember that large areas of the then centre of the world were already extensively cultivated at the time of Christ's birth and considerably changed by human influences, and that in the past 2,000 years nature has been exploited, even despoiled, often quite irrationally and without any thought for future generations, we begin to understand the startlingly desert-like, sadly monotonous emptiness of the Ebro valley in Castile, the Sicilian interior and some of the Dalmatian islands, which resemble the frightening picture of a moonscape. Forest land which today all civilised countries regard as one of their most valuable natural treasures, until comparatively recent times was nothing but the source of much desired timber. The best known example is Venice, whose palaces stand on the stems of Dalmatian forests. Homer's Ithaca, an Ionian island which as recently as the sixteenth century boasted large oak forests, is today overgrown by the dark thickets of the maquis. Where the ground was exhausted, the forests destroyed and the dead eroded limestone laid bare, there, as in large parts of Greece, the 'garigue' or even the rock heath prevail, i.e. open vegetation of hairy or thorny dwarf shrubs which lead a miserable existence in fissures of the bare rock. Excessive pasture of small ruminants prevents the growth of any young plants.

Thus natural forests are extremely rare in the countries round the Mediterranean and there are only a few remains to show what the country may have looked like once and could in parts still look like today (the evergreen oak forest near the monastery of St Francis of Assisi, the pine forests of Ravenna, the cork oak forests of Sardinia and the olive groves of the Ionian island of Corfu). Wheat fields, vineyards and olive trees today cover the once wooded country. Much larger and more characteristic of Mediterranean vegetation are the wide expanses which have no utilitarian value: the maquis, and often impenetrable thickets of mostly evergreen shrubs which only in specially favourable positions grow to more than 6 feet in height, but normally are barely as tall as a man. Even during the dry summer the maquis mercifully covers the thirsty land with its dark green. The sun has no power over it. It carefully preserves the precious water reserves of the soil. Its most characteristic representatives, *Quercus ilex* and *coccifera, Arbutus unedo, Laurus nobilis, Phillyrea,* the evergreen *Rhamnus alaternus, Myrtus communis* and *Pistacia lenticus,* have coarse, thick-skinned leaves which allow only very little moisture to evaporate. But resourceful nature knows more ways than one to preserve water. Tiny leaves are covered with a dense grey felt which reduces evaporation considerably (many papilonaceous plants, such as *Teucrium polium* and *Phlomis lychnitis).* Other shrubs simply shed most of their leaves when the dryness of summer sets in and largely cease to function *(Calycotome, Euphorbia dendroides);* another group of plants excellently adapted to the peculiarities of the Mediterranean climate (winter rains—summer drought), and therefore represented by great numbers and many species, are the bulb and corm plants, which grow leaves and flowers in the spring after the winter rains; as the seeds ripen, the plant grows one or more new bulbs or corms for the following year. It then withers and disappears at the onset of the drought *(Scilla,* narcissi, tulips, *Muscari,* etc., and all orchids). A last group comprises the annuals, almost invariably small plants which develop from seed to flowering plant during the rainy season and die away after having borne seeds in their turn.

Therefore, the summer visitor to the Mediterranean coast sees only the few eccentrics of the plant world which defy every law of nature and insist on flowering in the dryest season *(Daphne gnidium, Smilax aspera, Ceratonia siliqua).* In general the range of colours is small: the dark green of the maquis, the grey of the rocks and rock heath, the light brown of the dry soil, and, all the more striking, the intense blue and green of the sea.

But how different a picture in the spring! Anyone who sees it for the first time can only stare and stare again at unimaginable splendour. The maquis is like an overflowing garden, branches of broom bow down under the weight of golden blossoms, not a leaf to be seen. In the morning

the slopes are white with the snowy petals of the cistus *(Cistus salvifolius)*. They wither the same afternoon but for two weeks or longer new buds open every morning. The tiny white flowers on the slender branches of *Erica arborea* look like sugar icing and between them flower blue *Lavandula stoechas, Rosmarinus officinalis* and *Salvia officinalis,* and more and yet more broom—a symphony in yellow. And there is a scent in the air which cannot be described but must be experienced. Blossoms, honey and resin: how right was the Corsican Napoleon when he said that he would recognise his homeland blindfold by the scent of the maquis.
In the open grassy or rocky places between the shrubs there is not an inch to spare: tulips and anemones in pale purple and fiery red *(Anemone stellata* and *coronaria)*, daisies *(Anthemis chia)*, yellow compositas and above all the bizarre little faces of orchids. They are exotic little strangers skilfully pretending to be furry insects. Under the olive trees the wheat already stands foot high, but the field is red with poppies, the vineyards are yellow with South African oxalis *(Oxalis cernua)*—can one dismiss these wild flowers as weeds? The flora of the Mediterranean countries is so rich in genera (at a very rough estimate about 10,000 flowering plants) that even the hardened botanist makes new and surprising discoveries every spring and returns laden with new treasures.

The Southern Crimea - the Riviera of Eastern Europe, and the Nikita Gardens

PROFESSOR H. WALTER

The traveller who, after traversing the wide plains of Eastern Europe, with their forests in the north and endless steppes in the south, where corn is grown today, reaches the Crimean peninsula and suddenly catches sight of the Black Sea from the heights of the Crimea Mountains, feels himself abruptly removed to a sub-tropical country. This coastal strip, only a few miles wide and a little over 30 miles long, occupies a unique position in Eastern Europe in regard to climate, landscape and vegetation.
The Jurassic plateau is called Yaila, a Turkish word meaning pasture. From a height of 4,921 feet its southern edge falls steeply down to the sea and protects the narrow coastal area at its foot from the cold north-easterly winds of the Eastern European winter. The average temperature of the coldest month is 40° F. and that of the hottest 75° F., although short periods of frost may occur and temperatures drop as low as 8° F. Therefore, in some sense it would be an exaggeration to describe the country as sub-tropical, though it is justified in comparison with the icy winters of the north. A comparison with the French or Italian Riviera is more correct, but it, too, is to be taken with a grain of salt.
Orange and lemon trees, which can be seen in sheltered spots on the Riviera, do not survive in the open in the Southern Crimea. One would look in vain for the evergreen oaks of the Mediterranean mountains. They are replaced by *Quercus pubescens* and *Juniperus excelsa.* However, in addition there are a number of plants which correspond exactly to those of the Mediterranean countries, such as *Jasminum fruticans, Pistacia mutica, Cistus tauricus, Ruscus aculeatus,* the sumach *(Rhus coriaria)* and, occasionally, *Arbutus andrachne.*
The resemblance to the Riviera is even more striking when we look at the gardens. Tall, slender cypresses, stone-pines, *Magnolia grandiflora* and *Trachycarpus excelsa,* magnificently flowering *Albizzia julibrissin,* the silvery leaves of olive trees and the red flowers of pomegranates, to-

gether with southern fruit, like almonds, figs and persimmons. Fields of purple lavender and roses, cultivated for the purpose of extracting rose oil, conjure up a southern landscape which seems incredible to the Western European and enchants the Eastern European accustomed to a rougher climate.

The isolated appearance of the strange plant world of the Southern Crimea is due to climatic conditions which are very different from those of the rest of Eastern Europe, and most closely resemble the Mediterranean climate. The winters are not only mild but also very rainy. At the south coast of the Crimea between the Cape of Foros in the west and Aju-Dag, the 'bear mountain' jutting out into the sea near Gursuf, in the east, rain falls chiefly in winter, as in the Mediterranean, while the summers are very hot and dry. Further east along the south coast beyond Alupka and towards Feodosiya and Kerch the climate changes: maximum precipitation occurs in the summer months and the winters are colder.

Here in the 'Riviera of the East' are the famous Nikita Gardens, the botanical gardens with research institutes founded in 1812 at the instigation of the governor general of New Russia, the Duke of Richelieu. The botanist Christian Steven was its first director from 1812—1824 and he was succeeded by Hartwis (1824—1860). The area of these gardens, which are situated a little over six miles east of Yalta, comprises over 865 acres. They extend from the shore of the Black Sea to a height of about 984 feet. There is an arboretum of about 173 acres with thousands of different timber and ornamental trees from Mediterranean countries, Japan, China, California, Mexico, etc., most beautifully arranged from a garden-architectural point of view. Among them are laurel and camphor trees, evergreen oak, agaves and *Musa basjoo,* as well as *Sasa disticha, Cocos australis* and *Citrus trifoliata,* the only citrus tree that survives the climate, though it does not bear edible fruit. Sixty-two acres are set aside for trial orchards, including a rich assortment of southern fruit trees. Each of the 400 known kinds of peaches are represented by four trees. The trial vineyards take up another 178 acres and contain 500 Russian, 500 West European and about 300 Asian vines. In addition there are plantations of industrially important plants from which volatile oils are extracted, such as lavender, rosemary, camphor-basilicum, iris, hyssop and roses.

The rest of the area is a national park and serves the preservation of native vegetation which is increasingly endangered by housing development and the growing tourist traffic.

Higher up on the slopes of the Crimea Mountains there begins the region of *Pinus laricio,* subspecies *pallasiana,* with its beautifully straight and mighty trunks. *Quercus pubescens, Carpinus orientalis, Sorbus domestica, Acer steveni,* closely related to *Acer hyrcanum,* and others form the undergrowth. Among the shrubs *Cornus mas* and *Cotinus coggygria* are particularly striking. Higher still, especially on steep rocky slopes, the Caucasian pine is replaced by a species of pine, *Pinus hamata.* Finally at the upper edge of the mountains, in the valleys of the plateau and on the gentler northern slope of the Crimea Mountains, the beech prevails and forms large junglelike forests in regions which in the summer are shrouded in clouds. These beeches in the Crimea are far removed from the Central European distribution area of beech *(Fagus silvatica),* but equally far from the Caucasian beech *(Fagus orientalis).* Therefore, it is interesting to observe that there are beech forms in the Crimea which sometimes resemble more the one and sometimes more the other and seem to form a bridge between them. Some botanists even insist that there is a specifically Crimean beech.

Descending through the beech forests down the northern slope and into the Crimean plain, the traveller traverses within a short distance about as many zones of vegetation as he would on the long journey from Central Europe to the Caspian plain, for after a narrow belt of deciduous forests, where the hornbeam is very prevalent, we arrive at the lower region of oak forests and

thus the wooded steppe. Lower yet and somewhat more northerly, grassy steppes and feather grass steppes were once common, but today they have been replaced by cultivated land, while the desert-like wormwood steppe remains in the northernmost part, since without irrigation it can be used only as pastureland. On the shores of the Siwasch or 'rotten sea,' which almost completely separates the peninsula from the mainland, we find extensive salt plant societies resembling those of the Caspian plain.
The Crimea thus presents within a small space a rich plant world and very varied types of vegetation because of the differing climatic conditions north and south of the Crimea Mountains.

Botanical Gardens and Parks in the Soviet Union

NINA PAVLOVNA NIKOLAYENKO

The flora of the Soviet Union is rich and varied. It comprises about 20,000 genera of higher plants. The plant world of Central Asia, the Caucasus Mountains and the Far East is particularly varied in its forms. One of the most important problems of botanical gardens is the acclimatisation of plants. The introduction and selection of new plant cultures presents its own difficulties.
There are more than 80 botanical gardens in the USSR. They contain native plants as well as specimens of the world flora, offer a selection of garden flowers peculiar to their districts and give advice on vegetable and flower cultivation.
By far the largest, though not the oldest, botanical garden is the Main Botanical Garden of the Academy of Sciences of the USSR in Moscow. Together with the adjoining parklands, it extends over an area of 988 acres and contains the largest selection of tropical and sub-tropical plants in the Soviet Union (more than 1,000 species). Its collection of flowering plants in the open comprises 44 genera, 233 species and more than 5,000 varieties, including more than 2,000 varieties of roses. There are a great number of the following perennials: 410 tulip varieties, 375 iris varieties, more than 200 peony varieties, 160 phlox varieties, 350 gladiola varieties, 450 dahlia varieties and about 1,000 others.
The exhibition area of the flora section is divided according to zones. There is an arboretum, an alpine garden, a garden of evergreen plants, a rosarium and special sections for collections. Beautiful lakes accommodate aquatic plants and plants growing on the edge of the water. The garden has collections of roses, Korean chrysanthemums, peonies, phloxes, gladiolas and azaleas. The work done on the selection of plants and the cultivation of orchids is particularly interesting.
The oldest botanical garden of the Soviet Union is also in Moscow, near the University.
The botanical garden of the Botanical Institute of the Academy of Sciences of the USSR in Leningrad was founded in 1714 under Peter I. Many agricultural and garden plants, which today are common throughout the country, were first cultivated here. The Arboretum (40 acres) contains about 700 species and varieties of trees and shrubs. The nursery garden has over 1,000 species and varieties of grass-like perennials.
The rock garden presents a rich collection of alpines from Western Europe, the Caucasus Mountains, Siberia and Central Asia, the Himalayas and North America. The garden has some branch establishments in other parts of the Soviet Union. There is a collection of some 250 species and varieties of lilies. Director Rodionenko and Dr Silina are in charge of the biological, morpho-

logical and taxonomical study of lilies and tulips, and Dr S. Saakov is responsible for the cultivation of roses and palm trees.

There are 2,500 species of tropical plants in the greenhouses. The collection of rhododendrons and azaleas consists of 100, the cactus collection of more than 500, the *Aracea* collection of more than 100 and the fern collection of 150 species.

There are several botanical gardens on the shores of the Black Sea in the Caucasus Mountains. Five and a half miles outside the city of Batumi, in the picturesque country of the Green Cape, there are the botanical gardens of Batumi, founded in 1912. This is the hottest and most humid place in the Soviet Union. The collection of living plants from various sub-tropical regions of the earth in these gardens contains more than 4,000 species and sub-species. The gardens cover an area of 267 acres and include a park, plant-geographical sections, agricultural and trial plantations, nurseries, greenhouses and propagation areas. The trees and shrubs in the flora section are grouped together according to areas of origin. There are nine such sections: East Asia, Australia, New Zealand, Himalayas, Mexico, North and South America, Mediterranean countries, moist sub-tropical Caucasus area.

There are 1,400 species and varieties in the rosarium. New roses are bred and about 100 varieties have been chosen as being specially suitable for moist sub-tropical regions. There are also nurseries for camellias and gladiolas.

The city of Tiflis also possesses a botanical garden. Its park is not very big but most picturesque. It contains a mountain stream, high bridges, glens, a slope studded with shrubs, local and foreign rocks, an interesting rock garden on the sides of a hill and a flower garden on its top. The gardens are most suitable for the study of the rich flora of wild flowering plants. Expeditions to the Caucasus Mountains are frequently arranged and yield a rich harvest of interesting plants for the botanical collections and the park. Near the gardens there is the Botanical Institute which specialises in the study of irises, peonies and lilies. It has bred many natural varieties and hybrids. N. Kacheladse has conducted some most successful research work in connection with *Oncocyclus*, a sub-group of the iris family. About ten varieties of this sub-group grow in the Caucasus Mountains, the most beautiful of which is *Iris iberica*, and several varieties and hybrids have been grown and some pretty hybrids evolved. The botanical gardens of the city of Suchumi are one of the sights of the Black Sea coast. Here the visitor may admire a collection of sub-tropical plants and a large selection of aquatic plants. In recent years hardy chrysanthemums have been grown in the garden of Jadrova-Kolakovskaja.

Anyone who has ever visited Sochi knows the local arboretum. It covers an area of 124 acres and is famous for its architectural features. Its centre is occupied by a rather steep slope with an unexpectedly beautiful vista of the sea. To the right and left of the main building and the road forming the axis of the park, there is a network of avenues and paths, arranged in the shape of an amphitheatre, with some well constructed resting places. The ornamental steps which lead up to the slope are particularly memorable. On each side of the steps and in harmony with the surroundings there is a pleasing row of cypresses bordered by oleander bushes.

The arboretum contains the most varied collection of exotic plants to be found on the northern shore of the Black Sea, in all more than 600 varieties. The collection of Caucasian and other sub-tropical plants is famous, as is the display of palms and aquatic plants. The arboretum is especially beautiful in the spring, when the magnolias blossom, and in the autumn, when trees and shrubs are clothed in magnificently glowing colours.

In the city of Adler, not far from Sochi, there is one of the prettiest sub-tropical spots of the USSR—the park of the *Sovchose* or 'Southern Cultivations.' Its most interesting feature is the arboretum (30 acres), laid out in 1910 after a design by A. Regel. From here the visitor has a grand view of the snow-covered peaks of the Caucasus Mountains and the limitless panorama of the blue sea. Steep slopes, lakes fed by natural springs and artistically planted banks combine to create a fairy-tale beauty. The park contains plants from every continent and region of the world. Its comparatively small area affords room for 5,000 trees and shrubs, including 325 species and sub-species. About 80 per cent of the park is devoted to evergreen and coniferous trees. In spring the fine collection of flowering mahalebs and fields of tulips, narcissi, hyacinths and various azaleas and rhododendrons are particularly attractive.

Almost in the centre of the narrow shore belt of the peninsula (south coast of the Crimea), 3³/₄ miles east of Yalta, there are the Nikita Botanical Gardens. Mountain ranges of 3,600 to 4,200 feet above the sea rise in the north, while the southern shore is washed by the warm, never freezing waters of the Black Sea. This coastal region differs considerably from the rest of the peninsula. It has an arid, sub-tropical character. From May to October the climate is hot and dry with temperatures of up to 95° F. and often no rain at all.

In 1962 the Nikita Gardens celebrated the 150th anniversary of their inception. They occupy an area of 62 acres and include 12 scientific departments and laboratories and two branch establishments. The Gardens specialise in the introduction, selection and agro-biological study of garden plants, fruit-bearing plants and plants which contain volatile oils. They also deal with the biology of pests and diseases and their control and conduct physiological, biochemical, cytological and embryological research into plant structure. Unique in the dry south of the country is the aboretum (74 acres) with a most interesting collection of 70 different coniferous trees. There are also many plants from East Asia, North America and other parts of the world. Altogether the Gardens contain 1,125 species and 580 sub-species, 1,600 varieties of roses and 1,500 species of different ornamental plants. The selection of roses for sunny regions is supervised by W. Klimenko, that of cannas, chrysanthemums and phloxes by I. Sabelin, and that of clematis by A. W. Olosenko.

There are several botanical gardens in Siberia, most of them established quite recently. The oldest garden is in the city of Tomsk and associated with the University. It was founded in 1885 and covers an area of more than 247 acres. Its collections contain about 2,500 species. There are more than 900 species of tropical and sub-tropical plants in the greenhouses, a particularly fine collection of azaleas and some noteworthy century-old palm trees in the tropical section. One of the greenhouses contains some 50 species of desert plants and 2 basins with tropical aquatic plants—*Victoria crutiana* and *Victoria regia,* lotus, water lilies and others. There are also many varieties of gladiolas, dahlias and irises in the garden.

The branch establishment of the Academy of Science in Kola, on the Kola peninsula north of the Arctic Circle, has an arctic rock garden. It was founded in 1931 and covers an area of 741 acres. In these unfavourable climatic conditions many new varieties are being developed and plants are selected for cultivation in the arctic region.

The most interesting of the botanical gardens in Central Asia is that at Tashkent. Here the development of new varieties is conducted according to the method of related groups, and the garden, therefore, has a great many collections of the groups in which it specialises, such as Penstemon, *Rudbeckia,* anemones, peonies, carnations, *Muscari, Ipomoea, Quamoclit* and passion flowers. There are 88 varieties of barberry, 20 of *Deutzia,* 8 of *Forsythia,* 14 of *Hypericum,* 80 of *Lonicera,* 40 of syringa, 43 of Christmas roses, 72 of *Cotoneaster,* 150 of *Crataegus,* 125 of roses, 29 of lilac, 13 of elder, 10 of *Buddleia,* 42 of clematis, 30 of Virginia creeper, etc. The tree collections consist of 10 varieties of walnut, 7 of *Carya,* 23 of oak, 11 of *Robinia,* 9 of *Gleditschia,* 4 of *Catalpa,* 26 of ash, 19 of lime, 15 of elm, 42 of poplar, 62 of willow, 42 of apple, 43 of maple, and 40 of birch.

Dr S. Rusanov has bred several bybrids of yucca and the American hibiscus, and S. Botchanzev specialises in tulip hybrids. The collection of botanical tulips numbers 71. Research work is being done with *Eremurus, Fritillaria,* as well as iris, *Ostrovskia, Morina,* anemones and *Acantholimon.*

On the Baltic coast near Leningrad there are a number of outstanding creations of Russian garden architecture, the Pushkin, Pavlov, Petro-Dvorez, Lomonosov, Gatchina and Pravda Parks. They were extensively damaged in the Second World War, but reconstruction started immediately after the end of hostilities.

Petro-Dvorez is situated 15½ miles outside Leningrad. Its central section is an example of eighteenth-century landscape gardening with water as one of its main features, displaying fountains, cascades and canals. The main axis of the park is marked by a canal bordered by an avenue of fountains. Long, perfectly straight avenues of ancient trees lead to fountains and gazebos.

The palace gardens of Gatchina are 28 miles distant from Leningrad. They consist of three parks—the Dvorzovy (palace park), the Priorazki and the Sveriniez (deer park)—and altogether cover an area of 1,730 acres. The centre is occupied by the palace and the adjoining park with its dark avenues and austere architecture. The parks were first laid out in 1766. The Dvorzovy Park is an example of the landscape style of garden architecture. There are a number of lakes, the most beautiful of which is the emerald-green Serebrjany Lake (silver lake). Water occupies about one third of the park area. Large meadows are interspersed with picturesque little copses of many white willows.

Pushkin, a former Tsarist settlement, is generally called a garden city. The palace and gardens occupy an area of 1,483 acres and include several parks, which were created in the course of two centuries. They were first laid out in 1718 and from then on constant alterations were made. Their most characteristic features are the shady avenues of ancient lime trees, with statues of white marble and pavilions, and the sunny meadows, their edges studded with groups of trees and shrubs. They form a perfect backgrounds to lakes and ponds. The Pavlov Park extends over an area of 1,250 acres and lies 17 miles south of Leningrad and at a distance of about 2½ miles from Pushkin Park. The park was laid out in the late 18th century on the grounds of the Pavlov forest. It has preserved the natural features of the landscapes. Sun-lit clearings alternate with shady, even gloomy, woods, open country with enclosed squares decorated with beautiful statues, wide avenues with overgrown paths alongside the banks of ponds.

The palace and park of Lomonosov lie on the shore of the Gulf of Finland, 25 miles from Leningrad. The lower park was first laid out in a regular pattern, which assumed a more natural character in time. The upper park represents a union of landscape and artistic style. Straight, shady avenues blend with open fields and copses. Glens and ponds provide effective variety.

There are some magnificent old parks in the vicinity of Moscow, e. g. Archangel, Kuskovo, Kusminki, Ostankino, Uski, Zarizino, Mzyri, Gorenki, Voronzovo, Glinki, Brazevo and others.

Among the parks in the Ukraine, Trostjaniez and Sofijevka are particularly noteworthy. The arboretum of Trostjaniez is situated in the south-eastern part of the Tshernigovsk region, 28 miles south of Bachmann railway station, and extends to the outer part of the Donez-Sulskaja forest steppe at an altitude of 450—600 feet above sea level. The park covers an area of 519 acres and contains shrub collections and a tree nursery. It possesses some 550 species and subspecies and varieties, among them 100 species of coniferous trees. It is an outstanding landscape park with many rare and valuable plants. There are many ponds, valleys and artificial hills.

The National Park of Sofijevka (in the city of Uman) is a famous example of 18th century landscape gardening and is noteworthy for its artistic perfection. Water, fields and trees, archi-

tecture and sculpture together form a harmonious whole. The amphitheatrical arrangement was chosen not only to display groups of trees and architectural creations to the best advantage, but also for ornamental purposes in the distribution of lakes, basins, fountains, waterfalls and streams. Rocks are widely used in the general composition of the park. The trees consist mostly of local and exotic species.
There are also many ornamental parks on the south coast of the Crimea, e. g. at Gursuf, Alupka, Livadja, Alushta and Simeis. The Pushkin Park of Gursuf (early nineteenth century) is one of the oldest monuments of garden architecture in the Crimea and is associated with one of the most important periods in the life and work of the Russian poet Pushkin. The park at Alupka adjoins the palace of Count Voronzev. It extends from the shore to an altitude of 150 feet, in the south-eastern part to 210 feet above sea level. Livadja and Oreanda, former tsarist properties, are the most important parks on the south coast of the Crimea and occupy an area of about 395 acres on the slopes of the Mogabi Mountain.
In the coastal region of the Caucasus Mountains, the beautiful Sinop Gardens in the city of Suchumi, the Kur Garden at Gagra and the District Gardens of Batumi and Suchumi are also worth a mention.

The Flower Island of Teneriffe

PETER MORITZ

Teneriffe, the largest island of the Canaries, offers the visitor not only magnificent bathing beaches, but, above all, a great variety of plants which are unique in the splendour of their colours and shapes.
Four factors are responsible for the equitable climate which has earned for Teneriffe the justifiable epithet 'Island of Eternal Peace.' Teneriffe is situated on the same latitude as Cairo and Florida and about 218 miles west of the African coast in the middle of the Atlantic Ocean. It covers an area of some 782 square miles and in the Pico de Teide rises to an altitude of 12,190 feet above the sea. The Canary Current is a southerly branch of the Gulf Stream. It runs from north to south and cools down the waters heated by the tropical sun. The north-east trade wind originates off Cape Juby on the African coast, where, descending from a great height, it hits the surface of the sea. It reaches the northern flank of Teneriffe as a pure sea wind saturated with moisture and causes the formation of clouds which descend as mist and rain on the island. These clouds, providing moisture and shade, also divide the island into three climatic regions: the region below the clouds, the region in the clouds and the region above the clouds.
The visitor to Teneriffe thus enjoys a climate which varies little in winter and summer, the mean temperature of the region below the clouds being about 69° F., of the region in the clouds about 61° F. and of the region above the clouds about 49° F. The wide-spread idea that the summer season in the Canary Islands is too hot and, therefore, unsuitable for tourists is entirely false. For obvious reasons it is impossible to mention more than a few of the plants that are to be found in Teneriffe.

The Migrant Plants

Among the migrants there is a great number of attractive flowering plants. How did they get to the island? In so far as they are natives of Europe and the nearby African regions, they were undoubtedly transported in the stomachs and among the plumage of birds of passage. A few plants from Central and South America may have been carried to the Canary Islands by the Canary Current. Husk-like seeds of American plants have certainly been washed up on the shores of Teneriffe. On two occasions a German botanist, who lived in Teneriffe for many years, observed exotic plants entirely unknown to him in some tiny villages on the coast. When he asked people how they had obtained these plants, he was told that the fruits or seeds had been found washed up on the beach. However, in general man is responsible for the distribution of plants. Two examples to illustrate this fact: from its home in South-East Asia the banana tree has spread in two directions. Towards the west it leapt the Indian Ocean, traversed the African continent and reached the Canary Islands. The Spanish historian Oviedo, a contemporary of the conquistadores, reports that from there the banana tree was introduced into the Dominican Republic in 1516 and in 1535 further, into Peru. By that time it had probably already reached a few places on the west coast of America. From South-East Asia man had taken it eastward by way of the Pacific Islands.

Until the end of the Second World War the Californian poppy *(Eschscholtzia californica, Papaveraceae)* was largely unknown in Teneriffe. Today it is not only common in gardens, but has proliferated widely throughout the island and grows wild at altitudes of between 2,200 and 6,000 feet. It is said that the seeds first reached Teneriffe in a shipload of maize from the Gulf of Mexico.

The tulip tree *(Spathodea campanulata, Bignoniceae)* with its large red, luminous chalice flowers, comes from tropical Africa. The home of *Plumiera alba, Apocynaceae,* with its leaf rosettes and delicately scented white, yellow-lined flowers, is in the Antilles. *Pandanus edulis, Pandanaceae,* on the other hand, with its head-sized fruits, migrated from the Isle of Madagascar to Teneriffe. *Grevillea robusta, Proteaceae,* accomplished a long journey: it comes from Australia. An umbel of fiery-red blossoms and pods about 24 inches long characterise the decorative *Poinciana regia, Papilionaceae,* which is a native of Africa and India. *Hibiscus rosasinensis, Malvaceae,* a large flowering relative of our hollyhock comes from China. *Bougainvillea glabra, Nytaginaceae,* was first discovered some 200 years ago in Brazil by the French admiral and circumnavigator Antoine de Bougainville. *Datura arborea, Solanaceae,* with its pendulous white trumpet-shaped flowers, is a native of Peru and Chile and poisonous like all nightshades. *Aristolochia elegans, Aristolochiaceae,* grows in the tropical regions of the Old and the New World. Its large flowers, patterned in yellow and brown, are traps in which insects are held captive until pollination has taken place. Therefore, it is not a carnivorous plant. The most beautiful ornamental shrub of Teneriffe is *Euphorbia pulcherrima, Euphorbiaceae.* It was discovered by the North American ambassador Poinsette on the Mexican tableland. At Christmas time it displays its glowing colours along the highroad of Teneriffe. Some tropical fruit trees have also found a second home on the island, e.g. the mango tree, a native of Indonesia, with its agreeable plums which can weigh more than four pound; *Carica papaya, Caricaceae,* with its most wholesome papaya fruit; *Ficus carica, Moraceae,* from the Mediterranean regions; *Persea gratissima, Lauraceae,* from tropical America, with its avocado pears; *Eriobotrya japonica, Rosaceae,* from Japan, with its spicy medlar-like fruit.

The Native Plants

To the botanist the native plants of the island are much more interesting. About 1,500 different species are to be found in Teneriffe, about 450 of which are endemic, i.e. their distribution is confined to the Canary Islands, sometimes even to one particular island or to a small area on one of the islands.

The Region below the Clouds (up to 2,300 feet)

The Canarian date palm *(Phoenix canariensis, Palmae)* grows everywhere, sometimes singly, sometimes in small groups, although in its wild state it inhabits only the lonely *barrancos* (glens). The Canarian dragon tree *(Dracaena draco, Liliaceae)*, the most famous member of the Canarian flora, also thrives in the *barrancos*. Its uncouth shape, which has remained almost unaltered since the mesozoic age (60 million years ago), invites comparison with the pachyderms of the animal world. Its reddish resin has excited the imagination of travellers even more than its shape. It was believed to turn into 'dragon's blood' and to be possessed of strange powers. Next to the dragon tree, *Euphorbia canariensis, Euphorbiaceae*, is the most striking and may be termed the characteristic plant of the region. Its milky juice is poisonous and in its pillar-like trunk the plant stores the rainwater of the wet season against the dry summer. Some endemic relatives of this plant show leaf rosettes in the late spring which disappear in summer, or they manage without any leaves. The genus *Sempervivum* forms another extensive group. *Sempervivum lindleyi, Crassulaceae*, grows in close association with euphorbias, and the original inhabitants of the island already knew that its juice afforded an effective antidote against the dangerous poison of the euphorbia. *Kleinia neriifolia (Compositae), Chrysanthemum frutescens (Compositae)*, the Canarian wormwood *(Artemisia canariensis, Compositae), Periploca laevigata (Asclepiadaceae)*, the red cistus *(Cistus vaginatus, Cistaceae)* are only a few of the endemic plants of this region, where the Canarian banana *(Musa nana, Musaceae)* and the tomato are also being cultivated for export.

The Region in the Clouds (2,300—6,580 feet)

The vegetation in this region is far richer in species than that of the other two. Laurel woods *(la laurisilva)* prevail in the north-east, on drier slopes heather *(el fayal-brezal)* and on sandy soil pine forests.

The latter consist mainly of Canarian pines *(Pinus canariensis, Pinaceae)* with needles 12 inches long. In the last 25 years an area of 27,182 acres has been afforested with pines. The heath is dominated by tree heather *(Erica arborea, Ericaceae)* which in Teneriffe may reach a height of 33—49 feet. Its roots provide the valuable briar wood from which tobacco pipes and dice are fashioned. The laurel woods of the Canaries are the living replica of the temperate rain forests common in Europe in the Tertiary. They are composed exclusively of plants, the seeds of which were brought to the island by birds of passage (chiefly rock pigeons which still nest there). Various laurel trees *(Laurus canariensis, Apollonias canariensis, Ocotea foetens*, all *Laureaceae), Ilex canariensis (Aquifoliaceae), Notelaea excelsa (Oleaceae), Visnea mocanera (Theaceae)* are a few plants otherwise known only through fossils dating from the Tertiary. Nothing has so far come to light about the origin of the *Arbutus canariensis, Ericaceae*. Two of the most beautiful endemic plants, *Canarina campanula, Campanulaceae*, and *Digitalis canariensis, Scrophulariaceae*, grow in the laurel woods. The most peculiar fern of the Canaries is *Adiantum reniforme, Polypodiaceae*. Evidence of this plant in the shape of leaf impressions dating from the pliocene (12 million years ago) has been found in Europe. The Canarian laurel woods can therefore confidently be regarded as a living botanical museum of the European Tertiary.

The Region Above the Clouds (6,580—12,188 feet)

The bare volcanic ground, together with the dry climate at these altitudes, are responsible for the desert-like nature of the region. The shrub belt above the forests consists mainly of *Cytisus proliferus (Papilionaceae)* and *Adenocarpus viscosus (Papilionaceae).* The ridge of 7,216 feet and the giant crater of the Canadas, from which the Pico de Teide rises a further 4,920 feet, bear a monotonous vegetation consisting of *Spartocytisus nubigenus, Papilionaceae.* This globular furze bush, taller than a man, dominates the region. In place of an extensive list, I would only mention two of the rarest flowering plants anywhere, which are largely responsible for Teneriffe's name 'Island of Flowers.' The one is *Echium bourgaeanum, Borraginaceae,* whose relatives we can admire also in the other two zones. It grows to a height of 6½—13 feet and occurs at 7,216 feet within an area of only 2½ acres. I once saw about 100 plants there with budding flower stalks, 30 of them in full flower, a sight which one does not easily forget. The other is the Teide-violet *(Viola cheiranthifolia, Violaceae).* It occurs nowhere else but on the cone of the Pico de Teide at altitudes of between 6,872—12,103 feet. When the snow melts in April and the top layer of pumice stone has dried out and stores the heat of the sun for the night, when the frozen soil below the pumice scree has thawed to a depth of about 2 inches but still remains icy and rigid, this modest little plant brings forth its first leaves and amethyst-blue flowers with yellow stripes. Standing at first dawn on the edge of the crater and looking towards sunrise, you see Teneriffe and the other islands of the archipelago far below and a Teide-violet may grow at your feet, while on the scraggy rocks at a height of 11,990 feet a blue-grey Teide-finch is preening itself. That bird was surely instrumental in spreading the violet to these altitudes.

Primeval Madagascar

PROFESSOR WERNER RAUH

'He who travels to Madagascar will enter a primeval world and immerse himself in a mystery of the earth,' wrote Friedrich Schnack in his book *The Grand Isle of Madagascar.* Indeed, some parts of the '*Grande Île*' may make the visitor feel that he is standing in a museum of living fossils.

Today it is generally agreed that Madagascar, the Comoro Isles and the Seychelles are remains of the legendary country of Gondwana which connected Africa with India until it broke up in the mesozoic era and disappeared under the waters of the ocean. Although separated from the African continent by a mere 218 miles of the Mozambique Channel, Madagascar has but few plants and animals in common with neighbouring Africa, and some biologists justifiably regard it as a separate continent. Because of the early separation of the isle, the evolution of flora and fauna went its own way and produced forms which cannot be found in any other part of the world. In the words of a French scientist of the nineteenth century, Madagascar is 'a secluded shrine into which nature retreated to work on designs she does not employ anywhere else.' In Madagascar we find plants which by rights should not be extant at all, since we are unable to gather any information about their origin, their relatives or their proper place in the plant order. But there are only a very few places on the island where it is still possible to reconstruct a picture of its former and original condition or of its wealth of botanical oddities. The cultural habits of the original inhabitants, practised over many centuries and up to the present time, have led to large-scale destruction of vegetation due to regular burning before the onset of the summer rains. Every year the flames consume more and more plants.

The visitor to Madagascar at the end of October and beginning of November witnesses a grand and beautiful, but at the same time frightening spectacle. Large areas are on fire; flames glow from the tops of the mountains as they noisily consume the dry vegetation. After the conflagration the country is a sorry sight. Black lies the ground, every sign of life has been destroyed; only here and there a charred tree stump points upwards to the sky. Scorched earth in the truest sense of the word. Thus today almost 75 per cent of the original vegetation has vanished, especially in the central highlands which occupy about three-quarters of the island. They were once a forest area of incomparable beauty—some remains bear witness to that. To-day the central plateau is a steppe, desolate, monotonous, deeply furrowed by erosion. It is necessary to undertake long and arduous journeys on the island, which covers an area of 241,094 square miles, to reach the inaccessible, rain-swept east coast and the desert-like dry regions of the south-west and south in order not only to see but to experience the last remains of a vegetation which is unique in the world. But what is still to be observed here must fill every botanist not only with enthusiasm but with awe.

Particularly impressive and rich in botanical experiences is the journey along the west coast from the little port of Morondava down to the southern tip of the island at Cape St Marie, on a narrow, sandy track which often loses itself in dense thorny scrub. This is the '*région sous le vent*,' the region under the wind, and the zone of least precipitation on the whole island. Plants preferring dry soil, with small, frail leaves, thorn-studded succulents and lianas combine to form a forest, rich in species and often impenetrable, which during the short rainy season clothes itself in fresh verdure, but during the larger part of the year shows hardly any life. Its most characteristic features is the giant Baobab or monkey-bread tree, together with the *Adansonia grandidieri,* a typical Madagascan species. It is true that Baobabs are also to be found in the Central African savannah, but there they are represented by only one, whereas in Madagascar there are a full dozen species. The greatest of these, compared with which the sufficiently large African monkey-bread tree appears like a dwarf, is the above mentioned *Adansonia grandidieri,* which the Madagascans call '*Renala*' or 'mother of the forest.' It is the elephant among plants, for with its mighty, tower-like stems, 98—131 feet tall and 20 feet in diameter, it is one of the giants of the plant world. Compared with the stem, the branches are surprisingly insignificant, and the leaves last only for a few weeks. The Baobabs are probably the largest succulents of the plant world. Their stems serve as giant reservoirs against the dry season. They pump themselves full of water and the wood is soft and spongy and of no commercial value. In particularly dry years the watery bark is sometimes fed to cattle, so that they may quench their thirst. Since the Baobabs tower far above the rest of the vegetation, they are excellent lightning conductors, and their trunks are frequently to be found on the ground where they have been felled by lightning. Walking through such a monkey-bread forest, the traveller truly feels himself carried back to primeval geological eras, to a 'museum of living fossils.'

Further south precipitation gets increasingly scarce and the vegetation alters its character. The Baobab forests remain behind and are replaced by impenetrable thickets of thorny scrub, which is especially typical of the district of Androy, the 'land of thorns.' Almost every plant is prickly with thorns, as, for instance, the large *Euphorbias,* the various species of *Pachypodium* or thick-foot plants, another typical Madagascan plant group. Their barrel-shaped, water storing stems grow to a height of 10—16 feet and are covered with hard spiky stipules modified to thorns. But the picture is dominated by those strange, thorn-clad plants to which from a botanical point of view Madagascar owes its reputation as a 'secluded shrine.' They are representatives of the small family of *Didieraceae* which are confined to the south-west of Madagascar. Their name commemorates the great French coloniser and amateur botanist Grandidier, to whom we are indebted for the first detailed description of Madagascar. The *Didieraceae* are trees or shrub-like plants (to date 11 different species are known) whose strong thorns and tall shape call to

mind the Hedge Cactus of South America. These remarkable and unique plants could, therefore, be called, 'the cacti of the Old World.' Some representatives, like *Alluaudia* and *Didiera* species, form regular forests, whose existence, however, is also gravely threatened. Every botanist regards this plant group with awe. Although their flowers have been known for some time, until recently there was some doubt as to their taxonomical position. The Didiera forests are not only rich in other strange and rare vegetation, they are also the playgrounds of the Madagascan lemurs, magnificently coloured chameleons and the famous Madagascan star turtle. The Didiera forests extend to the very south of the island in varied forms, although large areas have been destroyed and replaced by sisal plantations. On the south-eastern tip of the island, in the vicinity of the little port of Fort Dauphin, the vegetation changes again. This is the '*région du vent*', the region of the wind, an area under the influence of the rain-laden trade wind which throughout the year provides the entire south-east coast with considerable rainfall (up to 127 inches!). The eastern part of the island, largely taken up by a mountain range of some 4,921 feet running from north to south, therefore presents a striking contrast to the dry west and south-west. While in those parts dry forests and thorny scrub characterise the physiognomy of the landscape, the east is dominated by abundant vegetation, and evergreen tropical rain forests with all their associated flora cover the hillsides. The trees are festooned with epiphytes, ferns, different species of Clubmoss, gorgeous orchids and billowing hummocks of moss. Lianas intertwine with the branches and a rich ground flora covers the decaying mould. The tropical rain forests also hide many strange plants. To name only a few, the famous Madagascan orchid *Angraecum sesquipedale, 'l'étoile de Madagascar,'* whose flowers carry a spur of some 12 inches in length into which a moth inserts its equally long proboscis to get at the nectar: the equally famous *Neodypsis decaryi,* one of the rarest palms on earth, the leaves of which, in contrast to all other palms, take the shape of a three-sectional fan. The most striking of all plants, however, is the 'travellers' tree,' *Ravenala madagascariensis,* a tree-like banana plant, whose long-stemmed leaves are shaped like a bi-sectional fan. The plant owes its strange name to the fact that large quantities of water are stored in the huge leaf scales and provide a reservoir for the traveller in the dry season. The *Ravenala* was originally an inhabitant of the primeval forests, but after their destruction it spread so rapidly as to form large forests of its own which survive even the annual burning. Thus the *Ravenala* forests, covering large areas along the east coast, are a typical symptom of secondary vegetation and of plant destruction.
Madagascar is a country of contrasts, of biological treasures and oddities, one of the last remaining plant paradises of the world, the survival of which is seriously threatened by insane exploitation. If drastic steps are not taken in the near future to stem the tide of destruction, the day will not be far off when '*primeval*' Madagascar will be nothing more than the desolate '*Île rouge*' which is already indicated by the present state of the central plateau.

The Origins of the Flora of South Africa

DR M. R. LEVYNS

When the early travellers broke their voyages at the Cape, they were puzzled and fascinated by the unusual plants they found growing on and around Table Mountain. At first it was mainly the oddities that claimed their attention. Thus we find plants such as *Stapelia variegata* (Carrion Flower) and *Haemanthus rotundifolius* (April Fool) amongst the earliest to be illustrated in the botanical books of that time. However, by the time Van Riebeeck landed, many of the plants, now known collectively as the Cape Flora, were familiar to botanists in Europe. Proteas, heaths, and other striking plants, seeds of which had been taken to Europe, were much prized in gardens, and this particular assemblage of plants was regarded as representing the flora of the whole of Southern Africa.

As the country was opened up it became apparent that the Cape Flora was by no means the only flora. We now know that it occupies a very small part of South Africa. Because its members were concentrated in the mountainous country of the south-west it was the first South African flora to be studied. It is a flora which cannot survive in places with either a very high or a very low rainfall and has a marked preference for those parts where the winters are wet and mild and the summers dry and hot. It grows best on poor soils such as those of the mountains of the Western Cape.

Although this flora is concentrated in the south-west, it would be wrong to conclude that there are no signs of it elsewhere in Africa. There are clear traces of it scattered throughout Africa, mainly on mountains, as far north as Ethiopia. Patches of Cape vegetation, often separated from one another by many hundreds of miles, are like islands in a vast sea formed by the modern tropical African flora. Identical or closely related species are frequently found on these island refuges, notably in the heath zone which occurs at high altitudes on the mountains of East Africa. Proceeding from north to south, especially in the east, the islands of Cape plants continue to be found, becoming progressively more frequent. Thus south of the Swartberg all the scattered mountains of the Little Karoo have cappings of Cape plants, while the flora of the lowlands is entirely different. These islands have great significance when we attempt to trace the origin of the Cape Flora. In recent studies it has been recorded that often the more primitive members of some of the larger genera are to be found on the outliers within the tropics, whereas in the south-west many of the species are advanced and occupy restricted geographical areas. The most obvious conclusion to be drawn from the facts of distribution is that there was once a widespread flora of the Cape type in Central Africa. Such a conclusion is supported by the belief of palaeobotanists that a droughtloving flora occupied much of Africa soon after the flowering plants came into being. This flora is supposed to have given way during a later period to a moisture-loving forest flora, but as yet the evidence is incomplete. However, a past history of this nature would fit the facts of present-day distribution and explain the numerous patches of Cape plants throughout much of Africa. It we accept this view, the islands of Cape plants must be regarded as relics of a very old African flora which was forced to retreat when moister conditions made its members yield to competitors better able to withstand a heavy rainfall. The flora appears to have migrated southwards, leaving traces on the mountains, until in the south west corner its wanderings came to an end. There it met a climate well suited to its needs. This led to a burst of evolutionary activity, and new species, new genera, and even new families arose. Evolutionary processes are slow and so we are forced to conclude that the Cape Flora reached its present headquarters a very long time ago.

At one time the theory of a southern origin for the Cape Flora was upheld by many prominent botanists, and there are still some who cling tenaciously to this view. The obvious, though remote, affinity of the flora of south-western Australia with that of the south-western Cape stirred the imagination and was largely responsible for the suggestion that both had had their origin in some southern land. Theories of land bridges which have since foundered beneath the sea and, later, the theory of continental drift have been invoked in support of the theory. The amazing discontinuities displayed by the Cape Flora in Central Africa and the comparative lack of these in the south make it difficult to imagine how anything but a movement from north to south could account for the indubitable facts of distribution.

The migrations of plants can in no way be likened to the movements of a flock of sheep, every member of which obediently follows the direction along which its fellows are travelling. In any community of plants some are much more capable than others of adjusting themselves to changes in climate. Such plants may be able to adapt themselves to conditions other than those under which they evolved and may in course of time join a plant community to which they did not originally belong. The case of the genus *Phylica* appears to illustrate this. In its features and pattern of distribution in Africa it is a typical Cape genus. However, in addition to its main centre of distribution, there are species on many of the islands around Africa, such as St Helena, Tristan da Cunha, Madagascar, and others. *Phylica* has never been recorded farther north than the southern end of Tanganyika. Such a genus may well have had a southern origin but, having reached Africa, later joined another migratory stream moving towards the south. Though the probabilities are that most members of the Cape Flora travelled southwards through Africa to their presents stations, a few others like *Phylica* may have had a southern origin.

Another African flora with a better claim to a southern origin for several of its members is the *Temperate Forest* Flora. Forest of this type was well known to the early settlers who found it in the ravines and on the eastern slopes of Table Mountain. Unlike the Cape Flora which consists of shrubs with small leathery leaves, the Forest Flora is composed mainly of evergreen trees with ferns forming a carpet below and climbers, such as the Monkey Rope, festooning the branches. *Yellow-woods* and *Ironwoods* are conspicuous members of the forest community. Near Cape Town and in the west generally, forest of this type never grows on exposed slopes but is confined to sheltered places such as ravines where the inevitable drought of summer is tempered by the presence of moisture in the soil. Further east, though the rainfall is not necessarily greater, it is more evenly distributed throughout the months of the year. Under such conditions forests which are confined to the kloofs in the west, flourish in the open. Thus we find such well-known forests as those at Knysna and the Tsitsikama Forest in the Humansdorp Division. They have all the constituents of the forests in the west but many more besides. Among the trees of the forest and streamside are some which have a strong claim to a southern origin. Prominent among these is the genus *Podocarpus* to which the yellow-woods belong. In the past *Podocarpus* and its allies were widespread in the Southern Hemisphere. Their fossil pollen-grains have been recorded in most places in the south, even in the rocks of Antarctica and the sub-Antarctic islands, places which to-day have a climate so severe that higher plant-life is impossible. Many of the habitable land-masses of the south have evidence that places, now too dry to support the growth of these moisture-loving trees, once had them in large numbers. An interesting illustration of this was discovered a few years ago near Cape Town when deep beneath the sand of the Cape Flats huge trunks of the giant *Outeniqua* Yellow-wood were found preserved from decay. Carbon-dating showed them to be between 30,000 and 40,000 years old. How these forest giants came to be lying there no one knows. Perhaps they formed part of an extensive forest which once clothed the southern tip of Africa, a forest which was almost exterminated by drought. Perhaps they were brought to their present resting place by ocean currents when the Cape Peninsula was an island. Future research may provide us with the clue which will enable us to solve the mystery.

There is not a scrap of evidence to suggest that *Podocarpus* and other trees closely related to it ever played an important rôle north of the Equator. They are true natives of the south. South African trees for which a similar claim may be made are *Cunonia* (Rooi Els), *Curtisia* (Assegai Wood), and *Brabeium* (Wild Almond). On the other hand some of our common forest trees have their closest relatives in the north. Such are the genera *Olea* and *Linoiciera* to which Olives and Ironwoods belong, *Ilex,* the holly, and *Celtis* to which the *Camdeboo* Stinkwood belongs. These are undoubtedly of northern origin. Thus we see that in its beginnings the Forest Flora probably received contributions from both north and south. Like the Cape Flora it has left traces throughout Southern Africa, telling us of its past glories, but its greater susceptibility to the effects of drought has rendered its records of the past even fainter than those of the Cape Flora.

Both the Cape and the Temperate Forest Floras have characters indicating their extreme age and there can be little doubt that they are older than any other African flora. Which of the two is the older, however, is a problem to which at present there is no solution. Possibly in the south the forest was in possession first, and this would explain the isolated patches of forest in the west, for as the climate became drier the forest could no longer exist in dry places and would yield to the better adapted Cape Flora, leaving merely traces of its former existence in sheltered places.

To-day most of Africa south of the Sahara is covered by a vast *Tropical African Flora* and its derivatives, such as the bushveld and grassveld of the Transvaal. This flora, though generally accepted as being much younger than the two previous floras, is old enough to have acquired an African character of its own. However, there are clear indications that many of its constituents have their closest relatives in the tropics of Asia and America. This suggests that it once formed part of a vast pan-tropical flora at a time when the distribution of land and water was very different from that which we know to-day.

The question may well be asked: is there any South African flora which is truly indigenous? The answer is: probably not. Yet there is one flora which seems more strongly South African than the others. That is the flora of the Karoo, especially the succulent Karoo of the west. So far studies on this flora have been of a taxonomic nature and little is known about distribution and past migration. But here too there are indications that some of its most characteristic members took part in vast migrations before reaching South Africa where a burst of evolutionary activity led to the production of some of the most curious plants known to man. A case in point is the group of succulents to which *Stapelia* belongs. The evidence available suggests that the group had its origin in southern Asia. Its path of migration ran eastwards through Arabia and Palestine to North Africa. A subsidiary path led to southern Europe and the Atlantic islands off the coasts of Europe and Africa, but no great development occurred in these places. In Africa, however, the case was different. The group spread throughout the length and breadth of the continent, including Madagascar. In the Karoo it attained its maximum development and once again we have a case in which evolutionary processes have been accelerated in the south-west.

Summing up, we see that in the four South African floras considered, the Temperate Forest Flora is the only one that is able to produce clear indications of a southern origin for a considerable number of its constituents. The Cape Flora has its quota of suspected southern elements, but the numbers are small in comparison with those which appear to hail from the north. The Tropical African and Karoo Floras have no trace of any migration from the south in the past. They are essentially African though they too in the remote past probably received contributions from without.

Proteas of South Africa

PROFESSOR H. B. RYCROFT

The proteas constitute part of what is perhaps one of the most interesting families of flowering plants in South Africa.

There are several reasons for this: many of the species are exceptionally beautiful, the flowering heads last particularly well in water, they demand very exact growing conditions, they have been known to overseas botanists for more than three centuries, and the protea is regarded as the floral emblem of South Africa. The species usually accepted as our national flower is the Suikerbos, correctly known as *Protea repens* L. but until recently usually called *Protea mellifera* Thb. In fact, this very species was adopted as the emblem for the Kirstenbosch Golden Jubilee of 1963.

From the earliest times the proteas of the Cape have attracted much attention overseas. Indeed, it appears that the first South African plant ever to be illustrated in literature was a protea. As long ago as 1605 a drawing and description of an old head of *Protea neriifolia* were produced by Clusius in his *Exoticum libridecem.* This was published 47 years before Jan van Riebeeck landed in Table Bay. Of course Clusius, who was professor of medicine and botany at the University of Leiden, did not call it *Protea neriifolia* but he likened the head to that of a thistle and called it *Carduus.* The name Protea was introduced more than a hundred years later.

World distribution of Proteaceae

The family Proteaceae occurs mainly in the Southern Hemisphere and consists of about 60 genera and 1,400 species. The greatest concentration is to be found in Australia with 37 genera and 750 species, Africa coming next with 14 genera and 400 species. The family is also represented in South America, Malaysia, New Caledonia, New Zealand, and Madagascar.

Most of the genera are endemic to the respective regions mentioned above but there are a few exceptions where genera are common to two regions situated sometimes at considerable distances apart. For example, *Embothrium, Orites, Gevuina, Lomatia,* and *Oreocallis* have species in both South America and Australia.

All the 14 African genera occur only in Africa, with the exception of *Faurea,* a more tropical genus, which has one species in Madagascar.

Distribution in Africa

In Africa the species are concentrated mainly in the south-western Cape where they constitute quite a prominent feature of the vegetation and the landscape. Eleven of the 14 genera occur only in the south-western Cape, where they are represented by about 200 species. They are *Aulax, Brabeium, Diastella, Leucadendron, Mimetes, Orothamnus, Paranomus, Serruria, Sorocephalus, Spatalla,* and *Spatallopsis.* Of the remaining three genera, two of them, *Leucospermum* and *Protea,* are mainly South African—38 of the 40 species of *Leucospermum* occur in South Africa, and *Protea* with about 130 species has 100 in South Africa. The species found outside the Republic extend as far north as Nigeria and Ethiopia. The last genus, *Faurea,* with 18 species, is mainly tropical and has only five species in South Africa.

Apart from being massed in the south-western Cape the *Proteaceae* of South Africa are generally found in certain fairly well-characterized regions. Where rainfall is adequate the plants are found in the areas covered by the geological systems known as Tertiary, Cretaceous, Karoo,

Cape, Waterberg, Malmesbury, Transvaal, and Basement Granite-Gneiss. Most species prefer well-drained, acid soil and are found more frequently on mountain tops and slopes than on the flats and in river valleys.

Origin of the Proteaceae

A combination of the present-day distribution pattern of the *Proteaceae,* the relationships between the genera and the scanty fossil remains that have been discovered might help to throw some light on the past history, migration, and evolution of this interesting family of flowering plants.

Did the proteas and their allies originate in the south or did they evolve in the north and then migrate southwards? Those who subscribe to the theory of a southern origin suggest that a great southern continent known as Gondwanaland existed many millions of years ago. In the very early history of plants this continent began to break up and eventually split apart to form South America, Africa, Australia, Antarctica, etc. This would help to explain the rather close relationship of some plant groups in these regions. It is also suggested that Australia and South America remained united for a long while after Africa had broken away, thus explaining the closer similarity between Australia and South America than that between Africa and the other two continents.

The other theory postulates that the ancestors of much of our South African flora originated in the Northern Hemisphere and that their descendants migrated along suitable corridors into the southern continents. In Africa, because of the great Sahara desert, the migration path would have been mainly along the slopes of the mountain ranges on the eastern side of the continent. The fact that proteas are still to be found at isolated places on the mountains all the way down Africa is claimed as proof of this theory. The isolated patches are regarded as remnants or relicts of a more or less continuous strip which lost most of its proteas due to progressive unfavourable climatic changes. Recently a Russian scientist, Dr S Samojilovitch of the Paleophytological Laboratory, Leningrad, has discovered what he suspects to be Proteaceous pollen grains in the Upper Cretaceous and Lower Tertiary sediments in Russia. If his suspicions are substantiated his discovery will lend further support to the 'northern origin' theory of our proteas.

The whole question of the origin, evolution, and migration of our unique flora is still rather shrouded in mystery but it is hoped that as new discoveries are made and new techniques applied a clear picture will emerge from the intricate jigsaw puzzle which we have at present.

Taxonomy and Nomenclature

After Clusius described and made the drawing of *Protea neriifolia* in 1605 lists of names and/or descriptions of *Proteaceae* were later published by Breyne, Plukenet, Petiver, and Ry; but the first really important work which included proteas was the *Index Alter Plantarum* published by Boerhaave in 1720. This book contains descriptions and illustrations of 24 species of Cape *Proteaceae,* 11 of which belong to the genus Protea as we know it to-day.

Boerhaave's work can be regarded as the first serious attempt at describing and classifying our Proteaceae.

A most important advance was made by the great Swedish botanist, Carl Linnaeus, originator of the binomial system of nomenclature, in 1753 when he published his monumental work *Species Plantarum.*

The names and descriptions of our proteas were based not on plant specimens but on the descriptions and plates in Boerhaave.

No further work was done on Proteaceae until another famous Swedish botanist, C. P. Thunberg, continued with the study of these plants. He travelled in South Africa during the period 1772 to 1775 and after his return to Sweden he published his *Dissertation on Protea* in 1781, in which he described 60 different species of the family. He was of course able to deal with the work more thoroughly than Linnaeus because he had actually seen and collected the living plants. It was a great thrill for me in 1960 to be able to examine all the specimens in Thunberg's herbarium which has been kept intact at the University of Upsala in Sweden, where both Linnaeus and Thunberg worked. I was able to clear up many problems which had previously been doubtful.

After Thunberg, various botanists dealt with Protea and at the end of the eighteenth century and at the beginning of the nineteenth we find that many excellent colour plates were published. That was at the time when the growing of proteas was very fashionable in England and in Europe.

Since then we have been able to study very many more specimens as a result of collections during the last half-century, and with more modern means of transport we have been able to make better acquaintance with the living plants in the field. In addition I had the opportunity three years ago of making a thorough examination of old specimens and literature in the more important herbaria in Britain and in Europe.

It is hoped, therefore, that in the not too distant future a new monograph will be published bringing our knowledge completely up to date.

Proteas round the World

Even before Van Riebeeck landed at the Cape in 1652 something was known about the flora of this country and plants were taken back to Europe by travellers who had called at the southern end of Africa.

It was much later, however, that there was a regular demand for Cape plants and that people were specially sent out for the sole purpose of collecting plants. Perhaps the first in this category were Thunberg and Masson who both arrived in 1772.

Thunberg, as we have already observed, came from Upsala in Sweden where he was first a pupil of Linnaeus and then his successor as professor of medicine and botany. He collected many specimens for scientific purposes and added much to the knowledge of the proteas. It was he who discovered *Serruria florida* (Blushing Bride), a member of the Proteaceae, in the French Hoek Mountains.

Francis Masson was sent out by the Royal Botanic Gardens at Kew to collect plants for the famous gardens. Altogether he spent nearly twelve years here. He discovered several new species of Protea and the specimens are at present stored in the British Museum of Natural History in London.

A wealthy merchant, George Hibbert, owned a famous garden at Clapham near London and apparently was particularly interested in growing proteas. He sent out James Niven who collected plants and seeds at the Cape at the end of the eighteenth century. His gardener was Joseph Knight, who apparently was more successful in growing proteas in England than they are to-day and in his publication of 1809 he lists more than 150 species growing in the garden. Other nurserymen also had success with proteas and at Kew there was a larger collection than there is to-day. They were also cultivated with pride—(and admired!)—in botanic gardens and palace gardens in various parts of Europe.

Towards the middle of last century interest in the growing of proteas seems to have been lost, partly perhaps on account of repeated failures due to a change in glasshouse practice when steam was used for heating. Proteas will not tolerate the hot, humid atmosphere required for tropical orchids.

Until comparatively recently there had been little interest in South Africa in the growing of our proteas. It was felt that they were 'wild' flowers which therefore did not deserve a place in the home garden.

Ideas have changed and, possibly as a result of the spectacular success that has been achieved at Kirstenbosch, proteas are now grown in all parts of the country where previously it was thought they would never succeed.

Although most of the showy species come from the winter-rainfall area of the south-western Cape it is remarkable how well most of them grow in the summer-rainfall area. In fact, in some parts of the Transvaal they seem to grow faster and flower earlier than they do in their natural homes.

To-day proteas are grown in many parts of the world, although not much success has been reported from Britain and Europe. In Australia and New Zealand they are cultivated very successfully and in large quantities and are very popular as cut flowers on the market and in florists' shops. They also seem to thrive in parts of California.

Diversity of the Genus

Although there are about 130 species of Protea only a comparatively few are of particular interest to the layman and most of these come from the Cape.

When Linnaeus chose the name protea for this genus of plants he named it after the legendary Greek god, Proteus, who was able to assume many different forms. Indeed, the proteas may be trees like *Protea arborea* or *P. multibracteata* or tiny dwarfs with only the leaves and flower heads showing above the ground level like *P. acaulis* and *P. scabra; P. Laevis, P. tenax,* and *P. cryophila* have underground stems and the leafy branches trail over the ground; the heads, as in *P. cynaroides* may measure 12 in. across or more, whereas in *P. odorata* they are 1½ in. or less; most species have their heads at the ends of branches, but a few like *P. humiflora, P. amplexicaulis,* and *P. cordata* produce heads laterally from the branches near the ground level.

Even within a single species there is often considerable variation: *Protea cynaroides* is an example, where at least two distinct forms appear to exist, and in the Port Elizabeth area at any rate they seem to be associated with altitude above sea level. At lower elevations the shrubs are usually reasonably tall, the leaves are comparatively narrow, the bracts are sharply pointed, and they flower in spring to summer. At the higher elevations, however, the shrubs are small, the leaves are broad, the bracts are rounded at the ends, and the flowering period is summer to autumn. Further study of the occurrence of these forms is required.

It is sad to have to admit that in many places proteas are gradually being exterminated. The main causes are repeated bush fires, flower picking, expansion of cities, towns, agriculture and forestry, and the encroachment of alien plants into the natural vegetation. *Protea repens (= P. mellifera),* for instance, was once abundant on the flats and lower mountain slopes of the south-western Cape and is now comparatively rare in these parts; *P. neriifolia* and *P. pulchra (= P. pulchella)* once occurred on the Cape Peninsula but are no longer to be seen growing naturally here.

It is encouraging to know, however, that there seems to be an awakening of interest in the preservation of our natural flora and in its cultivation, and we can only hope that none of the species that exist at present will ever become extinct.

In the Valleys of the Himalayan Cedars

PROFESSOR HERMANN MEUSEL

The species of the genus *Cedrus,* which in the later Tertiary were wide-spread in Europe, are today confined to isolated mountain ranges in the southern Mediterranean area. The beauty of these strong-stemmed and widely branching conifers has been praised in earliest times and their valuable timber used for many purposes. All that remains today of the once extensive forests of the Lebanon cedar in the Orient is a scanty little group, protected by a wall, amid bare rocks. How fortunate is the botanist who discovers larger forests of well-grown cedars in some places in the Central Atlas Mountains! In the rainy outer ranges of these mountains *Cedrus atlantica,* often in association with *Quercus ilex,* forms dense forests in which delicate evergreens, such as holly or dwarf bay, are able to spread. On the dry weather side of the mountains the trees appear as weather-beaten giants in loose sandy soil, together with ancient junipers *(Juniperus thurifera)* and the hard *Acantholium.* Where sufficient snow-cover provides the soil with ample moisture, the Atlas cedar shows a remarkable adaptability to differing conditions.

Since, with the help of some French friends, I had had the opportunity of viewing the cedar forests of the Central and High Atlas, it had always been my wish to see the famous deodara cedars of the Himalayan regions. In the mountainous countries of northern Baluchistan, Afghanistan and the western Himalayas *Cedrus deodara* inhabits the eastern distribution areas of the genus far removed from the habitat of the Mediterranean species, its relation to which resembles that of the West Himalayan *Quercus balloot* to the Mediterranean *Quercus ilex,* or of the West Himalayan olive *(Olea cuspidata)* to *Olea europea.*

While the Mediterranean cedars prefer to settle on open mountain ridges, the Himalayan cedars thrive best in enclosed valleys. In the outer ranges of the Western Himalayas, which come under the influence of the monsoon, evergreen oaks and large leafed Ericaceae, such as the tree rhododendron, dominate. Swelling hummocks of moss, sheltering many epiphytic ferns along the branches, indicate a high concentration of humidity in the atmosphere and ample rainfall. Mixed with this lush deciduous forest vegetation, the cedar occurs at most on dry rocky ridges or drier chalky soils.

The mountain tree is adapted to the contrasts of cold, snowy winters and dry, hot summers and thus dominates only in Himalayan valleys sheltered from the monsoon. In the mountainous regions at altitudes of between 4,500 and 8,000 feet extensive coniferous forests cover the slopes. Here *Cedrus deodara* is often accompanied by the blue pine *(Pinus excelsa)* with its delicate needles, and at greater heights replaced by the tall Himalayan fir *(Abies pindrow)* with its remarkably narrow head. It is indeed difficult to decide which of these three conifers is most to be admired. The lover of dark pine forests will prefer the firs standing as dark, slender pillars before a back-cloth of snowy mountains. How often we have admired the slender branches of *Pinus excelsa,* with its long pendulous needles, in Central European gardens. The first meeting with these trees in their natural habitat remains a memorable experience. But a view of the cedars outshines all such impressions. With their mighty trunks, strongly rooted in the rock, they appear to be true inhabitants of the mountains, but the loosely woven network of branches at the top fits the sunny climate of their southern habitat. They combine strength with elegance and the forests composed of cedars symbolise the victory of living nature over the hard conditions of the high mountains at the edge of the sub-tropical region.

Since the separation of Kashmir from India and Pakistan has made it difficult to float the valuable cedar wood down the Jhalum River and the Indian forestry commission has restricted pasturage, abundant regeneration of the cedar forests has taken place in the valleys. Young trees, which differ from those of other species, in having arched tops, can be found growing even on rocky ground. Their bunched needles on short shoots are often bluish-green in colour, while the needles of the older trees are usually green. Slender, like our mountain firs, cedars now grow up in the clearings. The charred trunks of old giants are evidence of a merciless exploitation in the past. But old live trees of 98 feet and more are also to be found, their broad tops resembling those of the Atlas and Taurus cedars.

Unlike the German forester Dietrich Brandis, who in the second half of the nineteenth century was employed as inspector-general of the British East Indian forestry commission, I have never seen deodara cedars as tall as 230 feet, but on the lower slopes in different parts of Kashmir I did see strong, slender trees which stand comparison with the tallest firs of the Black Forest. In the late autumn only isolated remains of the flora associated with the cedar forests were recognisable. The red-berried fruit system of *Arisaema* pointed to the strange fly-catching flowers of the East Asian flora, related to our Aaron's rod. *Aquilegia,* strawberry, lamp flower, hound's tongue, common avens and many other plants reminded me of the well-known sylvan flora of temperate regions. At the edge of the forest *Clematis grata,* a close relative of our *Clematis vitalba,* displayed its plummose pubescent fruit, and the slender arched branches of *Rosa moschata,* swinging up into the branches of the bluish-green cedars, were decorated with loose clusters of red fruit. As in all regions with dry summers, the deciduous trees showed vivid autumn colouring. As a significant companion of the cedar forests in the Western Himalayas, the low shrub *Parottia jacquemontana, Hamamelidaceae,* inhabits the clearings. When a forest region has been laid waste, *Parottia* spreads in all directions and, in the autumn, colours the sloping path with a vivid cadmium-yellow. The pinnate leaves of some species of sumach (for instance, *Rhus panjabensis*), which are common in dry forests, are characterised by reddish and orange tints. Barberries with clusters of blue berries, and red-fruited rock medlars are found everywhere in dry cedar forests.

Deciduous trees, however, are confined to moister habitats at the foot of slopes or in rocky gullies. Here, alongside ash and maple, there are broad walnut and chestnut trees, though most of them are badly damaged through the cutting of branches for cattle fodder. On terraces where mountain streams have deposited great quantities of gravel, the walnut tree forms natural little groups.

Where richer soil covers the foot of slopes and the bottom of valleys, the woods are replaced by fields of maize and wheat, and lower still by paddy fields. On arable ground only single trees remain as evidence of the original forest vegetation. On the deep soil of the terraced fields blue pines and cedars grow to considerable heights. Small streams are lined with alder and ash. Walnut and mulberry trees, the latter probably natives of these regions, are cultivated for their fruit. In autumn they decorate the fields with their colourful foliage.

The houses, frequently built of cedar wood, are surrounded by fruit trees and the spicy scent of decaying walnut leaves and cedar wood pervades the villages, where we are greeted by strong mountain peasants and merry children in colourful clothing.

A rich and varied landscape of fields and orchards, surrounded by dark forests on the slopes of snow-capped peaks, reminds us of scenes in the Central Alps, yet hints at the proximity of

India's tropical regions. Not only the manifold botanical observations, but also the unique aspect of the whole landscape keeps taking my mind back to the valleys of the Himalayan cedars and the wild nut trees.

Japan, the Homeland of Ornamental Plants

PROFESSOR HERMANN ULLRICH

A close study of the Latin names of plants at flower shows and in the catalogues of the larger tree and shrub nurseries reveals the fact that many names end in '*japonica*' or '*nipponica*.' Among the lists of other species called after authors, which normally carry the name of the species as a suffix and characterise the giver of the name, we find authors like Thunberg, Siebold, Trautwein, Zuccerini and Kaempfer, who made a special study of the plant world of Japan, along with Japanese authors like Matsumara, Kitamura, Makino, to name only the most important of them. This indicates that a great number of our horticulturally cultivated plants originate in Japan. If you take a specifically Japanese plant list, for instance, that in T. Makino's little standard work *Concise Pictorial Flora of Japan** or the larger work by the same author (from the same publishers), you will find that about a quarter of the plants listed carry the same characteristic species or author names, in some families even up to one third. Most of these species and sub-species are specifically Japanese and therefore count as endemics.

From the point of view of botanical history this is hardly surprising. Although in the geological past Japan was long a part of the Eurasian mainland, in more recent times a deep depression at the edge of the Pacific Ocean separated this chain of the highest peaks of an Asian border range. Botanically speaking, it also used to be connected with the Asian mainland and—as does the present archipelago—comprised regions of the northern temperate zone as well as sub-tropical regions with the corresponding floras. The later isolation, as always, gave rise to the evolution of descendants which by means of mutation distinguished themselves more and more from the original forms, which either evolved further or, to a lesser degree, became extinct. The ice ages have probably had less influence in Japan than in Europe, Asia and continental America, but vigorous volcanic activities played an all the more significant part and caused the development of small special areas of vegetation. Existing endemic forms were further augmented, though to a lesser degree, by the migration of floral elements from the Asian continent to the archipelago. Their names also indicate an exchange with Kamchatka, Sakhalin, Siberia, China, Korea and Manchuria in the north and west of the island chain, less with the Indo-Malayan area in the south, but more strongly again with Formosa via the Ryukyu Archipelago. Migration was particularly pronounced in the case of representatives which tend to be spread by wind, water or animals, while autochores, i.e. plants which spread by their own efforts, were added through human agents in the late Middle Ages and especially after the opening up of Japan in 1868. No exact details are known about the migration and spread of the cosmopolitans, the world citizens of the plant kingdom, which can be found in Japan today. Many of them have certainly been represented there for a very long time, as is shown by the first accounts of Japan's vegetation recorded by Kaempfer, Siebold, Thunberg and others.

Very soon after Japan had been opened up to world trade, the hitherto inaccessible and strange world of Japanese plants became available to western horticulture. The peculiar qualities of Japanese culture perhaps contributed least to this process—and does not do so today—for to

* Hokuryukan & Co., Ltd., Tokyo, in Japanese, with illustrations and Latin names.

the Japanese, at least those of the old school, a plant (or stone, mountain, animal or human) represents something unique whose form more than its colour corresponds to the European concept of 'flower.' In a European 'flower' or 'rock' garden, the western sense of beauty rejoices in the colourful splendour of the flowers as a whole and less in vegetative organs or the arrangement and shape of individual rocks. Artificially created mono-cultures are often preferred to single plants. The discerning old Japanese art of gardening, on the other hand, uses the individual plant, or very small groups of plants, to achieve a composition of mythological or aesthetic-contemplative significance. This finds expression indoors in the art of arranging flowers *(ikebana)* and the cultivation of dwarf trees *(bonzai),* a typically Japanese tradition, which may not be familiar to the reader of this book. Therefore, a massive display of flowers in the western style is hardly to be expected in Japan except perhaps in certain modern parks which have been created under western influence.

However, through the richness of its flora and the adaptibility of many of its representatives, Japan has given to the flower lovers of the world a great many of their favourites, such as the chrysanthemum, which have become indispensable to them and which play a distinguished part even within Japanese culture, for instance, as emblems—a golden chrysanthemum is the symbol of the imperial court.

The Japanese flora, supplemented by migrants which are being widely cultivated today, not counting the ferns but including the gymnosperms, comprises some 2,800 species. Amongst them certain families predominate, in most cases those which have made a significant contribution to the world assortment of ornamental plants.

In the first place, there are the *Compositae,* particularly the chrysanthemums which have already been mentioned, under the name of *Chrysanthemum indicum* L. which is synonymous with *Chrysanthemum indicum et japonicum* Thbg. Present-day ornamental forms are generally listed in five or six groups. One of them is specifically called the group of 'Japanese chrysanthemums.' Their flowers display a great variety of colours and shapes. They derive from old forms which were familiar and popular in Japan and China as early as the sixteenth century. *Kaempfer,* that traveller in Japan, gave them the name of *Matricaria japonica* and recorded the Japanese name *'kiku.'* As recently as the nineteenth century chrysanthemums were accepted by the western world as a welcome enrichment. They reacted very favourably to cultivation. Since they can be easily propagated by cuttings, hybrids and spontaneous mutations (sports) are perpetuated without trouble. This is not always the case with other *Compositae,* such as most other Japanese representatives of the same family, for instance, *Leontopodium japonicum,* the Japanese edelweiss.

Other *Compositae,* of which there are a great many in the Japanese flora, are not as well known or popular. Such species as *Cirsium, Arthemisia, Centaurea, Malotopus, Cacalia,* some asters, etc., should perhaps find more favour with gardeners and amateurs.

The magnificent *Lobelia sessilifolia* Lamb. *(Lobeliaceae)* which comes from Kamchatka, and is now wide-spread in Japan, certainly merits attention.

As a member of the family of *Campanulaceae, Platycodon grandiflorum* A. DC. should be mentioned. Through cultivation and selection some of its sub-species are now to be found in our gardens.

Among the *Caprifoliaceae,* the shrubs *Lonicera japonica* Thbg., the Japanese *weigelia,* also called *Diervillea* DC. has gained ground. Some species of snowball and their sub-species, which belong to the same family, have been introduced to European gardens, also the elder *Sambucus Sieboldiana* Blume. *Gardenia radicans* Thbg. *(Rubiaceae)* came to us as a house or greenhouse plant. It merits greater attention in its single as well as its double varieties. Among the *Thymeleaceae,* the scented *Daphne japonica* Thbg., which grows in the mountainous regions of its homeland, has become a popular rock garden plant. One of the Japanese *Elaeagnaceae* is *Elaeagnus multiflora* Thbg., whose fruits (variety *edulis*) are no longer tart and astringent but sweet and, therefore, quite palatable.

The Japanese mountain plant *Conandron ramondioides* S. et Z. belongs to the family of *Gesneriaceae* and is as yet regrettably rare in our cold greenhouses.

Callicarpa japonica Thbg., *Verbenaceae,* soon became popular on account of its red fruit—but also the white-fruited variety—and of its inflorescence, as did *Clerodendron fragans* Vent., which in addition has a strong but pleasant scent. The small *Buddleia japonica* Hemsl. *(Loganiaceae)* is also occasionally found in our gardens.

In its homeland the Japanese privet *(Ligustrum japonicum* Thbg., *Oleaceae)* is relatively exacting in regard to moisture, and varieties evolved by gardeners are not very hardy, since in Japan they need not withstand cold winters. Therefore, it is rather rare in western gardens. The Japanese lilac *(Syringa japonica* Decne.) and certain varieties of *Forsythia* have made a considerable contribution to the appropriate assortments. The Japanese cowslip *(Primula japonica* A. GR.), which in shady valleys in Japan grows up to 20 inches high, has had a decisive influence on the character of a whole section within the range of primulas cultivated by gardeners.

Particularly wide-spread and variable are the Japanese *Ericaceae.* The genus *Rhododendron* or *Azalea* occurs in many varieties and grows chiefly in woods and forests. *Encyanthus cernua* Mak. and *Andromeda japonica* Thbg. are also *Ericaceae* of Japanese origin. *Schizocodon soldanelloides* S. et Z. is quite attractive. It grows as a low shrub and its flowers resemble those of the beautiful soldanella. Like the latter it flowers very early in the year. Regrettably it has not as yet been widely introduced in our western gardens. Among the Dogwood shrubs, *Cornus Kousa* Buerg. is being acclaimed far beyond the borders of its native land. The *Aralias,* such as *Fatsia japonica,* with their many varieties, and *Hedera rhombea* S. et Z. are leaf plants which are most popular for indoor as well as outdoor cultivation in regions of a warm and moist climate. In their homeland they enliven the wintry landscape with a little green.

Stachyurus praecox S. et Z. is now also one of our earliest spring flowers. In Japan it grows on the slopes of moist valleys, together with azaleas, and contributes to Japan's enchanting spring atmosphere. Camellias, our popular but rather delicate indoor winter flowers, are common in Japan as wild growing shrubs. They grow or are planted in rows at the entrance to temple gardens. These tall shrubs with their white and red flowers, which grow yellow with age, present a curious picture: one shrub with flowers of three colours. *Thea chinensis* Sms. *(Camellia japonica* L. or other synonyms), which gardeners sometimes call pseudo-camellia, yields green tea and is widely cultivated as low shrubs in Central Japan, for instance, in the district of Kyoto.

Vitis heterophylla Thbg. and *Ampelopsis tricuspidata* S. et Z. *(Cissus thunbergii* S. et Z.) have become popular as indoor climbing shrubs, but the Japanese maple *(Acer palmatum* Thbg.) is quite hardy in our climate if the winters are not too cold, and in the autumn delights the eye with its red leaves. Of the leguminous plants, which are to be found as fairly tall trees in the forests of Japan, *Lespedeza Sieboldii* Miq., *Sophora japonica* L., *Cercis japonica* Sieb., occasionally decorate our exotic parks. The representatives of the family *Rosaceae* are numerous, and many of its genera are natives to the Land of the Rising Sun. The foremost of these is probably the genus *Prunus.* Ornamental plum and cherry trees and their many varieties blossom in midspring and play a considerable part in the cherry blossom festival of the Japanese, formerly perhaps a more contemplative, today a rather noisy way of honouring nature. Sorbus genera and others could also be mentioned. *Eriobotrya japonica* Ldl. is being cultivated as a fruit tree and is characteristic of many coastal areas of Central and Southern Japan. With us it is an exotic ornamental tree which enlivens the garden with its foliage and characteristic ramification. Many varieties of the Japanese spiraea *(Spiraea japonica* L. fil.) are to be found in Japan and it is somewhat difficult to understand why we seem only to favour the garden hybrids, for in their native land the pure strains delight the eye with their early gleaming blossoms at the edge of copses and woods. The Japanese quince *(Cydonia japonica* Pers.) I often found singly in the shape of a large spherical shrub in the classic historical gardens of Japan, such as the Ritsurin Park in Takamatsu and elsewhere. They are sometimes clipped in cubic shapes, as in the Kur Park, near the hot sulphurous springs of Beppu, where the warm ground causes the flowering season to be considerably earlier than elsewhere. Japan's flora also comprises many saxifragas, whose genera *Ribes, Deutzia, Astilbe,* etc., occur as small shrubs, while the genus *Saxifraga* may, under certain circumstances, dominate the botanical scene in the high mountains, where they grow as low shrubs or in hummocks, as they do sometimes in our rock gardens. Certain Japanese hydrangeas have become world famous for garden and indoor cultivation. The rich genetic material native to Japan, some species and varieties of which grow in the open there and are known as *Hydrangea japonica* Sieb., is generally treated as one group and would be better named *Hydrangea japonica* hort. so far as the cultivated strains are concerned. Even some *Crassulaceae,* such as *Sedum Sieboldii* Sweet. and *Sedum lineare* Thbg., to name only two, are to be found among the treasures of our succulent lovers; they might well add some other Japanese species. Among the *Ranunculaceae, Clematis florida* Thbg., *Actea japonica* Thbg., *Cimicifuga japonica* Spreng., *Aconitum japonicum* Decne. and *Anemone japonica* S. et Z. have left their native land to spread as varied wild and garden species all over the world. The *Berberidaceae, Magnoliaceae,* and *Nymphaeaceae* can only be mentioned briefly here, as also some *Polygonumaceae, Moraceae, Saururaceae* and other families.

Japan's flora is also rich in Monocotyledonous plants which in some areas may dominate the botanical picture with their beautiful flowers, particularly in late spring. Some species of *Orchidaceae,* so highly valued by their admirers, are also natives of Japan. I would mention *Taeniophyllum aphyllum* Mak., which curiously enough assimilates as a leafless plant with verdant roots, but produces relatively inconspicuous flowers. Some *Cypripedilum* species are all the more striking, particularly *Cypripedilum japonicum* Thbg., which carries a single flower above a cup-like collar of bracts, and many other species, some of them with several sub-species. The *Iridaceae* have enriched the large world assortment of their species by many new characteristics, especially through *Iris japonica* Thbg., *Iris Kaempferi* Sieb. They are most variable even in their native land, as shown in Makino's *Flora.*

It is quite astonishing how many lilies have evolved endemically in Japan. The genus Lilium alone, which has given its name to the family, is represented by several species. Most of them flower in spring and are to be found at Easter time in the flower markets of the large cities, most of them having very showy flowers.

Among the monocotyledons with calyces resembling petals are several Araceae. Their genera *Arisaema, Arum, Acorus* are to be found in certain restricted localities in the Japanese islands and again dominate the ground flora in spring. Not only their flowers, but their leaves are decorative, and for that reason these plants are often grown in our greenhouses and winter gardens. Other monocotyledons which characterise Japan's flora throughout the year by their proliferation and foliage, the many species of bamboo, for instance, can only be mentioned briefly in this book, which is chiefly devoted to flowering plants. Even apart from the lively and varied background it provides, Japan's flora has made a considerable contribution to the plant population of gardens and rooms all over the world.

The Plant World of Australia

PROFESSOR H. WALTER

The plant lover on a visit to Australia finds himself in an entirely new world. He sees hardly any plants with soft leaves like maple, lilac or clover. Almost all plants in Australia have leathery, hard or evergreen foliage. These are often rounded, needle-like, serrated or lobed (e.g. *Hakea*). In vain the visitor searches for the light green of our deciduous forests of beech, oak, ash, alder or birch. The forests of Australia are composed of only one genus—the eucalyptus, which is related to the myrtle. But of this genus there are some 600 different species which are not easily distinguishable from one another, even by the botanist. Among them are the tallest trees in the world which in the moist border regions of Australia grow to a height of 328 feet, and the lowest shrubs (mallee) whose woody stems form an enormous underground tuber. They grow on the edges of the dry Central Australian region. Eucalyptus plants occur in the lowlands at sea level and up to the tree line at 6,562 feet, where they are covered in snow for many months in the year. In Australia this one genus with its coarse, narrow olive-green leaves, which contain quantities of volatile oil, takes the place of the many varieties of trees to which we are accustomed. There are no coniferous trees. It is not surprising that to the European the eucalyptus forests appear somewhat monotonous, but the Australian loves them and draws a sigh of relief on catching sight of them again after a journey to Europe.

The eucalyptus leaves generally grow vertically and, in consequence, the forests appear light. In Australia they are confined to regions of 10—12 inches of annual rainfall. Where the climate is too dry for eucalyptus trees, they give way to acacia shrubs which in the flowering season are covered with little scented yellow balls like the plants which we buy in our flower shops under the incorrect name of 'mimosa.'

The acacias of inner Australia have delicate feathery leaves only as seedlings. As the plants grow, it can be observed how the leaves are gradually reduced while the stalks become larger and broader until finally they alone develop further. The often greyish-green, leaf or needle-like formations on the acacia bushes of Central Australia are, therefore, leaf stalks which take the place of actual foliage. Of this acacia there are also 400 species.

Altogether the Australian flora is reckoned to consist of 10,000 different species, 75 per cent of which are endemic, i.e. they occur nowhere else. These form the proper Australian element of the flora. Only in the damp tropical jungles of the north-east are there other types which remind one of those in the Indonesian islands. They are a foreign body within the Australian plant world, as are the Antarctic elements to be found in the south-east and in the alpine regions, especially in the Tasmanian mountains. They also occur in New Zealand and South America. Not only the Australian trees appear foreign to us, but also the floral shapes of many herbaceous plants, some of which are illustrated in this book. Very curious, for instance, are the 'kangaroo paws' *(Anigozanthus)* to be found on marshy ground, whose flowers look like the toes of a paw.

One of the most interesting plant families of Australia are the *Proteaceae,* which also occur in South Africa, although there they are represented by different species. They are especially striking to the plant lover during the flowering season. Although the individual flower is small, together they form a large and dense inflorescence, usually magnificently coloured. The fruit systems are equally curious. They often look like comical little gnomes when some of the fruits burst and show gaping valves.

The opening of the hard, woody seed vessels in Australia is an interesting phenomenon. The woody, hard, pear-shaped fruit of the 'wild pear' *(Xylomelon)*, for instance, remain closed for years until a forest fire heats them up temporarily and causes them to burst. But the seeds do not immediately drop out. They are attached to the wall of the seed-vessel by little teeth and only a fairly strong wind can shake them out. They fall on the cool ashes, which provide a good seed bed. These plants which depend on fire for their propagation are called 'fire plants.' Fire plays a significant plant in Australia, more than ever today. The farmers burn down the woods on purpose to destroy them, for timber is almost valueless in the poorly populated country. It cannot be exported because its great weight makes it unsuitable for building purposes or pulping. Sheep cannot graze in the woods, and so the farmers hold that, 'One blade of grass is worth more than two trees.' The most effortless way of killing the woods is to cut rings in the barks of the trees, which cause them to die in about a year's time. The dead wood is then reduced to ashes. With larger trunks this is not always immediately successful, and these tree corpses often remain for a long time accusingly pointing up to the sky. Meanwhile the ground round the marshes is lightly loosened, so that grass and clover seeds and phosphate fertiliser may be scattered from planes, and the pasture land is ready. The dimensions of the Australian countryside are very different from those in Europe or even North America. The farms are generally 2,471—24,711 acres, the 'sheep stations' further inland even 247,110—2,471,100 acres. There the sheep have to be content with extremely poor natural pasture, so that 124 acres are required to keep one sheep. In these areas the nearest neighbours are often 124 miles away. Every station, however, possesses a radio transmitter and is thus in contact with school and hospital centres. Children receive their lessons by radio and the doctor visits his patients by plane.

The Australian interior is by no means a desert. Wide areas are covered with salt bushes or acacia shrubs and serve as pasture land. At the edge of salt-pans there are often very pretty flowering plants. Areas of unmixed sand, or those in which no water is to be found, are called 'deserts,' although they have some vegetation. In the northern half of the continent the interior consists of grass land with scattered eucalyptus trees. At the 'stations' in these areas cattle are kept in place of sheep.

The Floral Splendour of the Philippines

DR MONA LISA STEINER

There is no more colourful picture than an avenue of fire trees *(Delonix regia)* with their umbrella-shaped tops crowded with fiery-red flowers against a deep blue tropical sky. Even the ground beneath the trees is overlaid with a gleaming carpet contrasting with the verdant surroundings. Forbes Park, one of the beautiful suburbs of Manila, the capital of the Philippines, welcomes us thus in the month of March, when the flowering season is at its peak. Although there hardly is a rest period in the tropics, December and May could be compared with spring and summer, when the splendour of the flowers reaches its height.

Long hedges of *Poinsettia (Euphorbia pulcherrima)*, covered all over with gleaming red hypsophylls, are still in full flower. Only double flowers are to be seen, the single ones having long since been discarded and replaced by better ones. While in the West we enjoy white and pink tree blossoms, in the Philippines there are a number of red flowering trees to be admired, such as the tall tropical tulip tree *(Spathodea campanulata)*: the deep red dapdap *(Erythrina variegata)* papilionaceous blossoms, which spring in countless tufts from strangely ramified branches: the red silk cotton tree *(Gossampinus heptaphylla)* with huge, fleshy five-petalled flowers, and many others. You may think you are meeting an old acquaintance, the laburnum, but look closer and you will see the difference. It is the tropical laburnum *(Cassia fistula)*.

The most striking ornamental shrub, to be found in almost every garden, is also the most obliging of all tropical shrubs, the *Bougainvillea*. This is not the monotonously purple *Bougainvillea* of our flower shops, which has long since been discarded, to be replaced by red, yellow, orange, white and deep purple varieties with greatly enlarged bracts. They grow as compact shrubs or in hedges which show hardly any green leaves, only masses of flowers. Yellow, white and red ixia and a great many wonderful tropical plants, not one of them known to us in the temperate zone, are to found in the gardens.

But all the splendour we admire in the gardens around Manila is not really characteristic of the Philippines. The cosmopolitan traveller will have seen most of these tropical plants already in Hawaii, Singapore, Jamaica or Ceylon. Are there then no ornamental plants peculiar to the Philippines?

The Philippines, the land of 7,000 islands, is one of the richest floral regions of the world with 10,000 different flowering plants. By comparison, the present-day European flora embraces some 16,000 species, but the surface area of the Philippines is only about as large as that of Italy. Of particular interest are the many endemic species, exclusively to be found in the Philippines.

Hawaii is often mentioned as a paradise of orchids, but botanically speaking, the Philippines have a far better claim to the epithet, since about 1,000 different species grow wild here, while Hawaii can lay claim only to three small and insignificant orchid species.

There can scarcely be an orchid grower in the world who does not know Waling-Waling *(Vanda sanderiana)*. This wonderful orchid, which as a wild flower is confined to a very small area of Mindanao, has become the ancestor of many *Vanda* hybrids. Apart from other beautiful *Vandas*, the delicate butterfly orchid and its different relatives are most fequently cultivated. Even the poorest native nipa-house of palm leaves and bamboo has a few coconut shells with white butterfly orchids hanging up in the large open windows. Almost throughout the year these orchids produce long pendulous panicles and sometimes a flower or two is cut down to adorn the hair of a beautiful young Philippine girl.

Epiphytic orchids grow on most of the trees in the gardens, especially species of *Dendrobium* which do not require too much attention. In March the scent of *Dendrobium anosum* pervades the air. The name is paradoxical because it signifies 'unscented.' The long clusters of purple flowers can be bought from hawkers who sell them in the streets of the suburbs.

In order to see the full range of endemic orchids you should visit an orchid show where Philippine species are displayed in all their richness and splendour.

But the orchid family is not the only one which can boast of rare ornamental plants. In most gardens there is a white-flowering shrub very rarely seen outside the Philippines, namely, 'Doña Aurora' *(Mussaenda philippica*, variety *Aurorae—Rubeaceae)*. There are many tropical shrubs which flower for many months in succession, but hardly one which is in full bloom throughout the year. 'Doña Aurora' loses its flowers only when, from time to time, it has to be pruned. Otherwise it is covered all over with white hypsophylls which, botanically speaking, are enlarged petals.

In recent years an interesting hybrid has been evolved, 'Doña Luz,' which resembles 'Doña Aurora' but flowers red. This most striking plant is a hybrid of *Mussaenda erythrophylla*, which

has one enlarged red petal, and the wild white variety. This Philippine plant is not as yet generally known, but already much sought after by gardeners the world over.
It is paradoxical that the Philippine ornamental plant *Medinilla magnifica,* so well-known abroad, is never cultivated at home, although it grows wild in the mountains of Luzon. The reason is to be found in the high temperatures which prevail in Manila and other cities. *Medinilla* grows high up in the mountains, where temperatures resemble those of temperate zones rather than the tropics. It is strange that of 107 wild species of *Medinilla* only one is being cultivated, although others have more vivid colours and more compact inflorescences.
There are flowers in almost all the colours of the rainbow, but nature does not produce many brilliantly blue-green flowers. It is said that Gadevine *(Strongylodon macrobotrys)* is unique in its colouring, which regrettably can hardly be reproduced. This liana forms enormous trusses, often 3—6 feet long, densely covered with flowers 2—3 inches long, which individually resemble bean flowers. At the edge of the jungle this woody creeper forms walls of gigantic height and width, hung with countless flowers and presenting an incredible picture. Although this is a leguminous plant, its fruit are round and as large as a head. They contain only a few seeds which unfortunately very soon lose their capacity to germinate.
The Philippine ornamental plants I have mentioned represent only a small selection of the best-known and most striking endemic flowers, which are of interest to gardeners throughout the world. But most of the exotic blossoms which flower in the seclusion of the steaming jungles still await the discoverer who will reveal their beauty and adorn the gardens of the world.

Hawaii — Dream Island of the Pacific Ocean

DR MONA LISA STEINER

Dream island of the Pacific, tropical splendour of flowers—the traveller arrives in Hawaii with such high expectations that he is afraid of being disappointed. But the sweet-scented *lei,* the garlands with which pretty Hawaiian girls welcome the traveller on his arrival at the airport or the quay, herald a visit which surpasses all expectations. How is it that there seem to be only fair, sun-tanned girls and broad-shouldered, handsome young men walking about the streets of Waikiki bare-footed and in bikinis or the shortest of bathing trunks? Everything radiates light, the sun, the white sands, the azure ocean, the eyes of kindly people.
But not only the girls are charming, radiant and beautiful; there is hardly another place in the world which can boast of such luxuriant vegetation. Plants, leaves, flowers and fruit seem to be larger, more brilliantly coloured, juicier and better developed than anywhere else. The giant leaves of green creepers climbing up the walls, look as if they had been dipped in oil—not a speck of dust anywhere. In many tropical countries the heat is oppressive and in the dry season the plants look a little dehydrated and dusty. Take a walk in Honolulu and you will discover what it is that has such a miraculous effect on man and plant—liquid sunshine. Not cloud in the sky, the sun shines, a slight haze covers the landscape, a fine spray bedews everything. You walk in your bathing suit without feeling chilly and admire the rainbow above the mountains. This fine drizzle which pleasantly freshens the atmosphere at least once a day is one reason for the healthy climate and luxuriant vegetation.
Quite incredible to most visitors are the enormous climatic contrasts within the shortest distances. At the foot of one side of the mountain the vegetation is luxuriant: 100 yards further the rainfall is less than half and on the other side of the mountain there is an almost complete desert, so dry that only a few xerophilous plants are able to grow. One side of a valley may be fertile, the

other as dry as dust. The reason for these contrasts lies in the trade winds, which take certain clearly defined courses. In certain places they hit the mountain side and precipitate rain, others they miss out altogether. Property prices rise with the annual rainfall and gardens are to be found chiefly in the moister regions, for watering can never be as effective as natural rain.

Let us take a look at the world-famous gardens of the pineapple barons and other millionaires. There are no fences, hedges, curtains, people are proud to show their homes and do not seclude themselves physically or mentally. Giant banana-like leaves of the Heliconia species with orange-red flowers in zigzag formation, erect or pendullous, are among the most popular background plants. Along with them grow enormous plants of the torchginger *(Phaeomeria magnifica)*, which show great red inflorescences in the centre far below the leaves. The red ginger *(Alpinia purpurata)* belongs to the same family of *Zingiberaceae*. It has long cone-like inflorescences which in a vase last for several weeks. Our nurseries often show the exotic *Strelitzia regina*, with tapering yellow bracts and a blue 'tongue,' but these give only a very faint indication of the size and splendour of the plants in Hawaii, although their native country is not Hawaii but tropical Africa. Many varieties of hibiscus also grow to perfection here, mostly not the usual forms with single or double flowers which are normally found in the tropics, but a giant strain with flowers the size of a plate. The native girls wear them in their hair in every imaginable colour (except deep blue). Among the most popular cut flowers are the beautiful varieties of *Anthurium* in white, red and pink. The shiny, waxy hypsophylls are hardly distinguishable from artificial flowers, which are also much used in Hawaii, though only in combination with natural flowers and leaves. The perpetually flowering *Allamanda cathartica* with its golden yellow bell-shaped flowers frames the doorways, and Bougainvilleas in many colours gleam among the luxuriant verdure. White *Hedychium coronarium* scents the air in the half-shade and yellow *Hedychium gardnerianum* grows among the deep red foliage of ti or *Cordyline fruticosa*.

Among the cut flowers are also orchids, especially *Vanda 'Miss Joaquim,'* which grows on the ground. These orchids are grown in vast fields, like carnations or roses in Europe. At the hotel no meal passes without an orchid nestling beside the plate or in the glass, and orchids lie on pillows as a goodnight greeting. Amateur and professional gardeners have perfected the art of cultivating orchids to the highest degree in the ideal climate of Hawaii. Amateurs, chiefly men, vie with each other in cultivating the most beautiful varieties which are being admired at orchid shows. The cultivation of orchids is fashionable in Hawaii and provides the main topic of conversation. That is one aspect of Hawaii—Honolulu, Diamond Head, Wakiki Beach: elegance, luxury, the paradise of the orchid, America in tropical disguise. But it is only one aspect. Apart from Oahu, the island on which Honolulu is situated, there are Maui, the island of grand valleys, Hawaii, the orchid island, and Molokai, the most primitive island, where traces of the original Polynesian life remain.

If you want to know Hawaii thoroughly you should visit the island of Maui and Haleakala with its unique national park, a giant crater 33 miles long which resembles a moonscape with symmetrical volcanic cones and other strange formations. This area is one of the most magnificent that Hawaii has to offer. The rocks are quite incredible in the splendour of their colouring, which changes with the times of the day. A journey up the mountains reveals a belt of tropical vegetation, but otherwise all is dry, barren and sandy. The vegetation is scanty, growing close to the ground, strangely twisted and equipped with every possible trick of nature to enable it to withstand the extreme dryness, intensity of light, winds and great contrasts of temperature. Yet this apparently infertile region contains the most interesting flora in the world, which is unique in many respects.

Here in the national park of Haleakala we find the real Hawaii, less luxurious and colourful but all the more impressive. Almost all the plants we admire in the gardens have been introduced and are, therefore, not characteristic of Hawaii; the endemic flora shows itself in the national park. Some botanists have likened these plants to dinosaurs, relics of a world which has long since passed away. This unique vegetation is found nowhere else on earth. How is this *flora relicta* to be explained?
Almost all the floral areas of the world are of continental origin. Geologically speaking, even an archipelago like the Philippines belongs to the continent. However, Hawaii is of volcanic origin and never had any connection with the mainland. How do flora and fauna evolve on islands separated from all other life?
It is assumed that the original vegetation was carried to the islands in the course of millions of years by gales, birds and ocean currents, and subsequently evolved in isolation. On the continents the battle for existence was hard, some families and species proved stronger and endured, others were eradicated. The plants which landed on Hawaii found different conditions and different enemies. The original fauna of Hawaii comprised very few species; prior to the arrival of man there were no mammals except bats. Many very primitive genera and species, which had no chance of survival on the mainland, continued to exist and in the course of millions of years new genera and species evolved in isolation. With the advent of man the endemic flora declined; goats, horses, cows, weeds, cultivated plants, ornamental plants slowly but inexorably annihilated the earlier vegetation.
To save the endemic flora from extinction national parks were established where representatives of this wonderful world of the past can still be found. Haleakala is probably the best known for its landscape as well as its flora. The most famous plant of the region is the Hawaiian silversword *(Argyroxiphium sandwicense)* which belongs to a genus endemic to Hawaii. The young plant resembles an agave with very dense foliage and has spiky, woolly silvery leaves. From a distance the young silversword looks like a silvery ball. When the plant has reached a height of about 20—23 inches, it develops striking yellowish-brown flowers, not unlike small sun flowers, which is not surprising for this strange plant is a primitive composite. It is also interesting to note that there are seven different insects which concentrate on this plant and threaten its existence.
For thousands of years the Hawaiian sandal wood has been much sought after. It comes from a small tree or shrub *(Santalum haleakalae)* with leathery dark green leaves and red four-petalled flowers which appear at the tips of the branches. The dry cores of the stems yield the scented sandal wood which has been so highly prized since man discovered it. The notable endemic genus *Hibiscadelphus* is related to the hibiscus, but it has become regrettably rare. Mamane *Sophora chrysophylla* in full flower presents a wonderful spectacle. Yellow papilionaceous flowers smother the shrub, contrasting beautifully with the deep blue tropical sky. They later develop into strangely twisted pods which are used for medicinal purposes. Families, of which we know only small representatives, here evolved tree-like genera; certain relatives of the violet, for instance, are woody plants. Very strange and equally unfamiliar are lobelias like *Clermontia haleakalensis* with tufts of lanceolate leaves, not unlike *Dracaena,* the dragon tree of the Canary Islands, a *Liliaceae.* Another surprise to the plant lover is the extremely delicate native begonia, *Hillebrandia sandwicensis.* Even the botanist well versed in the tropical flora has to confess himself unable so much as to guess at the family, the Hawaiian flora is so different from anything else in the world. Considering that 85 per cent of the endemic plants are different from those of other countries, it is no exaggeration to claim that Hawaii possesses one of the most singular and interesting floras of the world.

When the Atacama Flowers . . .

PROFESSOR GERHARD FOLLMANN

The traveller coming from the 'Green South' of Chile, which so closely resembles northern-hemisphere forest and pasture lands, and proceeding overland via Concepcion and Santiago to the so-called 'Grand North,' soon finds himself in desert country as grandiose as it is varied, yet terribly sterile. To this day the hunger and thirst march of the Spanish conquerors in the opposite direction appears almost unbelievable. It is not surprising that these stretches of rubble and sand, rock and salt, inimical to every kind of life, rarely interrupted by a dusty and apparently lifeless hedge cactus, caused the English scientist *Charles Robert Darwin* to remark that nowhere else in the world did the sun waste its rays to so little purpose. As on the west coast of Africa, the desert climate on the western slopes of the Andes is caused by relatively cool ocean currents: cold water sucked up from great depths by the Humboldt Stream running northwest parallel to the coast, almost continuously keeps the surface of the Pacific Ocean at a temperature lower than that of the mainland which is being heated by the tropical sun. In consequence, the air moved inland by the prevailing south-west winds, dries out and very little rainfall results. In the east the coastal desert of North Chile is protected against the rain-laden trade winds by the mighty barrier of the Andes. In 'good years' the south of the region has a rainfall of barely 2 inches, while in the north 'sporadic' rainfall of 0.4 of an inch has been recorded at intervals of 10—15 years. However careful one ought to be in the use of superlatives, it is no exaggeration to say that the north Chilean Atacama is absolutely the driest of all deserts. Nor is there any need to modify this statement because of a few strictly confined 'mist oases' on the slopes of some geomorphologically favoured coastal mountains, which show a relatively richer vegetation due to a moister local climate.

When at last it does rain, which means a brief downpour in the nature of a cloudburst, the so-called *llanos* (Spanish for plains) of the Atacama, miraculously turn green overnight, for the desert soil, despite long periods of drought, contains many viable seeds. Within a few days a colourful veil of flowers spreads over the rainsoaked regions, not by any means always throughout the whole Atacama, to its full extent of more than 625 miles from north to south, and the air near the ground is filled with the delicate scent of *Verbena, Calceolaria, Loasa, Heliotropium* and *Senecio.*

Hundreds of different species play their part in the phenomenon of the 'flowering desert.' Despite the pioneering work done in the last century by the German-Chilean botanist Rodolfo Amando Philippi, several of them are as yet insufficiently known, which is not surprising considering their rare and sporadic appearance and the isolated nature of the region. One or two of them may determine the colour of the ground for miles around: purple stretches *(Caladrinia)* alternate with sky blue ones *(Nolana)*, lilac-coloured ones *(Erodium)* with blue and white ones *(Scilla)* or light yellow ones *(Hippeastrum)*. The unreal appearance is underlined by the rigid and sombre background of the barren, stone coloured heights of the Andes.

However, is should not be imagined that these 'ephemeral' plants cover an area as densely as, for instance, does the vegetation of an alpine meadow. Although the individual plants grow fairly close together, they do not touch each other. A careful examination shows that there is much bare desert ground between them. Their most sparingly developed leaves and branches afford little coverage. The height of these desert plants ranges from less than 1/4 inch to about 12 inches, in exceptional cases 16 inches. On the other hand, their flowers are surprisingly large and, to a cursory glance over a wide area, give the impression of a dense carpet.

In the 'flowering Atacama' the number of individual plants to the square foot is extraordinarily high. In the rainy spring of 1961—the last previous rain had fallen in 1952—in some places we counted some 3,000 specimens to 10.67 square feet in the *pampa* (Spanish for steppe) of Copiapó at the centre of the observation area. (Visited again in the following year, the pampa showed itself so barren and empty that an unsuspecting observer would never even have guessed at its flowering potential. Not even withered traces of vegetation were visible. They had probably been blown away by violent desert storms.) These sporadic plant societies, therefore, provide an impressive contrast to the few perennial desert plants (succulents and dwarf shrubs) whose individual specimens often grow at intervals of 40 or more feet, which gives the impression that the region is almost completely devoid of plant life.

The plant societies of the 'flowering desert' consist of very different forms of life. We find chiefly annuals, curiously enough often without any of the familiar devices for the storage of water and for protection against evaporation. In very many of these short-lived desert plants the green stalks are overlaid with a red pigment (a protective layer of anthocyanin pigment, acting like a red filter); in very minute plants the leaves also are often red tinted. In these desert areas of most intense sunlight, protection against light is more important than protection against evaporation.

There are also a great number of plants growing from bulbs or corms mostly, however, in the shape of first-year newcomers grown from seeds. This shows that even these organs of survival, resistant and well protected by the soil as they normally are, are unable to withstand the murderous drought except in rare cases.

Annuals most frequently appear to have very rudimentary vegetative organs, swaying stalks and narrow, often feathery, delicate leaves. A few species have downy hair, others bear feathery or thread-like leaves on ramified stalks. Most of them have basilar rosettes from which the small feathery leaves rise either in a shallow arch—they are called *Adesmia* types after a very prevalent papilionaceous dwarf shrub—or with funnel-shaped, erect, very small leaves *(Plantago* type).

Most of the interesting dwarf varieties (desert violet, desert plantain, desert stork's bill) of the 'flowering Atacama' belong to the second group. With thousands of plants to 10½ square feet, they often form a dense carpet barely half an inch high. Most of these minute inhabitants of the desert bear only a single flower, even species which normally have more, as, for instance, the European varieties of stork's bill. More than half the weight of the total plant may be embodied in that one flower. Compared with their 'normal' size observed elsewhere, these dwarfs have often shrunk to less than one hundredth, an adaptation which is chiefly due to the extremely curtailed period of vegetation of one to three weeks, into which are telescoped every possible manifestation of life from germination to flower and fruit.

Another annual form of the Atacama plant society is equipped with a basilar rosette of thick, water-storing leaves. Usually the individual plants are larger and stronger. The foliage is broader, often arranged in diamond shape, glassy, and bare, and in many cases the surface is dotted with glandular pores. In these species the leaves develop rapidly, while the magnificent flowers, to which the water stored by the succulent leaves is available for some time after rainfall, develop more slowly. Characteristic representatives of this group are the portulacas *(Calandrinia* type), most of which are natives of the New World.

The third group of annuals, the parasites, should not be forgotten. Their webs of golden-yellow threads may cover all the other desert plants *(Cuscuta* type). They live preferably on plantain species and with their little balls of white flowers resemble the white bryony of northern fields, although the desert plant remains much smaller and finer. From the point of view of distribution, it is surprising to note that such highly specialised parasites are to be found in areas where conditions only just, and under exceptional circumstances, permit the ephemeral existence of dwarf plants.

On the other hand, the geophilous perennials have pretty uniform habits with narrow ephemeral leaves forming rosettes, from the centre of which rises the elegant flower shaft. In addition to the large flowering *Hymenocallis* species with yellow or red flowers *(Hippeastrum* type) which closely resemble our cultivated day lilies, the graceful, yellow to purple flowering oxalis species with bulbils are especially striking. A number of these beautiful and hardy desert plants merit cultivation as garden plants. It is not yet certain for how many years they can survive without rain in their natural habitat.

There are a very few micro-climatically favoured habitats where plants, which remain above ground, play a part in the 'flowering desert,' especially the recumbent dwarf bushes of Indian hemp *(Skythanthus* type), growing very few and far between, whose characteristically arched opposite seed vessels have given rise to the popular name of *Cuerno de Cabra* (Spanish for goat horns), in some places accompanied by *Leoncito* (Spanish for little lion), a yellow-flowered barbed *Opuntia,* barely 4 inches high.

No one can say how long the individual seed, from which a flowering plant eventually develops, has lain in the ground. But it is perhaps possible to answer the question as to the origin of the seeds of annuals in the 'flowering desert' where perhaps no plant life has existed previously for a decade or more, when one considers the wind conditions. The German plant geographer Josef Schmithüsen, for instance, believes that the seeds, fine and light as dust, are carried far into the Atacama by the prevailing south-westerly winds and derive from parent plants somewhere at the southern edge of the desert. It is possible that the Atacama is annually supplied with seeds from the south. The fact that the ephemeral Atacama plant societies consist of species which occur on the southern edge of the desert, seems to argue in favour of that assumption. The entirely different societies of the 'mist oases' on the Pacific edge of the Atacama, on the other hand, undoubtedly seem to have come from the north. Towards the north the number of species making up the colourful herbaceous ground cover decreases more and more, perhaps partly because of less favourable conditions in regard to available moisture.

The fauna of the 'flowering Atacama' is equally surprising. Lizards or their tracks may be seen even during the dry period. Many insects hover above the flowering herbage, and there are some birds, the size of a finch. Buzzards and vultures draw their circles in the sky. Foxes have also been observed. Even the dainty *guanacos,* relatives of the camel, come down from the high Andes to feast on the tender herbs on the few occasions when the *pampa* wears a coat of green. It is always a pleasant surprise to see cows and goats grazing among the flowers near the scattered settlements which usually owe their existence to the mining of some mineral. The farmers of the *haciendas* in the short valleys of the Andes, who normally have to grow food for their cattle on narrow irrigated fields, take the animals far out into the *llano* when it flowers. The *vaquero* (cowherd) has no shelter. Every fortnight he is supplied with fresh provisions, and once or twice a week he rides to the nearest mine to fetch water. Cattle are not watered, but have to be content with the moisture taken in with the plants. In any case, cattle cannot remain in the *pampa* for much longer than a month, that is, until the drying desert herbs are no longer able to meet their need of water. The cows have to be brought home then, although there is still enough fodder in the form of hay on the fields which until recently were resplendent with flowers. Woe to the cowherd who delays his homeward trek too long. Many skeletons of cattle along the road bear witness to the merciless hardness of life in the desert.

Plant Life in the Deserts of North America

PROFESSOR FRIEDRICH EHRENDORFER

No breath of wind, a harsh, inexorable sun beats down from the whitish July sky above the desert and the thermometer shows 106° F. Tall, branched pillars of giant cacti look unreal in the wavering, shadeless light. Between them the stony slopes are yellow and brown and bare. Only here and there some low, leafless shrubs and the rigid rosettes of the yucca cling to the ground. A heavy, lifeless silence broods over the land. At this, my first meeting with the desert of Arizona near Tucson, nothing could have been further from my thoughts than a comparison with the Garden of Eden. And yet this comfortless, heat-laden waste hides a miracle which invites just such a comparison. The winter brought more rain that usual and on a warm, radiantly blue May day in the following year, I stand again in the same desert. The word seems singularly inapt now, for the slopes are covered with a many-coloured carpet of annual verbenas, lupins, *Eschscholtzias* and many other flowers. Dense, milk-white vacemes now rise from the leaf rosettes of the yuccas. The encelia bushes have wrapped themselves in a delicate shade of grey-green and are radiant with yellow flowers. A busy swarm of insects buzzes above a sea of blossoms, humming-birds flutter among the Fouquieria whose sealing-wax red flower spikes sway on long, thorny branches. Even the bizarre giant *Carnegiea* cacti are now smooth with stored water and show a friendlier pale green. In the face of such contrasts it is tempting to take a peep behind the veil of mystery which surrounds the enchanted desert*.

The climatological map of the world shows that the heat deserts are concentrated along the tropics north and south of the equator: in the south-west of North America, and in North Africa and Arabia, on the west coast of South America, in South-West Africa and in Central Australia. These characteristic desert regions of the world are mainly due to the circulation of the trade winds. The reason becomes clear when we remember that warm air absorbs more moisture than cold air and that warm air rises because it is lighter than cold air. In the equatorial region, where the sun stands at the zenith, the air becomes hotter than anywhere else; it absorbs moisture and rises. But in rising it cools again and loses its moisture in the shape of tropical rains. The drained air masses now drift at great altitude away from the equator towards the north and south, descend over the tropics into lower strata, warm up again and become very dry in the process. The desert belt of our earth, therefore, lies in these regions. Finally the air masses return to the equator close to the surface of the earth as trade winds. The dryness of the regions between the tropics is increased by cold ocean currents touching warm coasts (dry winds travelling inland) and by mountain ranges between sea and land, and these facts are responsible for the actual position of our deserts.

In the south-west of North America there are three main hot desert regions: the Mohave desert (Death Valley and adjoining parts of Southern California and Nevada), the Sonora Desert (lower Colorado and Gila rivers in Southern California and Arizona, as well as adjoining regions in Mexico and Baja California) and finally the Chihuahua Desert (Central Mexico and adjoining parts of the USA in Texas and New Mexico). Mountain ranges, somewhat richer in rainfall, separate these three desert regions from one another. The hot cactus deserts continue northwards into the region of the Great Basin between Sierra Nevada and the Rocky Mountains, in the shape of semi-deserts with colder winters and wormwood steppes with sage brush *(Artemisia tridentata)*.

---

* D. T. McDougal, F. Shreve, H. Walter and D. I. Axelrod have made outstanding contributions to the solution ot the problems discussed in this article.

The plant world of the different deserts in the New World is very similar in character. Again and again we find the characteristic species of cacti, agaves and yuccas or the low desert shrub *Larrea* with its resin-scented, leathery leaves. However, there are also many differences due to the isolation of the individual desert regions from one another: the cactus *Carnegiea gigantea* (see illustration), for instance, occurs exclusively in the Sonora Desert, while the fantastic Joshua tree, *Yucca brevifolia* (see illustration), is one of the dominating plant forms in the Mohave Desert.

What are the conditions which make life difficult to the plant pioneers of the desert? In the first place, the extreme dryness. The annual rainfall in these regions amounts to no more than 12 inches, in some places to much less or no rain at all. In addition, desert rains are usually very unevenly distributed. In the second place, high temperatures. During most of the year evaporation accounts for more moisture than the supply of water by way of rainfall. These conditions cause the formation of landlocked salt lakes, as in the Salton Sea or the lake in Death Valley, California, both of which lie almost 328 feet below sea level. Extreme exposure to atmospheric conditions in the desert regions causes the rock to crumble and thundery rain washes gravel and scree down to the foreland, while in some places the wind piles up formidable sand dunes, as, for instance, in the desert of Death Valley and at the northern end of the Gulf of California. It is clear that the formation of vegetable mould as we know it is altogether out of the question. The regions can be put to agricultural use only with the aid of irrigation from artesian wells or by way of dams, but where this is being done, the desert soil, in so far as it is not briny, proves to be fertile and yields rich harvests of cotton, etc.

Scientific research has revealed the surprising fact that desert plants are no more economical in their water consumption than other plants. There exists a constant ratio throughout the world between a given amount of rainfall and the amount of foliage which it enables the plant to grow. Reduced rainfall thus enforces a breaking up of the plant cover and finally the retreat of the plant pioneers to ditches and depressions where there is a higher level of moisture in the ground. Every kind of intermediary stage is to be found between the semi-desert, with scattered vegetation, and the desert proper, which to all intents and purposes is devoid of any vegetation. The most striking and general characteristic of the desert plant is its capacity to endure dry periods which sometimes extend over many months. It is extremely interesting to observe how different plants, different constructional models evolved by nature, cope with the extreme conditions of the desert in different ways.

Cacti certainly represent the most striking forms of life in the North American deserts. They are the so-called stem succulents: leaves and axillary shoots are reduced to tufts of thorns and the stem has been transformed into a fleshy water reservoir. Most cacti have an extensive root system immediately below the surface and are thus able to take in rainwater very rapidly, whereby they may increase their weight by more than 30 per cent; the stems swell up and the ribs move apart in concertina fashion. The giant cactus *Carnegiea gigantea* grows very slowly but it can attain an age of 200 years, a height of 39 feet and a weight of 7 tons. Able to store from 440 to 660 gallons of water, such a giant is capable of surviving for more than a year without fresh water supplies. Cacti can take many different shapes, such as balls (for instance, *Ferrocactus),* hummocks (for instance, *Echinocereus,* see illustration), the tree-like branched species of *Cylindropuntia* (see illustration), and the flat shoots of *Platyopuntia.* In addition to the stem succulents, the North American desert contains the leaf succulents which store water chiefly in the leaves. A typical example are the agaves. Like cacti and many other desert plants, they possess a very thick, almost waterproof epidermis which reduces the loss of moisture in the dry periods to a minimum.

While cacti with their shallow root system are able to take up rainwater from immediately below the surface and then to store it, many desert shrubs draw their water from lower depths where it is protected against evaporation and remains available more or less regularly throughout the year. For this purpose these plants are equipped with a very deep-reaching and extensive root system; in many cases they are also able to apply extraordinary suction power (750 pounds to the square inch and more). In addition, during the critical dry periods many of these desert shrubs, for instance, *Fouquieria* and the acacia species *Prosopis* and *Acacia,* shed their tender leaves and only the bare branches, protected by an almost completely waterproof bark, survive. In other species, such as *Larrea,* the leaves remain but they are leathery and covered with a resin-like film or similar device to protect them against too much evaporation.

What happens to the quantities of water which during the rainy season in the desert are temporarily available in the strata close to the surface and exceed the demands of the cacti? They, too, are utilised by desert plants, mainly by those ephemeral species which in the space of six to eight weeks complete their life cycle from germination to the mature seed. Their seeds are extremely resistant to heat and drought, and may lie in the desert soil for many years without losing their viability. In years of poor rainfall they grow only sparsely, but in good years they germinate in their thousands and transform the desert into a veritable sea of flowers. These ephemeral plants (annuals) thus represent an effective regulative factor in the water supply of the desert. The species of this group have shallow roots and little suction power. Their growth is strictly attuned to the rainy seasons. In the eastern regions of the North American deserts with prevailing summer rains, the autumn flowering summer annuals are more dominant, in the western regions with prevailing winter rains, the spring-flowering winter annuals. The winter annuals with germination temperatures of 59—65° F., are akin to groups of the temperate zones, for instance, *Phacelia, Oenothera* (see illustration), *Senecio (Compositae)* or *Plantago* (plantain species); the summer annuals, with germination temperatures of 81—90° F., on the other hand, mostly belong to tropical groups, for instance, *Kallstroemia, Tidestromia* and *Allionia.*

Plants which become active only after the rainy season are equipped with bulbs or corms deep in the ground, whose foliage above ground completely disappears in the dry season. Especially attractive representatives of this type in the North American deserts are, for instance, *Calochortus* lilies and many larkspurs. Finally, the deserts contain some ferns, selaginellas, mosses and other primitive plants (algae and lichens), which are able to sustain almost complete dehydration, and in a shrunk or dried up state fall into a kind of rigor mortis. When moistened, they immediately grow green and continue to remain active as long as the favourable conditions last.

The capacity of desert plants to cope with extreme conditions is extraordinarily varied. The rich variety of species is distributed not evenly but in adaptation to the different regions within the hot deserts of North America, grouped in certain plant societies. Cacti, yuccas and agaves generally occupy the warm stony or rocky slopes. They are accompanied by certain shrubs, bulbs and grasses. Where in level places the soil is denser and less porous, *Larrea* often dominates wide areas. In landlocked, salty depressions it is largely replaced by a stem and leafless succulent species of goosefoot. On the heavy clay soil of the better drained lowlands we find a savannah-like vegetation with broad prosopis trees and grass or thornbushes in between. Also *Cylindropuntia* and *Platyopuntia* are frequent in these places. Water meadow trees, like poplars, willows and ashes are very occasionally to be found in desert regions in the immediate vicinity of some rivulet.

How did it evolve, this fascinating plant world of the North American desert regions? The examination of fossilised plants found in California and Nevada has shown that these areas now covered with semi-desert, in the late Tertiary, 1 to 10 million years ago, were occupied partly by evergreen sub-tropical forests and partly by summergreen mixed deciduous forests. At that time the climate was considerably richer in rainfall and more maritime than today on account of large inland lakes and the fact that the high coastal mountains (for instance, the Sierra Nevada) did not then exist. The present-day surface, climate and vegetation conditions evolved in the more recent geological past during and after the ice ages. The desert floras of North America, typified as they are by a great variety of characteristic forms, evidently cannot have evolved only in such relatively recent times. It is assumed that they evolved in the dry regions of Mexico and Central America in the early Tertiary and later found favourable conditions for a wide distribution and ramification. As plant pioneers of vast stretches of desert and semi-desert, they now determine the picture of large areas in the south-west of North America.

The Azalea Miracle in the Smoky Mountains

DR ELFRUNE WENDELBERGER

In eastern North America the wooded mountain range of the Appalachians extends for 1,625 miles from the 33rd degree of latitude to Newfoundland. Seeing the blue hills disappear in the haze from the coastal plains, no one would suspect the abundance of natural beauty contained in this country.

There are two national parks in the southern part of the mountains: the Shenandoah National Park in the heart of the Blue Ridge Mountains of Virginia and the National Park of the Great Smoky Mountains, connected by the Blue Ridge Parkway, a road of some 470 miles. The Smoky Mountains, which derive their name from the haze and mist often surrounding them, in their highest peaks reach altitudes of 6,500 feet and more. But the country is gently undulating, without steep rocks or stony heights. The forest, unending, lonely mountain woods, cover ridge and dale with their uninterrupted green cloak. In Europe at these altitudes one would find only alpine grassland, heath, lichens, or, at best, dwarf mountain pines but certainly no deciduous trees. But here we are at the 36th degree of latitude and, therefore, on a level with North Africa. Although thanks to the influence of the distant Labrador Current the climate is much more even, it is also much warmer than that of Europe and the period of vegetation much longer. In addition, the atmosphere is very humid on account of the proximity of the sea and the capacity of the rock to store water, and all these factors together favour the growth of trees.

Down in the valleys, in the shady gorges and on the lush mountain meadows straight, cone-shaped tulip trees *(Liriodendron tulipifera)* form a green cathedral, together with magnolias, often with giant scented white blossoms, yellow chestnut trees *(Aesculus octandra)*, sugar maple *(Acer saccharum)*, the western silver lime tree *(Tilia heterophylla)* and some others. Higher up there follow oak and chestnut forests with a confusing diversity of species and of various composition: American chestnut *(Castanea dentata)*, *Quercus prinus*, *borealis* and *alba*, white and hairy hickory *(Carya alba* and *tomentosa)*; still higher the red Virginian maple *(Acer rubrum)*. The sheer number of different species is overwhelming—in the Smokies alone there are more than 100 genera of trees and shrubs. In the higher regions of the peaks the deciduous forests are replaced by conifers of a northern character: red firs *(Picea rubens)* to begin with, together

with yellow birches *(Betula lutea)*; next, at higher altitudes, *Abies fraseri*, together with American mountain ash *(Sorbus Americana)*. On dry, rocky ribs exposed to the wind at all altitudes, there are several kinds of mountain pines, such as *Pinus virginiana*, *rigida* and *pungens*, mixed with *Quercus coccinea*.
Drive or, better still, walk through this country in June and you will see the woodlands for miles around turned into a vast flower garden. Rhododendrons ('azaleas') form the dense undergrowth of these forests from the valleys to the high ridges and are now aflame with blossoms. In damp gorges under the shelter of the hemlock fir *(Tsuga canadensis)* the white rhododendron *(Rhododendron maximum)* grows to a height of 26 feet and displays its snowy blossoms, occasionally blushing to pale pink. So closely do the shrubs stand together that no other plant is able to grow in the shade of the almost impenetrable maze of their coarse, leathery leaves.
In contrast, the flaming azalea *(Rhododendron calendulaceum)* blooms golden-red, orange and yellow, generally in warm, sheltered spots of the oak and chestnut woods. The sun shining through the foliage makes its colours glow and the air is filled with the fragrance of thousands upon thousands of blossoms. The ground below is carpeted with white, pink, yellow and red petals which the wind carries to the nearest brook, where they collect in the eddies. On steep slopes or where exposed rocks rise from the wood cover, the mountain blossoms with countless shrubs of the familiar purple rhododendron *(Rh. catawbiense)* which forms impenetrable thickets at altitudes of over 4,265 feet. No greenhouse and no park could possibly convey any idea of the luxuriant growth and abundance of blooms of this mighty shrub with its large pale to deep purple flowers. These 'heath balds' are sometimes interspersed with the rare Carolinian rhododendron *(Rh. carolinianum)*, with its light red flowers.
Less frequent is a low azalea with pale pink, very glandular flowers which emit such a bewitching scent that a single flowering shrub can be detected at long distances. But where this azalea covers a whole hilltop there is a great buzzing of bees and other insects which collect from miles around to drink the nectar.
The mountain laurel *(Kalmia latifolia)* is fairly independent of altitude. It grows like a weed from the roadside up to greater heights, although it generally remains below 3,937 feet. Its umbels are white to pale pink and on exposed slopes it forms a dense cover, the laurel heath, with which no tree can compete.
It is worth while examining a single flower from the many that form the umbel. The pink buds are like a work of art made from the choicest porcelain. From the outside the little niches in the petals which house the anthers appear as dainty humps. The open flower lends itself to an interesting demonstration: when the base of the stamens is touched with the tip of a pencil, they spring upwards and at the same time the anthers explode and scatter their contents. Thus an insect searching for nectar at the base of the stamens is dusted with pollen and carries it to the stigma of the next flower it visits.
In the depth of the impenetrable, lonely mountain forests, threaded by neither path nor track and hardly, if ever, visited by man, the shy lynx leads the life of a robber knight. The black bear, on the other hand, likes to beg for food by the side of the highway and to rummage through litter bins.
On sunny slopes you may find a dazzlingly red pink *(Dianthus virginica)*, and if you are lucky you will see an emerald-green jewel of the bird world. A strange humming sound, and a minute creature comes flying with lightning speed, hovers above the red flower, for a second dips its long beak into it and is gone. That was a humming-bird fetching its extra sugar ration from the flower and at the same time acting as pollinator. Most 'bird flowers' are a vivid red, visible to the eye of the bird but not to insects, and of a particular build. They do not provide the

landing platform indispensable to most insects but unnecessary to the hovering humming-bird. Their chalices are very deep and accessible only to the long beak of the humming-bird and their nectar is rich in quantity and rather liquid, satisfying the bird's need of energising food and quenching its thirst at the same time. The protruding anthers deposit the pollen on the forehead of the little bird and from there it reaches the equally protruding stigma.
Sometimes the tiny bird perches on a branch or more often a leaf which hardly stirs under its featherweight touch, and may be more closely examined. Back and head are dark to emerald-green, the throat is a vivid ruby-red (hence its name 'ruby-throat') and changes colour at every movement of the head. The most striking feature of the bird is its long, thin beak. The under-side is white, the tail short. Suddenly the humming-bird rises vertically (it can fly to the right or left like a helicopter) and disappears more rapidly than the eye can follow.
The wide forests, covering hills and valleys as far as the eye can see, hide many secrets. In the National Park of the Great Smoky Mountains their rich life, variety and beauty are preserved for future generations.

Conservation in the United States of America

FRED M. PACKARD

The broad expanses of the United States stretch from the hardwood forests of the eastern states across a thousand miles of treeless plains, over conifer-clad ranges interrupted with arid basins, from the Rocky Mountains to the Pacific. Beginning in the tropics of Florida, a traveller moves through successive life zones to the ancient Canadian Shield on the northern boundary; or, starting from the Sonoran deserts of Arizona, New Mexico and California, he may scale the Sierra Nevada Mountains extending northward all the way into British Columbia, passing through different belts of pine and spruce forests to the alpine meadows above timberline. Here, at elevations above 10,000 feet, he encounters conditions closely similar to the Alaskan tundra bordering the Arctic Ocean. Everywhere he goes, in each of the myriad ecological zones, he will find wildflowers characteristic of the particular biocoensis, some abundant, some unique. Perhaps the most spectacular display occurs in the Southwest, when, for a few weeks in March and April, the succulents burst into bloom. During most of the bone-dry year, the desert presents a bleak, forbidding appearance; much of the cacti is dusty grey-green and studded with wicked thorns. Then the rains occur, and the winter landscape of pastel mountains and smoke-grey sagebrush suddenly is painted with brilliant colour from the extravagent palette of an exuber-ant Creator.
The colours range from the large creamy-white flowers of the Joshua tree *(Yucca arborescens)* and saguaro *(Cereus giganteus)*, the yellows and oranges of the prickly pear *(Opuntia vulgaris)*, through the scarlets and reds of the cholla *(Opuntia fulgida)* and ocotillo *(Fouqueria splendens)*. Under the intense desert skies, the vividness is incredible to visitors.
In autumn the Appalachian ranges inland from the Atlantic coast present the eastern counter-part in colour. Here, with the first hint of winter chill, the leaves of the hardwoods turn to scarlets, ochres, bronzes and golds. Thousands drive through the Shenandoah and Great Smoky Mountains national parks to see at its finest a sight which is but hinted at in other parts of the world.
In the northwest corner of the country the Olympic National Park protects an incredible climax rain-moss forest of Sitka spruces 18 feet in diameter, with Douglas firs, western hemlocks and

incense cedars only slightly smaller. Carpeting the forest floor, rolling across downed logs which have been turning to soil for a hundred years, rising up the tree trunks 70 feet or more, is the golden sphagnum moss glowing in the moisture brought by constant fogs and rains from the nearby ocean. This mossy bed is so thick and luxurious you can sink your hand into it up to the wrist.

On the eastern and northern slopes of the Olympic Mountains, madrone *(Arbutus menziesii),* cascara *(Rhamnus purshiana),* and rhododendron are abundant; in the high elevations the alpine meadows are gardens of wildflowers during the summer.

America awakened to the urgency of safeguarding her botanical heritage toward the end of the nineteenth century. Ruthless logging of the greatest forests of the *Sequoias*—the sawyers left one tree standing in the Congrere Basin as a monument to themselves—led to the establishment of Sequoia National Park in 1890 to save the remaining forests and natural environment of 600 miles of wilderness in California; in 1940 the adjoining King's Canyon National Park provided protection to another 700 square miles. Under the Antiquities Act of 1906, which gave the President, as well as Congress, power to preserve Federally owned lands for scientific and cultural purposes, successive Presidents have designated many areas—some of them millions of acres in extent—as inviolate sanctuaries for their native plants and wildlife within the national park system.

Inspired by leaders like Aldo Leopold and Robert Marshall, the United States Forest Service has designated 14 million acres within the national forests as Wilderness, Wild or Primitive areas. Unlike the remaining portions of the national forests, which contain the primary commercially utilized stands of timber in Federal ownership, these latter areas are stringently protected. No roads enter them, and no timber is cut. Their primary purpose is to preserve natural ecology and appearance for human enjoyment. Although livestock grazing is permitted, these magnificent scenic regions support an abundance and variety of wildflowers.

The national wildlife refuge system, comprising more than 28 million acres administered by the Federal government primarily to benefit birds and mammals, also protects the principal marshlands of the country, essential habitat for many native flowers. Impressive as this accomplishment may be, there is national concern about excessive draining of other wetlands, with consequent loss of the natural habitat for water plants and waterfowl, sinking of ground water tables, increasing acidity of the land, and other damage. A forceful program is under way to salvage as much wetland as possible by educational, legal and financial measures.

Some of the finest botanical environments have been safeguarded by various State governments. Every State has a park commission, and a number of them have established state parks that are the equivalent of national parks. Here, for the most part, strict protective policies ensure that the natural flora will not be lost. The Anza-Borrego Desert State Park, in California, contains 460,000 acres, mostly virginal and some yet unexplored. This, the second largest state park in the nation, protects a rich variety of desert flora.

Cumberland Falls State Park, Kentucky, was purchased by conservationists determined to save it from a planned hydro-electric dam, then presented to the state. One of its more unique features is the 'moonbow' formed when the mist caused by the fall's plunge rises from the basin below to reflect the bright moonlight.

Throughout the country, in the Adirondacks and Catskill mountains of New York, in the Porcupine Mountains of Michigan, in the headwaters of the Mississippi River in Minnesota, the roadless lakelands of central Maine, in the 'sea of grass' of central Florida, and in many other states, primeval forests and mountains, lakes and rivers, plains and deserts, the state parks retain the beauty of aboriginal America.

These are all governmental actions, but they are due directly to public sentiment. Each of these programs, every national and state park, wilderness area, wildlife refuge, or other reserve, has been created because one or a few Americans felt strongly enough about the preservation of the natural to take personal action. They dreamed their dreams, and led others to share their enthusiasm. They inspired their public officials, and where they could not inspire, they exerted the over-riding force of public opinion. They fought for their causes in the legislative halls and government offices; and they never ceased until victory was won. They did not always win, of course; but as public interest grew and conservation has become a household word in America, they have succeeded ever more frequently.

Nor did they rely solely on government action. They formed civic organizations, not only to marshall support for their causes, but also to act where the government could or would not serve. The National Audubon Society purchased dozens of sanctuaries, patrolled them and safeguarded vital faunal and floral environments. The Sierra Club has played an important part in almost every effort to save natural landscape in the western states, and in many national issues. The Izaak Walton League of America raised thousands of dollars to help buy private lands endangering the Superior Canoe Boundary Waters in Minnesota, a vast primitive lakeland the U.S. Forest Service has reserved for traverse by canoists and campers. The Nature Conservancy was founded to purchase, with donated funds, outstanding examples of every botanical ecotype for scientific research—the equivalent of the strict nature reserves of other countries, but usually not under governmental administration.

In addition, there are many smaller and more specialized private organizations. The Wildflower Preservation Society, the Garden Club of America, the National Council of State Garden Clubs are but a few examples of national groups dedicated to the preservation of wildflowers throughout the country. Nearly every state has a garden club, and most large cities have several garden or wildflower clubs. These groups have been instrumental in gaining official protection for many vanishing species; through their efforts, for example it has been made illegal in many of the southeastern states to pick the flowers of the dogwood *(Cornus florida)*, the wild *Azaleas* and *Rhododendrons*, or the mountain laurel *(Kalmia latifolia)*.

Some of America's loveliest wildflowers are seldom seen, although they once were common—trailing arbutus *(Epigaea repens)* with fragrant pink and white flowers; the fringed gentian *(Gentiana crinita)*, with blue, delicately fringed corolla; cardinal flower *(Lobelia cardinalis)*, the only red Lobelia, and a number of lilies and orchids. But many more varieties are returning to their native habitats because of twin campaigns of education and protection.

America has travelled a long way from the days when men could exploit and destroy without thought or hinderance. It has been said that a man could spend his lifetime visiting the protected land of this country. Yet there is an equally long road yet to travel. Millions of acres of once verdant grasslands lie unrepaired from the ravages of decades of overgrazing. The days of 'cut out and get out' forestry have almost ended, yet too many of America's forests and woodlots are still badly managed, and efforts to ensure permanent preservation of a remnant of wilderness still provokes outcries from those interested mainly in exploitation. All over the nation, streams and lakes are hideously polluted. Only in the last few years have any significant funds been made available to restore health and productivity to America's waters.

Most critical of all, perhaps, is what U.S. Secretary of the Interior Stewart L. Udall calls 'the quiet crisis.' With growing population, increased incomes, and extraordinary mobility—combined with a new interest in the natural out of doors—the American people are seeking outdoor recreation at an accelerating rate that threatens the very tranquillity and release from the tensions of modern life that they desire. There is danger that in their eagerness to appreciate nature, the people will destroy it.

America is beautiful, and she has acted vigorously to safeguard that beauty. If the lands and their resources that have been preserved are assured permanent protection, and if a reasonable amount more, commensurate with the increased demand for open space, is set aside for its own sake and free from unwise exploitation, the quiet crisis can be met.

Fortunately, the American people are vigorous, vocal and insistant. They want their children to be able to experience the wonder of the natural creation, the flowers and forests, animals roving free, a clean and healthy land. They have the vision and determination to see that the future of this country is as beneficent as its past.

Botanical Gardens, Parks, and Floral Regions

Abbreviations:
BG = Botanical Garden
RVS = Recommended Visiting Season
SF = Special Features
GH = Greenhouse(s)

The figure in brackets indicates the year of foundation.

Where not otherwise stated, the garden (park) is open to the public throughout the year.
Although, thanks to the co-operation of many flower-lovers in every part of the world, the following list of botanical gardens throughout the world may come very close to the actual situation, some of the questionnaires sent out have not been returned or not been filled in completely. The registration of parks and floral regions in the open countryside depends very much on the individual opinions of botanical advisers, and the list cannot claim to be complete.

Europe

Austria

Alpinum Bad Aussee, Sarstein 38, Styria (1918), 1,316 sq. yds.

RVS: May to July. Open 1st April to 30th October. SF: Alpine plants, partly in societies. Two sections: American and Asian flora. Access: Pötschen Road from Bad Aussee 2 miles to 'Tannenwirt' (inn), where there is also a bus stop. Narcissi in full flower at Bad Aussee from 15th May to 10th June.

Mayr-Melnhof Alpinum at Frohnleiten near Graz (1950), 5 acres

RVS: May to July. SF: One of the largest collections of alpine plants in Europe (about 6,000 species), especially many saxifragae. Metasequoia (33 ft. high). The alpinum is situated about 18 miles north of Graz. Five minutes' walk from the railway station of Frohnleiten.

Botanical Gardens of the University of Graz, Schubertstrasse 51 (1888/89), 44 acres (GH 603 sq. yds.)

RVS: May to June. Open April—October, closed on Sunday and Holiday afternoons. SF: System of angiosperms in the shape of a genealogical tree.

Botanical Gardens of the University of Innsbruck, Sternwartestrasse 15 (1910), 5 acres (GH 1,076 sq. yds.)

SF: Alpinum, especially Southern Alps, endemics, parasites (especially mistletoe).

Alpine Garden of the University of Innsbruck on the Patscherkofel Mountain (1929), 2 1/8 acres, 6,560 ft. above sea level

RVS: Mid-May to end of August. Mondays to Fridays all day, otherwise by arrangement. SF: Collections of native plants of the alpine regions, especially Rhododendron ferrugineum, Primula, Saxifraga, Sempervivum tectorum. Access by funicular railway from Igls near Innsbruck. 320 yds. further to the west the private trial grounds 'Hohe Mahd' for the cultivation of crops in mountainous regions and Pinus cembra plantations.

Botanical Gardens of the Land Kärnten (Carinthia), Klagenfurt, Kinkstrasse (1865), 5 acres (GH 180 sq. yds.)

RVS: Summer. Open from 9 a.m. to 3.30 p.m. SF: Flora of the Southern Alps.

Botanical Gardens and Arboretum of the City of Linz a. d. Donau (Danube), Roseggerstrasse (1952), 12 acres (GH being extended)

RVS: April to June (alpinum), March to May (native flora), May to July (cacti). SF: The centre of the Gardens is taken up by symmetrically arranged beds with ornamental plants, adjoined by some sections of native plants: plants of the pond, the riverside woods, the marshy meadow, the mixed forest; a section for plants of the Wels Heath is under construction. In the eastern part an ecological section is being built for azaleas and wild rhododendrons. The alpinum occupies a separate site. The section under construction is to contain a systematic representation of the botanical world, a heath garden, irises, ponds for water and bog plants, beds for biological and morphological themes; a garden for medicinal and kitchen herbs. *Greenhouses*, including a tropical house with Victoria cruciana basin, a house for cacti and succulents (with 1,200 species of cacti and 300 species of African succulents) and an orchid house for tropical orchids and hothouse plants.

Alpine Garden Rannach near Graz (1954), 9 acres, 2,092 ft. above sea level

RVS: Mid-March to end-June. SF: Plants of the East and West Alps. Railway station St. Veit, 7 miles from Graz or by bus. 1¼ hours' walk from St. Veit on well signposted roads.

Alpine Garden Rax—below the 'Otto House' on the Raxalpe (1950)

RVS: Summer months. SF: Alpine flora of the Raxalpe.

Castle Gardens Salzburg-Hellbrunn (1612—1619), 148 acres (GH small orangery for flower shows)

RVS: Spring, autumn. SF: Native flora, some exotic plants, landscaped park.

Alpine Garden Traunkirchen, Salzkammergut (1933), 2 acres (GH 60 sq. yds.)

RVS: April to June. Open April to 30th September. SF: Alpine flora. Plants from all parts of the world. Access: 10 minutes from Traunkirchen railway station; on the motorway Bad Ischl—Gmunden, steamer stop Alpengarten and Hotel 'Am Stein.'

Alpine Garden Vorderkaiserfelden near Kufstein/Tyrol (1926), 4,541 ft. above sea level, 455 sq. yds.

RVS: Mid-May to end of August. SF: Native plants of the Kaiser Mountains and a small collection of plants of the West and South Alps—protected plants. Access: from Kufstein on foot in 3¼ hours by roads signposted by the Alpenverein.

Mariazell/Steiermark, Styria. Famous for daffodils in the countryside surrounding Mariazell.

RVS: Mid-May to mid-June.

Greenhouses in the Public Park Wels (GH 407 sq. yds.)

RVS: April to May. Open March to October, 2—6 p.m. SF: Large collection of cacti.

Alpine Garden in the Federal Gardens 'Belvedere,' Vienna III, Prinz-Eugen-Strasse 27 (1803/1865), 2,870 sq. yds.

Open from 15th April to 30th June. SF: Oldest of European alpine gardens. Contains some 6,000 species from every continent, all hardy in the prevailing conditions. A very few are protected from excessive winter moisture by fir branches or leaves or cloches. They have a common desire for light and water, which the plants of the steppe share with the plants of the mountains. Regional grouping has been abandoned in order to make full use of the available space. However, aesthetic considerations are widely taken into account.

During the war years the garden was neglected and also sustained some damage. In 1945 it was restored and in 1950 again opened to the public. The number of visitors is steadily increasing and in the record year of 1960 reached a total of 27,000, which is sufficient evidence of the popularity of this botanical treasure house in the garden city of Vienna.

Most plants in this collection are perennials and some reach the considerable age of 20 to 30 years and more. Apart from a pear tree which is 200 years old, the present doyens of the collection are the 'terrible broom' of this historic garden and the slightly younger Rhamnus pumila.

The collection is constantly being enriched and extended by exchange with 180 botanical gardens throughout the world—some 5,000 seed samples are sent out annually—by purchases and frequent expeditions into the mountains. The garden contains plants from the European, Asian, American, Australian mountain regions, as well as from the high plains and rocky steppes of Africa and Asia. There are also cultivars of decorative alpine flowers to suggest what can be done to increase the charm of a small private garden.

Botanical Gardens Schönbrunn, Vienna XIII (1753), 5 acres

SF: Old trees and shrubs. (The Palm House of Schönbrunn is separate from the Botanical Gardens.)

Palm House, Vienna XIII, Schloss Schönbrunn (1882), 2,870 sq. yds.

RVS: Spring. SF: 3 houses: Show house with flowers; Palm and Orchid house; tropical, ornamental and industrial plants.

Botanical Gardens of the University of Vienna, Vienna III, Rennweg 14 (1754), 21 acres (GH 4,186 sq. yds.)

RVS: Open April to October. SF: Orchids and succulents.

The Botanical Gardens of Vienna

are closely tied to the great tradition of the Viennese botanical school. Even before the scientific gardens were laid out, the imperial court owned collections of rare trees in Emperor Maximilian's castle and palace gardens at Ebersdorf, later at the hunting lodge 'Neugebäu'. The first 'Hortus Medicus' was laid out in 1665 at Rossau, though it was later abandoned. At the suggestion of her physician van Swieten, the great Empress Maria Theresia in 1753 founded the 'Dutch Botanical Court Garden of Schönbrunn' and in the following year the university garden at the Rennweg. The Botanical Garden of Schönbrunn has been enriched by means of many journeys to all parts of the world and used to contain the largest Proteaceae collection in the world. The history of the university garden—for a long time a purely ornamental garden in the French style—is closely connected with the most famous names in Viennese botany, Jacquin, Endlicher, Kerner von Marilaun, Wettstein von Westersheim.

Professor Gustav Wendelberger

Botanical Gardens of the Hochschule für Bodenkultur, Vienna XVIII, Gregor-Mendel-Strasse 33 (1896, 1945), 2½ acres (GH 598 sq. yds.)

RVS: April to October. Saturday afternoon and Sunday closed. SF: Arboretum.

Belgium-Luxembourg

Parc d'Anlier, Luxembourg, 13,591 acres

SF: Arboretum.

Provinciaal Domein Rivierenhof (Garden 'Rivierenhof'), Turnhoutsebaan 246, Deurne-Antwerp (1923), 326 acres (GH 538 sq. yds.)

RVS: May to October. SF: Rosarium and Arboretum, Alpinum. Access by Antwerp—Turnhout road.

Jardin Botanique d'Anvers (Antwerp), BG

SF: Over 2,000 different exotic plants.

Fondation Ligne, Section Conservatoire, Château de Belœil (Hennegau), park belonging to the Princes of Ligne, Belœil Palace (Hennegau), (mid 19th century)

RVS: April to October for the rose cultures; the rest of the garden is private and not open to the public. SF: 10,000 rose plants, 3,000 of them old varieties from Bengal. Access via Mons on the Mons—Leuze road.

Rosarium 'Le Pachy,' Bellecourt (Hennegau) (1909), 25 acres

RVS: End-June to September. SF: The rosarium of Le Pachy is one of the largest in the world. Old and new roses line some 9 miles of garden paths. Access via Brussels—Nivelles—La Hestre—Bascoup. Bellecourt route Nationale 5, from Anderlues to Mariemont.

Jardin au Domaine du Sart Tilman, University of Liège, 134, Route du Condroz, Boncelles, 494 acres

Visits by permission of the director.

Groenendaal Arboretum Brabant (1897), 25 acres

SF: Arboretum. About 9 miles south of Brussels.

Arboretum Géographique de Tervuren, Drève du Duc, 106, Brussels, 247 acres (1 GH)

SF: Tree species of northern regions.

Jardin Botanique de l'Etat, Brussels-Meise (1870), 225 acres (GH 2½ acres), BG

RVS: May to September. SF: Arboretum, in GH species from the Congo. Access: about 6 miles north of Brussels on the motorway to Antwerp.

Plantentuin de Rijksuniversiteit Ghent, Ledeganckstraat 33 (1797), 7 acres (GH 3,588 sq. yds.), BG

RVS: May to October. Open Sundays from 9 a.m. to noon, Thursdays 2—5 p.m. SF: Orchids, Begonias, Cacti, exotic plants, alpinum. On Route Nationale 1 (Brussels—Ostend).

Parc National 'Hautes Fagnes,' 6,178 acres

SF: Sub-alpine flora.

Arboretum Kalmthout, 22 acres

Open Wednesdays and Sundays. SF: Rhododendron, Hamamelis; various shrubs; Prunus, Malus, Rubus; roses.

Parc National de Lesse et Lomme (Province of Namur), district of the parishes of Rochefort, Han-sur-Lesse, Over et Auffe, Resteigne, Eprave, Wavreille (Province of Luxembourg) (1954), 2,470 acres

RVS: Spring, June, September. SF: Orchids, Gentians. Access by highways Nos. 35 and 49.

Jardin Botanique de l'Institut de Botanique de l'Université de Liège, 3, rue Fusch (1835), 10 acres (15 GH)

SF: Bromelias, Begonias.

'Provinciaal Domein Vrijbroek,' Hombeeksesteenweg 262, Mechelen (1930), 99 acres (GH 239 sq. yds.)

RVS: May to October. SF: Rosarium. Access from Brussels—Antwerp road.

Parc National Olloy-sur-Viroin (Province of Namur) (1959), 294 acres

RVS: Spring, June. SF: Orchids. Access via Couvin, highway No. 5, Province of Namur.

Château Rœulx-Roseraie (Rosarium), Hennegau (1960), 12 acres

RVS: June to September. Open April 1st to October 31st from 10 a.m. to 6 p.m. Closed on Tuesdays. Access via Soignies, 5 miles.

Parc National 'Raymond Mayné,' Torgny (1948), 10 acres

RVS: May to June. SF: Orchids, Gentiana germanica, Anemone pulsatilla, Iberis amara. Access: about 4 miles from Virton and 17 1/2 miles from Florenville.

Réserve Naturelle de la Warche 'Abbé Charles Dubois' (1948), 27 acres

RVS: Spring and summer. SF: Ranunculaceae, ferns. Access: a little over 1 mile from Robertville on the Malmedy—Robertville road.

Bulgaria

Jardin Botanique de l'Université, 49, rue Moskowska, P.O. Box 157, Sofia (BG)

Hortus Botanicus Academiae Scientiarum Bulgariae, Tolbuchin 15, Sofia (BG)

Jardin Botanique de la Faculté d'Agriculture, Sofia

Czechoslovakia

Botanical Gardens of the Komensky University, Bratislava, Karloveská cesta 390 (10 GH)

RVS and open: May to October. SF: Roses, Festuca, Orchids.

Botanical Gardens of the University J. E. Purkyně of Brno, Kotlářská 2

Garden for Medicinal Plants, Brno, Třída obranců míru 10

Botanical Institute of the Academy of Science, Alpine Garden Černolice, Pošta Ritka (1935), 27 acres (GH 36 sq. yds.)

RVS: April, May. Visits by permission of the director. SF: Plants of mountain and high mountain regions, especially of the Alps and Carpathian Mountains. Access by Prague—Dobřiš (13 1/2 miles south-west of Prague). Railway station Všenory.

Botanical Gardens of the Pedagogic Institute, Košice, Mánesová 17, 86 1/2 acres (GH 2,083 sq. yds.)

Open on Sundays in the morning.

North Bohemian Botanical Gardens, Reichenberg (Liberec), Purkyňová 3

Arboretum Mlyňany SAV, Vieska nad Žitavou, Pošta Slepčany, okres Nitra

Botanical Gardens ČSAV Prague-Průhonice (1962), 637 acres

SF: Alpinum, Rosarium, fruit trees, Rhododendron collection.

Hortus Botanicus Universitatis Palackianae, Olmütz (Olomouc), Fierlingerova 10

Botanical Gardens of the Karl University, Prague, Benatská 2 (1360 Hortus Angelicus, from 1897—1898 Na/Slupi), 9 acres (GH 2,033 sq. yds.)

RVS: May and June. Open May to October. SF: Alpinum, succulents.

Arboretum Nový Dvůr, p. Stěbořice u Opavy (Troppau), 50 acres (3 GH)

RVS and open: March to October. SF: Woody plants for industrial areas.

Botanical Gardens, Tábor

Botanical Garden (Krajska botanicka zahrada) Plzeň-Lochotín, Karlovarska 61

Botanical Garden of veterinarian faculty of Agricultural University (Botanicka zahrada veterinarini faculty Vysoké školy zemědělské) Brno, Palackého 13

Botanical Garden of agricultural faculty of Agricultural University (Botanicka zahrada agronomické faculty Vysoké školy zemědělské) Brno, Zemedelská 1

Botanical Museum-Garden Neutra, Bojnice (Botanicka zahrada nitranského musea, Bojnice zamek)

American Garden Chudenice (Americká zahrada Chudenice u Klatov)

SF: Arboretum.

Arboretum Kysihýbl near Baňská Štiavnica

SF: Arboretum.

Denmark

Forstbotanischer Garten Charlottenlund, 10 acres

SF: Conifers.

Gisselfeld Kloster, Have, Haslev (1560), 86 acres (GH 1196 sq. yds.)

RVS: June to July. SF: Arboretum, tropical and sub-tropical plants. Orchids. 27 1/2 miles from Copenhagen on National Route A 2, then 5 miles west.

Den Kőnigl. Veterianer og Landbohøjskoles Haver, Bűlowsvey 13, Copenhagen V, 20 acres (5 GH)

SF: Hardy shrubs.

Arboretum Hørsholm, 93 acres

Visiting by permission of the director. SF: Conifers.

Wűstenarboretum Hvedde, Kibaek, 46 acres

SF: Desert plants.

Botanical Garden of the University of Copenhagen, Øster Farimagsgade 2 B, Copenhagen-K (1871—1874), 24 acres (GH 3,388 sq. yds.)

RVS: May to September. SF: Alpinum, Begonias, Orchids from Thailand, Succulents, Cacti.

Blomsterløg Parken, Langesø F. (1957), 10 acres (GH 34 sq. yds., more under construction)

RVS: May. Open during flowering season only, daily 10 a.m. to 8 p.m. SF: Spring bulbs.

England and Wales

University College of Wales Botanic Gardens, Aberystwyth, 25 acres (6 GH)

Visits by permission of the director.

Beaulieu Abbey, Beaulieu, Hampshire

Open daily from 10.30 a.m. to 6 p.m., November to March Sundays only, 11 a.m. to 5 p.m. SF: Narcissi and other spring flowers.

Birmingham Botanical and Horticultural Society, Westbourne Road, Edgbaston, Birmingham 15 (1829), 14 acres (GH 1/2 acre), BG

RVS: May. SF: Begonias, Cacti, tropical plants, succulents, flora of the Himalayas.

The University Botanic Garden, Department of Botany, Birmingham, 8 acres (12 GH)

Visits by permission of the director. SF: Collection of wild potato plants, plants of Mexico and Central America.

Borde Hill Gardens, Sussex (19th cent.), private arboretum

SF: Chinese plants, conifers, Ericaceae, Cunninghamia konishii (Formosa), Camelliae, Quercus alnifolia (Cyprus), Nerina hybrids.

Botanic Garden, Lister Park, Bradford 9, Yorkshire (1903), 2 acres (1 GH)

SF: Industrial plants, medicinal plants, European alpines, Compositae.

The University Botanic Garden, Bristol

Open weekdays.

Caerhays Castle Gardens, Cornwall

SF: Pinus radiata, Cedrus lebani, Quercus robur, Ulmus campestris, Camelliae, Ilex, Rhododendron, Acer.

University Botanic Garden, Cambridge (1761), 37 acres (GH 1/2 acre)

RVS: Spring. SF: Large tulip collection, Philadelphus, hardy plants, geographically arranged rock garden, chronological collection of plants introduced into British gardens from the earliest times to 1950 (Ephedra, Begonia crispula, Jaborosa integrifolia).

Chatsworth Gardens near Bakewell, Derbyshire

Open 1st April to 7th October, Mondays to Fridays 11.30 a.m. to 4.30 p.m., Saturdays and Sundays from 2—6 p.m., Bank Holidays from 11.30 a.m. to 6 p.m. SF: Artistic landscaping.

Chelsea Physic Garden, Royal Hospital Road, Chelsea, London, S.W. 3 (1673), 4 acres

Visits by experts and students only by permission of the director. SF: Taxus baccata, Catalpa bignonioides, Amicia zygomeris, Cyclamen rohlfsianum, Romneya coulteri.

Compton Acres Gardens, Canford Cliffs Road, Dorset, between Bournemouth and Poole

Open from 21st April to 30th September daily from 1.30—5 p.m., Mondays from 10.30 a.m. to 5 p.m. SF: 7 separate gardens. Sub-tropical plants, rock gardens, Japanese garden, gardens of different European countries, Palm court.

Botanical Garden, University Science Laboratories, South Road, Durham (1923), 3 acres

Visits by permission of the director. SF: Native flora, Viola, Primula, Sisyrinchium.

Botanic Garden 'Myddelton House,' Enfield, Middlesex, 7 acres (2 GH)

Open once a year. SF: Snowdrops, autum crocus, crocus, medicinal plants.

University of London Botanical Supply Unit, Elm Lodge, Englefield Green, Surrey (1839), 21 acres (9 GH)

Visits by permission of the director.

Garden of the Department of Botany, University of Exeter, Exeter, Devon

Visits by permission of the director. SF: Conifers.

Winkworth Arboretum, Hascombe Road, Godalming, Surrey, 96 acres

SF: Acer, Ilex, Magnolia, Prunus, Sorbus, Rhododendron, Stewartia, Styrax, Viburnum.

Haddon Hall Gardens, near Bakewell, Derbyshire

Open 2nd April to 31st October, 11 a.m. to 6 p.m., closed on Sundays (in October 11 a.m. to 4 p.m.), and on 22nd April, 10th June, 5th August from 2—6 p.m. SF: Roses, hanging gardens.

Hafod-ty Gardens, Bettws Garmon, Caernarvonshire, Wales

SF: Rock and aquatic gardens. Azaleas, Rhododendrons, flowering shrubs.

Nymans Gardens, Handcross, Sussex, 30 acres

Open April to October, Wednesdays, Thursdays, Saturdays, Sundays and Bank Holidays, 2—7 p.m. (or till dark). SF: Rare conifers, shrubs and other plants, bog plants.

Harewood House, near Leeds, Yorkshire

Open April to September, Sundays, noon to 6 p.m.; 7th—28th October: Tuesdays noon to 5 p.m.; 23rd April, 12th June to 28th August, Wednesdays and Thursdays, 10 a.m. to 6 p.m. 2nd/3rd May to 26th/27th September, 10 a.m. to 6 p.m.; Easter, Whitsun and Bank Holidays, 10 a.m. to 6 p.m. SF: Terrace gardens, narcissi, rhododendron, azaleas, roses.

Northern Horticultural Society Gardens, Harlow Car, Harrogate, Yorkshire, 45 acres (4 GH)

SF: Rhododendron, roses, alpinum.

Bedgebury National Pinetum, Hawkhurst, Goudhurst, Clanbrock, Kent (1925), 69 acres

RVS: Early June. Open daily till dusk, except Christmas. SF: Numerous conifers. Belongs to Royal Botanic Gardens, Kew.

Hidcote Manor Garden, Hidcote Bartrim, Gloucestershire

Open 1st April to 15th October, except Tuesdays and Fridays, from 11 a.m. to 8 p.m. (no admission after 7 p.m. or 1 hour before dark). SF: Many rare plants, artistic landscaping.

University of Hull, Botanic Garden and Experimental Garden, Thwaite Street, Cottingham, Hull, Yorkshire (1877), 4½ acres (2 GH)

Visits by permission of the director. SF: European and tropical ferns, Apocynaceae, Asclepiadaceae.

Royal Botanic Gardens Kew, Richmond, Surrey (1759), 300 acres (GH 5 acres)

RVS: March to May. Open, in winter from 10 a.m. to 4 p.m., or to dusk; in summer, from 10 a.m. to 8 p.m. SF: 25,000 different plants from all parts of the world and many collections of rare plants. Cycadeas, rhododendron, orchids, palms, roses, heather, ferns, alpinum, insectivores, and industrial plants, succulents, Australian flora.

The Royal Botanic Gardens at Kew

The county of Surrey spreads like a fan round the south-west borders of London and away from the main road we find charming, typically English scenery.

Here on the banks of the Thames, on the threshold of London, there are the world-famous Royal Botanic Gardens of Kew. They were founded by Princess Augusta (1759) and her like-minded son George III. In 1841 they were taken over by the State, and in 1897 Queen Victoria donated some parkland on condition that it should be allowed to retain its semi-wild condition.

Today the gardens cover an area of 300 acres and Queen Victoria's wish is still being respected. Kew Gardens are mainly devoted to science. Their chief tasks are: 1. the exact identification of plants; 2. the passing on of information in the botanical field. The Gardens are a rich source of botanical material (seeds and living plants) for all part of the Commonwealth and the world in general. They played a significant part in the development of the rubber and cocoa industries.

Prominent Buildings:

The Pagoda,
built in 1761 by Sir W. Chambers, octagonal, 10 storeys high.

The Flag Staff,
fashioned from a Douglas pine, 370 years of age, 226 ft. tall.

King William's Temple,
built 1837 under William IV.

Temple of Bellona,
built 1760 by Sir W. Chambers.

Temple of Arethusa,
also built by Sir W. Chambers.

Temple of Aeolus,
built on a hill in 1761 by Sir W. Chambers.

Mokushi Mon,
replica of a famous Japanese gate on the Moss Hill. Remarkable for the beauty of its proportions and fine carvings.

General Museum,
built in 1857. The main collections are kept here.

Reference Museum,
not open to the public. Contains reference books about specimens kept in the Museum.

Timber Museum,
containing every kind of timber and tree.

Orangery,
built in 1761, Sir W. Chamber's masterpiece.

The Palm House,
a glass and iron construction, built from 1844—1848 by Decimus Burton. For a long time it was the largest glasshouse in the world. It is 361 ft. long The wings are 30 ft. high; the central section 66 ft. high.

Kew Palace
(the Dutch House). Red brick in the Dutch style. Built in 1631 on the foundations of a farmhouse which was once the residence of the Earl of Leicester, a favourite of Queen Elizabeth I.

The Hothouse,
one of the largest glasshouses in the world. Resembles the Palm House, completed in 1899.

Marianne North Gallery,
a collection of 848 flower paintings, the life work of the Victorian artist Marianne North. She worked from 1872—1885 in many different parts of the world.

Glasshouses:

No. 1 Araceae House;

Nos. 2—3 Fern Houses; one tropical, one humid (2 A) and one cool.

No. 4 The Winter Garden (cruciform):

No. 5 Succulent House.

Nos. 7—14 The T-Glasshouse; in the central and hottest part, the giant water lily, Victoria amazonica.

No. 7 & 8 Form the stem of the T and contain plants from the Cape Province, begonias and tropical hothouse plants.

Nos. 11 & 12 Tropical industrial plants.

Nos. 13 & 14 Orchids.

No. 15 Water Lily House.

No. 25 The Alpine House, unheated, supplement to the rock garden.

The Palm House contains living tropical plants of both hemispheres; palms and Cycadeas.

The Park

Rhododendron Valley and Bamboo Garden

George III's landscape architect Brown designed the miniature valley. The most beautiful rhododendrons of the country flower here in the shade of tall Lebanon cedars and deciduous trees. The 20 species originally planted here 100 years ago have increased considerably. The splendour of their colouring at blossom time is indescribable.
The bamboo comes from China, Japan and the Himalayas.

The Limestone Garden

designed in 1944. On the right, native plants; on the left, foreign plants. Mostly rosette and hummock plants.

The Flower Garden

A rose pergola divides it into two parts, with rows of parallel beds to the right and left. The plants are grouped according to families. For instance, the compositae occupy 29 beds, while smaller families share one bed. The exact number of species and varieties cultivated here varies but on average there are 6,000 different species. Many of them are exotic or annual plants in need of constant care and attention which have to be raised from seeds every year. The sun flower and aster collection is probably the largest in the world and provides a magnificent display of colour.

The Hill Garden,
snowdrops, crocus and narcissi flower beneath elms, walnut, chestnut and Spanish chestnut trees.

Cambridge Cottage Garden

It is made to look as old-fashioned as possible: lilies, cherry trees, camellia 'Kimberley,' Chinese trees and shrubs.

Queen's Cottage and parkland

Donated by Queen Victoria, this woodland, extending over 210 acres, is threaded by a single path. Oaks, ashes, elms, beeches and willows grow close together, with blackberry thickets at their feet. In spring the clearings are carpeted with bluebells. More than a hundred species of birds nest in the trees.

The Rock Garden

Alpine plants from the temperate zones in all parts of the world.

The Barberry Valley

The Lake

is one of the most remarkable sights of Kew. It covers an area of 4 acres and has several islands. American bog cypresses (Taxodium distichum) grow along the banks in addition to many native bog and aquatic plants, Iris siberica and water lilies. Water birds hatch on the islands.

The Water Garden

British aquatic and bog plants.

The Pond

Taxodium distichum, willows, poplars.

The Water Lily Pond

A collection of water lilies, iris, primulas, etc.

The Heather Garden

The Rose Garden

Noteworthy plants throughout the year:

January—February: Snow heather, snowdrops, hellebore, witch hazel
March—April: Camellias, crocus, forsythia
Early April: Narcissi
April—May: Cherries, ornamental apple trees, lilies, magnolias, tulips, wisterias
April—June: Rock plants
Late May: Bluebells
May—June: Azaleas, blue poppy, chestnut trees, iris, rhododendron
June—July: Lilies, flowering shrubs
July—September: Roses, water lilies, summer flowers
September—October: Belladonna lilies, heather, asters
October: Autumn colouring
October—December: Fruiting trees and shrubs

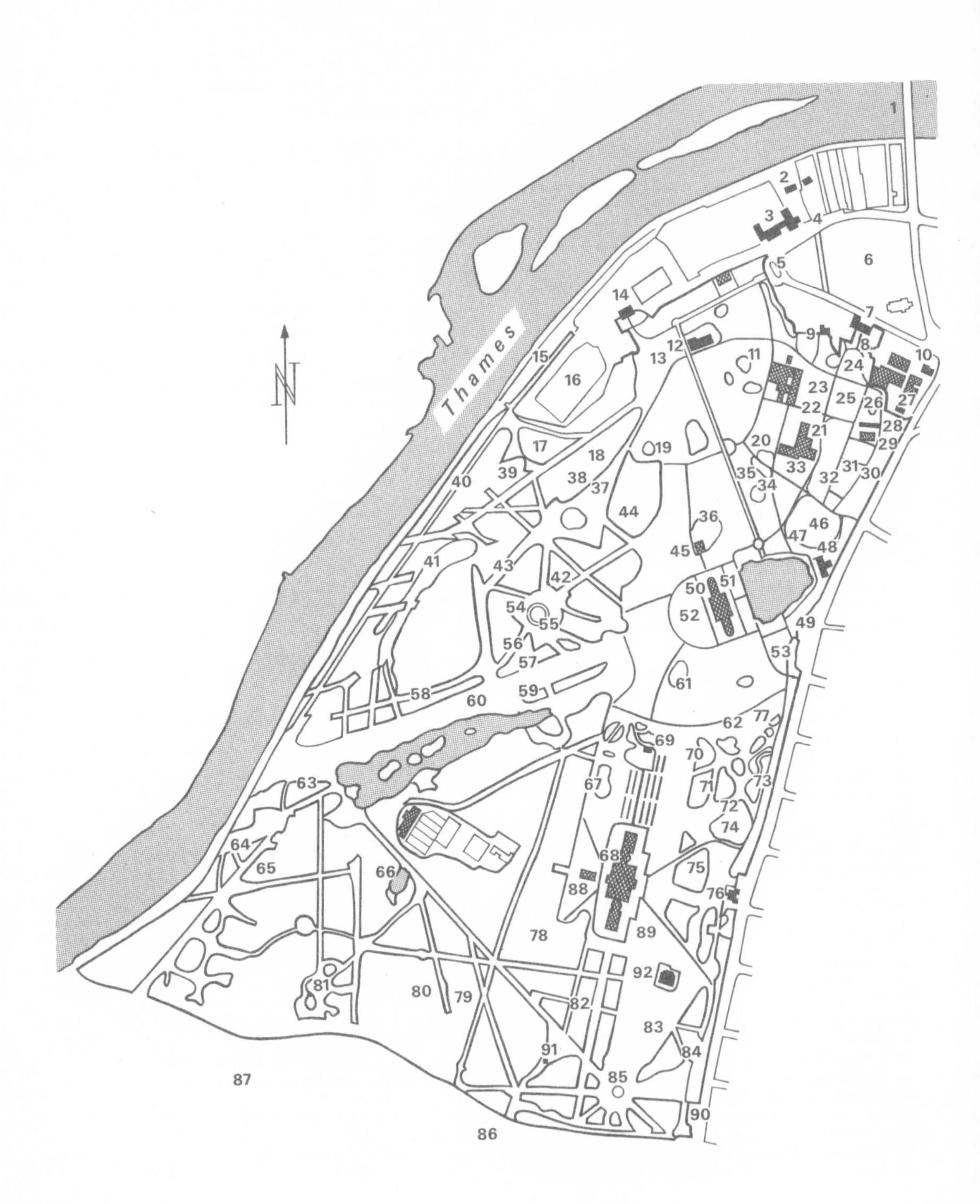
Thames
N

Garden of Leonard Maurice Mason, Talbot Manor, Fincham, King's Lynn, Norfolk, 21 acres (13 GH)

SF: Tropical and sub-tropical collections. Orchids, begonias.

Haulfre Gardens, Town Hall, Llandudno, North Wales, 11 acres (11 GH)

SF: Alpinum, trees and shrubs of the coastal areas.

Botany Department Experimental Gardens, The University, Leeds 2, 1 acre

Visits by permission of the director. SF: Hybrids.

The University of Liverpool Botanic Gardens, Ness-Neston, Wirral, Cheshire (1948), 60 acres (GH 897 sq. yds.)

RVS: April to August. SF: Alpine flora, Ericaceae, primula, aquatic plants.

South London Botanical Institute, 323, Norwood Road, London, S.E. 4 (1838), 1 acre (1 GH)

Open weekdays from 3—10 p.m., except Thursdays. SF: A variety of wild growing British plants.

Great Dixter Gardens, Northiam, Sussex

Open 20th April to 30th September, daily from 2—5 p.m., except Mondays, Good Friday and Bank Holidays. SF: Many different genera, hedges and perennials, tropical plants.

University Botanic Garden Oxford, High Street, Oxford (1621), 7½ acres (9 GH)

RVS: June—September. Sundays closed from noon to 2 p.m SF: Iris, summer flowers.

Penjerrick Gardens, Cornwall

SF: Rhododendron, Australian tree ferns, hybrids.

Gwylly Gardens, Portmeirion near Penrhyndeudraeth, Merioneth, Wales

Open Easter to October from 10 a.m. to 5 p.m. SF: Wild gardens and woods with subtropical plants, rhododendron, azaleas, hydrangeas.

Index to the Map of the Royal Botanic Gardens at Kew

1 Kew Bridge
2 Mycological Institute
3 Herbarium
4 Car Park
5 Main Entrance
6 Lawn
7 Timber Museum
8 Medicinal Garden
9 Director's Office
10 Administration
11 Turkish Oak
12 Orangery
13 Oriental Plane Tree
14 Kew Palace
15 Queen Elizabeth's Lawn
16 Tree Nursery
17 Poplar
18 Birch
19 Asters
20 Limestone Garden
21 T-Glasshouse
22 Cacti House
23 Lime Tree
24 Lilac
25 Iris Garden
26 Water Garden
27 Jodrell Laboratory
28 Reference Museum
29 Alpinum
30 Pergolas
31 Roses
32 Rock Garden
33 Orchids
34 Beech
35 Rhododendrons
36 Crab Apple Hill
37 Princesses' Way
38 Heather
39 Elm
40 River Walk
41 Rhododendron Valley
42 Oaks
43 Tulip Walk
44 Ash
45 Water Lily House
46 Temple of Aeolus
47 Plane Tree
48 General Museum
49 Temple of Arethusa
50 Palm House
51 The Queen's Beasts
52 Rose Garden
53 Water Tower
54 Azalea Garden
55 Magnolias
56 Nut Walk
57 Hazel Nut Tree
58 Chestnut Walk
59 Alder
60 Syon Avenue
61 Japanese Cherries
62 Clematis
63 Pine
64 Willows
65 Snowdrops
66 Water Lily Pond
67 Box
68 Greenhouse
69 King William's Temple
70 Hibiscus
71 Barberries
72 Tamarisks
73 Camellias
74 Flag Staff
75 Maple
76 Marianne North Gallery
77 Temple of Bellona
78 Holly Walk
79 Larches
80 Cypresses
81 The Queen's Cottage
82 Pear Trees
83 Acacia Walk
84 Walnut Tree
85 Pagoda
86 Old Deer Park
87 Royal Mid-Surrey Golf Course
88 Australia House
89 Pagoda Walk
90 Lion Gate
91 Japanese Gate
92 Cafeteria

Agricultural Botany Gardens, Cutbush Lane, Shinfield, Reading, Berks. (1918), 3 acres (8 GH)

Visits by permission of the director. SF: Triticum, Aegilops, Fragaria.

Sheffield Park Gardens near Uckfield, Sussex

Open April to October, Wednesdays, Saturdays and Sundays, 2—7 p.m. (October noon to 5 p.m.). SF: Spring bulbs, rhododendron, azaleas, rich collection of autumn flowers.

University Botanic Garden, Southampton, 3 acres (3 GH)

Beaumont Hall, Stoughton Drive South, Leicester, 3 acres (7 GH)

Open Mondays to Thursdays, 10 a.m. to 5 p.m.; Fridays 10 a.m. until dusk; closed Saturdays and Sundays.

Botanic Gardens Stourhead, near Mere, Wiltshire

Open daily from 11 a.m. to 7 p.m. From October to March closed on Tuesdays and Fridays. SF: One of the most beautiful landscape gardens of Europe. Rhododendron.

Bodnant Gardens, Tal-y-Cafn near Conway, Denbighshire, 60 acres

Open April to October, Tuesdays, Wednesdays, Thursdays, Saturdays and Bank Holidays, 1.30—4.45 p.m. SF: One of the most beautiful and well stocked gardens of the country. Terraces, rare shrubs (especially rhododendron) and trees. Accessible by Eglwysbach Road, E. of A 496.

Arboretum Westonbirt near Tetbury, Gloucestershire, 115 acres (2 GH)

SF: Acer, rhododendron, conifers, deciduous trees.

Tresco Abbey Gardens, Tresco, Isles of Scilly

Open weekdays 10 a.m. to 4 p.m. SF: Sub-tropical garden with plants from all parts of the world.

G. H. Johnstone Garden, Trewithen, Cornwall

SF: Plants from China, Magnolias, Acer, Ilex, Camellia.

Sissinghurst Castle Garden, Sissinghurst, Kent

Open 24th March to 31st October, 10 a.m. to 7 p.m. SF: Spring flowers, roses, grass garden, autumn flowers.

Savill Gardens, Windsor Great Park, Berkshire, Crown Property, 20 acres

Open March to October, 10 a.m. to 6 p.m. SF: Spring, summer and autumn flowers, flowering shrubs and trees.

Valley Gardens, Windsor Great Park, Berkshire

RVS: May to June. SF: Rhododendron, azaleas.

The Royal Horticultural Society's Gardens, Wisley, Ripley, Woking, Surrey (1904), 303 acres (GH 2,774 sq. yds.)

RVS: May to September. Open weekdays, 7.30 a.m. to sundown (or 7.30 p.m.); Sundays open to members only. SF: Rhododendron, heather and rock garden, alpine plants, trial grounds for various garden plants. Singularly well stocked and noteworthy. Between Cobham and Ripley.

Museum Gardens, York (1840), 10 acres

Finland

Arboretum Mustila, Elimäki (1902), 297 acres (5 GH)

RVS: June to July, September and October. SF: Deciduous trees and conifers, rhododendron.

Botanical Gardens of the University of Helsinki, Unioninkatu 44 (1833), 12 acres (GH 1,435 sq. yds.)

RVS: June to September, closed Tuesdays and Fridays.

Botanical Gardens of Oulu, Kasarmintie 7 (1960), 12 acres (GH 478 sq. yds.)

RVS: June to August. SF: Alpine and arctic plants.

Garden Research Institute Piikkiö

Accessible by bus from Turku.

Botanical Gardens of the University of Turku/ Ruissalo (1956), 18 acres (GH 957 sq. yds.)

RVS: April to October. Open all the year, Sundays from noon to 2 p.m. only. SF: Tropical orchids, about 700 species, especially natural varieties.

Horticultural School Lepa

SF: Show cultivations of alpine plants and perennials.

Garden of Baron Paavo v. Pandy, Kultalathi

North of the Arctic Circle, the northernmost garden of Europe.

France

Jardin Botanique d'Alford (Seine) (1765), 3,826 sq. yds. (GH 120 sq. yds.)

Visits by permission of the director. SF: Botanical school garden.

Jardin Botanique de la Ville d'Amiens (Somme)

Jardin Botanique de la Faculté de Médecine, Angers (Maine & Loire)

Station Botanique de la Villa Thuret, Antibes (Alpes Maritimes) (1856), 10 acres (GH 1,435 sq. yds.)

RVS: April to June. SF: Exotic flowers and plants; palms, eucalyptus. Important arboretum, subtropical and Mediterranean species mostly.

Centre de Recherches Botaniques, Station Expérimentale 'La Léonina,' Beaulieu-sur-Mer (A. M.) (1951), 7 acres (GH 837 sq. yds.)

RVS: April to November. Purely scientific centre and open only to persons engaged on scientific work. SF: Various fruit and vegetable plants; exotic plants.

Jardin Botanique de l'Université et de la Ville de Besançon (Doubs), 1, Place Maréchal Leclerc (1890), 5 acres (GH 454 sq. yds.)

RVS: May to November. Open 8 a.m. to noon and 1.30—5.30 p.m. except Saturday afternoons and Sundays. SF: Victoria regia, scientific collection of 2,000 species; alpinum, ferns, aquatic plants, medicinal plants, rosarium.

Jardin Botanique de la Ville de Bordeaux, Terrasse du Jardin Public (Gironde)

Jardin Botanique de la Ville et de l'Université de Caën (Calvados), 5, Place Blot, Normandie (1736), 1¼ acres, in addition 6¼ acres park (GH 957 sq. yds.)

RVS: Spring and summer. SF: Native flowers of Normandy, medicinal plants, succulents and exotic plants, rock flora.

Réserve Naturelle de la Camargue, Delta of the Rhône, South of France (1928), 37,167 acres (National Park)

RVS: March to June. Access via Arles and Saintes Maries-de-la-Mer. Permission to visit must be applied for in advance; the number of visitors is very restricted and permission to visit is generally confined to students and persons engaged on scientific work. Application to Maisons de la Capelière et du Salin de Badon, Camargue. SF: The plain of Camargue, known as a bird sanctuary, also comprises the seven islands of Rièges, south of Etang de Vaccarès. The magnificent vegetation of the islands makes a complete contrast to the rest of the Camargue. Flora: Lonicera, gladiolas, irises, narcissi, lianas, Mediterranean shrubs, juniperus phoenicea.

Jardin de la Villa Roquebrune, Cap Martin, Rivièra

RVS: April, July and August. SF: Stone-pines, plants of South Africa, Aster fruticulosus, succulents, cacti, pelargonia, Scabiosa cretica from Sicily. Situated on a picturesque peninsula between Monaco and the Italian border.

Jardin 'Cevenol' au Parc National Le Caroux (Hérault) (1962), 478 sq. yds.

RVS: May; open on Sundays and Holidays. SF: Native flowers of the Cévennes. Access: 11½ miles from Lamalou les Bains along the old forest road, Rosis—Cambon, near Douch.

Réserve Naturelle Mont Canigou (Pyrenées Orientales), 9,136 ft. above sea level, especially the area around Chalet Hotel des Cortalets (National Park)

RVS: July. SF: Rhododendron ferrugineum and Cytisus purgans forming dense flower carpets. Especially noteworthy among the rocks of the mountain ridge, Primula latifolia, Primula viscosa and, somewhat lower down, Senecio leucophyllus. Access: Perpignan, up the Tet Valley to Prades, whence road to Vernet. A few miles short of Vernet, on the left narrow mountain road to Chalet Hotel des Cortalets, whence 1½ hours' walk to the summit.

Jardin Botanique de la Ville de Dijon (Côte d'Or), 1, Avenue Albert Ier (1771), 5½ acres

RVS: May to September. SF: Native plants and several collections (6,000 different plants).

Les Jardins à Evry-Petit-Bourg (S. & O.)

SF: Rosarium.

Les Jardins au Domaine de Prafrance, Générargues (Gard) (1854), 99 acres, 15 of which occupied by bamboo collection (5 GH)

RVS: March to October. Open 9 a.m. to noon and 2—7 p.m. SF: Renowned bamboo collection, more than 32 species; Arboretum (Sequoia gigantea, Magnolia, etc.), rhododendron, liriodendron, azaleas.

Les Jardins à Gonesses (S. & O.)

SF: Spring bulbs.

Parc Grands Murcins, Roanne (Loire) (1934/36), 5 acres (GH 1³/₄ acres)

RVS: May to October. SF: Arboretum—conifers (firs, cedars, pines), plane trees, etc.

Les Jardins à Grasse (Alpes Maritimes)

RVS: June to August. SF: Large flower fields (cultivations for manufacture of perfumes, cut flowers). Syringa, roses, tuberoses, broom, lavender, pines.

Jardin Botanique de l'Ecole Nationale d'Agriculture, Grignon (S. & O.) (1875), 2 acres (GH 179 sq. yds.)

RVS: June to September. SF: Ecological collection, limestone plants, collections of graminaceous and leguminous plants.

Rosairie l'Hay-les-Roses (Seine), 2, Avenue Jean Jaurés (1895), 28 acres (Park and Rosarium)

RVS: June. Open June and first week of July from 10 a.m. SF: Rose Museum; old rose varieties, modern roses, ornamental roses; botanical and historic roses.

Jardin La-Tronche-sur-Mer (Vendée)

SF: Bulb cultivations.

Station Biologique et Alpinum au Col du Lautaret (Hautes Alpes), 6,722 ft. above sea level (1903), 3¹/₂ acres

RVS: July. Open from 15th June to end of September. SF: Alpinum with 3,000 alpine plants and the rarest rock plants in the world. 56 miles from Grenoble and Briançon. Accessible by car.

Station d'Acclimatation Botanique du Château de la Tour de Montmuilhe, La Col-sur-Loup (Alpes Maritimes) (1931), 30 acres (GH 36 sq. yds.)

RVS: May to October. Visits by permission of the director. SF: Araceae, asparagus. Access: 11 miles from Nice, 13 miles from Cannes. From Cagnes-sur-Mer take Route de Vence. Bus from Nice.

Jardin Botanique de la Ville de Lille (Nord), Faubourg de Douai (1947), 27 acres (GH 3,547 sq. yds.)

SF: Orchids, succulents, begonias, bromelias.

Jardin Botanique de la Ville de Lyon, Park de la Tête d'Or (1857), 15 acres (GH 1³/₄ acres)

RVS: May to October. SF: In addition to an arboretum, the garden comprises an alpinum with most alpine plants and the rarest rock plants of the world, excepting Africa, a total of 2,000 species. The alpinum covers an area of 2,392 sq. yds. Rosarium with 1,200 species, among them historic roses. 1,200 rare flowering shrubs. Sub-tropical and tropical flora, rare aquatic plants (Victoria regia, etc.), succulents, liliaceae, orchids.

Jardin Botanique—Faculté de Médecine et Pharmacie, 4, Avenue Rockefeller, Lyon (Rhône)

SF: Pharmaceutical plants. Open to scientists only.

Jardin Botanique, Parc Borély, 52, Avenue Clôt-Bey, Marseille VIII.

Serre de la Madone, Val du Gorbio, Menton (about 1920), 19 acres (GH 139 sq. yds.)

RVS: April, June and July. SF: Sub-tropical plant collection. Araliaceae (Oreopanax capitatus, O. dactylifolius, O. echinops).

Jardin Botanique de la Ville de Marseille, in Parc Borély, 52, Avenue Clôt-Bey, Marseille (1880), Botanic Garden, 5 acres; Centre de Multiplication: 3 acres, both within Parc Borély, 43 acres (GH 1,794 sq. yds.)

RVS: June to September. SF: Rosarium (1¹/₄ acres) with 2,500 plants of 230 different species.

Jardin Botanique de la Ville de Metz (Moselle), Rue de Pont-à-Mousson (1867), 11 acres (GH 897 sq. yds.)

RVS: 1st April to 15th November. SF: Roses, dahlias, bulbs, tropical and sub-tropical plants.

Jardin Botanique de l'Université de Montpellier (Hérault), Boulevard Henri IV (1593), 14 acres (GH 1,435 sq. yds.)

RVS: January to March for orchids; late May for native flowers. Summer for other plants. Open 8 a.m. to noon and 2—6 p.m. In winter closed on Saturday afternoons and Sundays. SF: Pancratium; aquatic plants; Egyptian lotus (flowers in July); arboretum, tropical plants, orchids.

Jardin Botanique de la Ville de Nancy, Rue Sainte Catherine (1758), 12,338 sq. yds. (GH: 537 sq. yds.)

RVS: April to October. Open 8 a.m. to noon and 1.30—5 p.m. SF: Alpinum, medicinal plants, tulips, irises, dahlias.

Jardin Botanique de la Ville de Nantes (Loire Inférieur) (1680), 17 acres (GH 3,588 sq. yds.)

RVS: April to September. Open 9 a.m. to noon and 2—6 p.m. except Tuesdays. SF: Arboretum, magnolias, camellias (240 species), orchids, cacti.

Réserve Naturelle de Néouvieille (Pyrénées) (1934), 5,436 acres, 5,740 to 10,144 ft. above sea level

RVS: Summer and early autumn. SF: Festuca eskia, F. spadicea, Carex curvula, rhododendron, Arctostaphylos uva ursi, Lycopodium annotinum, Salix daphnoides, S. nigricans, Erica tetralix, Molopospermum cicutarium, Comarum palustre. Accessible via Lourdes or Bagnères de Bigorre. Accommodation available in the hotels of the two side valleys at Barèges and Aure.

Jardin Albert I, Nice

SF: Giant yucca.

Nice

SF: Plant cultivation for the manufacture of perfumes, cut flowers.

Arboretum et Fructicetum Nogent-sur-Vernisson (Loire) (1823—1873), 247 acres (GH 120 sq. yds.)

RVS: Spring and autumn. Visits by permission of the director. SF: Conifers (250 species); Fructicetum Vilmorinianum; trial grounds for forest trees (148 acres).

Jardin Botanique de la Faculté de Pharmacie, 4, Avenue de l'Observatoire, Paris 6e, 2 acres

Visits by permission of the director. SF: Medicinal plants.

Jardin des Plantes, Paris, 57, rue Cuvier (1635), 34 acres (GH 3¼ acres)

RVS: May to October. SF: Alpinum; botanical collection for educational purposes, classified according to Engler; medicinal plants, winter garden; horticultural collection for educational purposes with antique and modern varieties; glasshouses with plants of the desert regions (a total of 17,000 species). Access from Metro station Jussieu or Austerlitz.

Jardin de Ville, Paris, 3, Avenue de la Porte d'Auteuil (1895), 25 acres (GH 3½ acres)

RVS: March to October. SF: Azaleas, chrysanthemums, palms, orchids, succulents, bromelias.

Réserve Naturelle de Pelvoux (Isère), Hautes Alpes (1914), 81,299 acres, 5,000 ft. to 13,123 ft. above sea level

RVS: Summer. SF: Sub-alpine, alpine and snow plants. A part of the national park is closed to the public. Situated on the Pelvoux (12,972 ft.), one of the highest peaks of the Massif de l'Oisan. Accessible via Chamonix and Grenoble.

Jardin Botanique 'Le Thabor' de la Ville de Rennes, 5, Boulevard de la Duchesse-Anne (1860), 25 acres (GH 239 sq. yds.)

RVS: May to September.

Jardin Botanique de la Ville de Rouen, 114, Avenue des Martyrs de la Résistance (1836), 25 acres (GH 2,990 sq. yds.)

RVS: Spring and summer. SF: Ecology; alpinum; Victoria regia; insectivores, orchids, exotic plants.

Réserve Naturelle de Saint Crépin (Hautes Alpes)

RVS: Spring. SF: This national park is devoted exclusively to the preservation of Juniperus thurifera. Accessible via Chambéry and Briançon (valley of the Durance). Accommodation at Saint-Crépin.

Jardin Botanique 'Les Cèdres,' Saint Jean Cap-Ferrat (Alpes Maritimes) (1924), 37 acres (9 GH)

Visits by experts only after application to the owner: M. Marnier-Lapostolle, 91, Boulevard Haussmann, Paris. It is necessary to supply evidence of qualification as botanist or specialised horticultural nurseryman. SF: Comprehensive collection of exotic plants, cacti, agaves, succulents, ferns, etc.

Jardin Botanique et Alpinum 'La Jaysinia,' Samoëns (Haute Savoie) (1906), 9 acres

RVS: Spring to autumn. SF: The largest herbarium of alpine plants in France; laboratory for scientific research. Flora: complete range of alpine plants, geographically arranged; aquatic plants found in mountain regions. Access via Geneva, Annemasse, Bonneville. Accommodation at Samoëns.

Jardin Botanique de l'Université de Strasbourg, 7, Rue de l'Université (Bas Rhin) (1879), 18½ acres (6 GH)

Visits by arrangement with the director. SF: Alpinum, arboretum, aquatic plants, cacti, tropical plants, systematic collection.

Jardin d'Acclimatation de la Société d'Horticulture, Toulon

SF: Native and exotic plants.

Jardin Botanique de l'Université de Toulouse, 2, Rue Lamarck (Haute Garonne), 2½ acres (3 GH)

Closed on Sundays and Holidays.

Jardin Botanique de la Faculté de Médecine et Pharmacie de l'Université de Tours, Boulevard Tonnellé (1842), 1¾ acres (GH 2,392 sq. yds.)

RVS: May to October. SF: Native plants of the Touraine, medicinal plants.

Arboretum et Alpinum Vilmorin, 2 Rue E. d'Orves, Verrières le Buisson (1815), 7 acres

RVS: May to June. Visits by permission of the director. SF: Conifers, alpinum.

German Democratic Republic

Botanischer Garten of the City of Altenburg, Bezirk Leipzig, Heinrich-Zille-Strasse (2 GH)

Open 1st May to mid-October, in fine weather only. Tuesdays to Saturdays 2—6 p.m.; Sundays and Holidays 10 a.m. to 1 p.m. and 3—6 p.m. SF: Hardy plants, ornamental plants. Geographical section; medicinal plants, protected native flora, biological and plant-sociological sections. Cacti and succulents.

Brocken-Oberharz see Halle-Wittenberg

Forstbotanischer Garten des Instituts für Forstwissenschaften Eberswalde der DAL zu Berlin, 64 acres

Open on Sunday afternoons in summer.

Institut für Kulturpflanzenforschung Gatersleben der Deutschen Akademie der Wissenschaften zu Berlin

Conducted tours by permission of the director. SF: Mutations of Antirrhinum, Hordeum, Lycopersicum, Wisterias.

Botanischer Garten der Technischen Universität Dresden, Dresden A-16, Stübelallee 2 (1890), 7½ acres (GH 1,196 sq. yds.)

Open 1st April to 15th October.

Schlosspark Pillnitz near Dresden

SF: Dahlias.

Schau- und Versuchsgarten of the Martin Luther University of Halle-Wittenberg, Brocken-Oberharz, 4,784 sq. yds.

Open June to September from 11 a.m. to 2 p.m. SF: Alpines and arctic plants.

Botanischer Garten der Ernst Moritz Arndt University of Greifswald, Grimmer Strasse 88 (1763), 17 acres (GH 1,555 sq. yds.)

RVS: Outdoors, spring and summer. Closed on Sunday and Saturday afternoons. SF: Orchids and primulas. Alpinum, rhododendron, moor bed plants.

Botanischer Garten of the Martin Luther University of Halle-Wittenberg, Halle/Saale, Am Kirchtor 3 (1698), 7 acres (9 GH)

RVS: June to October. SF: Eurasian steppe plants and plants of the Canary Islands; cacti.

Botanischer Garten of the Friedrich Schiller University of Jena, Goethe-Allee 26 (1584 as medicinal garden), 12 acres (GH 1,507 sq. yds.)

RVS: April to September. Open: outdoors, 9 a.m. to noon and 2—5 p.m. GH, 10 a.m. to noon and 2—4 p.m. every day except Saturdays. SF: Plants of the Balkan Peninsula, the Middle East, Central Asia, alpinum, cold greenhouse plants, Primulaceae, succulents.

Botanischer Garten of the Karl Marx University of Leipzig, Linnéstrasse 1 (1542), 6 acres (GH 1,316 sq. yds.)

RVS: March to September. Open weekdays in summer 7 a.m. to 7 p.m., in winter 8 a.m. to 5 p.m., and on Sundays throughout the year from 9 a.m. to noon. SF: Alpinum, orchids, succulents, tropical and sub-tropical plants, lime and moor plants, morphological and biological sections.

Botanischer Garten für Arznei- und Gewürzpflanzen (medicinal and kitchen herbs), Oberholz near Leipzig

Parkanlagen Bad Muskau, Bezirk Cottbus (1815), 494 acres

Famous landscape park founded by Count Pückler, early 19th century.

Botanischer Garten Potsdam-Sanssouci, Maulbeerallee 2

Karl Foerster, mass cultivation of perennials, cultivation of and research in hardy flowering perennials, Potsdam-Bornim

Botanischer Garten of the Wilhelm Pieck University of Rostock, Doberaner Strasse 143

Rosarium Sangerhausen, Steinberger Weg 3 (1903), 30 acres (1 GH)

RVS: June to September. SF: Old roses of all classes, and wild roses. Largest collection in the world: 6,000 species and varieties.

Forstbotanischer Garten Tharandt near Dresden, Dippoldswalder Strasse 7 (1811), 45 acres (2 GH)

RVS: April to October. SF: Important forest trees, rare dwarf trees, rare low perennials.

Staatliche Schlösser und Gärten Wörlitz near Dessau, three different parks: Wörlitz (1764), 277 acres; Oranienbaum, 82 acres; Luisium, 34 acres

German Federal Republic

Wittelsbacher Park and Stadtgarten Augsburg, 32 acres

SF: In the park the Rudolf Diesel Memorial Gardens in the shape of a Japanese landscape garden.

Botanischer Lehr- und Schaugarten of the City of Augsburg, Augsburg, Parkstrasse 15 a (1936), 5 acres (GH 776 sq. yds.)

RVS: In the open, May to September. Greenhouses, December to March. SF: In the open, Tulip show, ground-covering shrubs resistant to dry conditions, ground-covering shrubs for shady places, heath and moor plants, dendrological section; greenhouses, cacti, Bromeliaceae, Orchids.

Botanischer Garten Berlin-Dahlem, Königin-Luise-Strasse 6—8 (1646, 1897—1909), 103 acres (34 GH)

See article below by Dr J. Gerloff

Botanischer Garten in Bielefeld, Am Kahlenberg 16 (1911), 9 acres

RVS: March to September. SF: Alpinum, Rhododendron.

Botanischer Garten of the Rheinische Friedrich Wilhelms University, Bonn, Meckenheimer Allee 171 (1818), 21 acres

RVS: Throughout the year. Open Mondays, Wednesdays, Fridays 2—7 p.m. (October 1st to March 31st, 2—5 p.m. From March to 1st to October 1st Sundays 9 a.m.—1 p.m.). SF: In the greenhouses, plants of the tropical rain forest, Orchids, Succulents. During the summer months, Victoria regia, tropical swamp and aquatic plants. In the open, phylogenetic systems 1,400 species, floral ecology, fruit ecology, plant-geographical section about 1,000 species.

Botanical Gardens Berlin-Dahlem

Königin-Luise-Strasse 6—8 and Unter den Eichen 5—10 (1646, 1897—1909 moved to its present situation at Berlin-Dahlem by A. Engler).

The Botanical Gardens of Berlin-Dahlem cover an area of 103 acres and are among the largest in the world. Intended to serve scientific purposes, they are also of educational value to the whole population. With their beautiful landscaping, they attract even the layman not especially interested in botanical matters. The gardens are supplemented by a modern botanical museum.

In the open the gardens are divided as follows: Plant-geographical section, arboretum, taxonomical section, section of cultivated and medicinal plants, aquatic and swamp section, two morphological-biological sections and some ornamental gardens. Special mention should be made of the extensive plant-geographical groups and the even larger arboretum, the two sections of which occupy by far the largest part of the gardens. The former, displaying the most important plants of the northern temperate zone, are world famous, for no other gardens possess a geographical section to be compared with this one in layout and size. Particularly striking is the presentation of the great sweep of mountain ranges from the Pyrenees, the Alps, the Carpathians, the Balkans, the Middle East and the Caucasian Mountains to the Himalayas and West China. Japanese and North American plants, including those of the Rocky Mountains, occupy a large area. The arboretum comprises a taxonomical (i.e. arranged according to families) selection of trees which are hardy in the climate of North Germany. The gardens owe their landscape effects to the park-like lay-out of the rich dendrological section and the plant-geographical section, aided by some very pretty lakes.

The greenhouses accommodate some 6,000 different species under cultivation, among them a special collection of some 1,500 orchids, 1,000 cacti and 100 begonia species. Since there are on average 3—4 specimens of every species, the greenhouses altogether contain at least 20,000 individual plants.

The contents of the greenhouses are grouped according to geographical, taxonomical, ecological and economical considerations, as follows:

1. Six geographical houses (African succulents, South African plants, American succulents, American Bromelias, Australian and East Asian plants).
2. One Araceae house.
3. Two orchid houses (one tropical, one sub-tropical).
4. One tropical fern house.
5. One house each for dicotyledenous and monocotyledenous tropical cultivation plants.
6. One tall house (53 feet) for sub-tropical plants with two large annexes, one for tree ferns and one for flowering plants suitable for indoor cultivation.
7. One house for tropical aquatic plants, where during the four summer months the two Victoria species dominate the picture.
8. A large tropical house ('palm house') containing a vast panorama of tropical scenery which, however, has not yet been restored since the destruction of the entire gardens in 1943, although restoration began in 1963. The house has an interior height of 82 feet, a length of 197 feet, a width of 98 feet and a cubic capacity of some 57,858 cubic yards. It is one of the sights of Berlin.

On average some 200,000 to 300,000 people visit the gardens annually and a scientifically and horticulturally controlled exchange of plants and seeds is conducted with over 300 other botanical gardens and nurseries in Germany and all over the world.

Dr J. Gerloff, Custodian

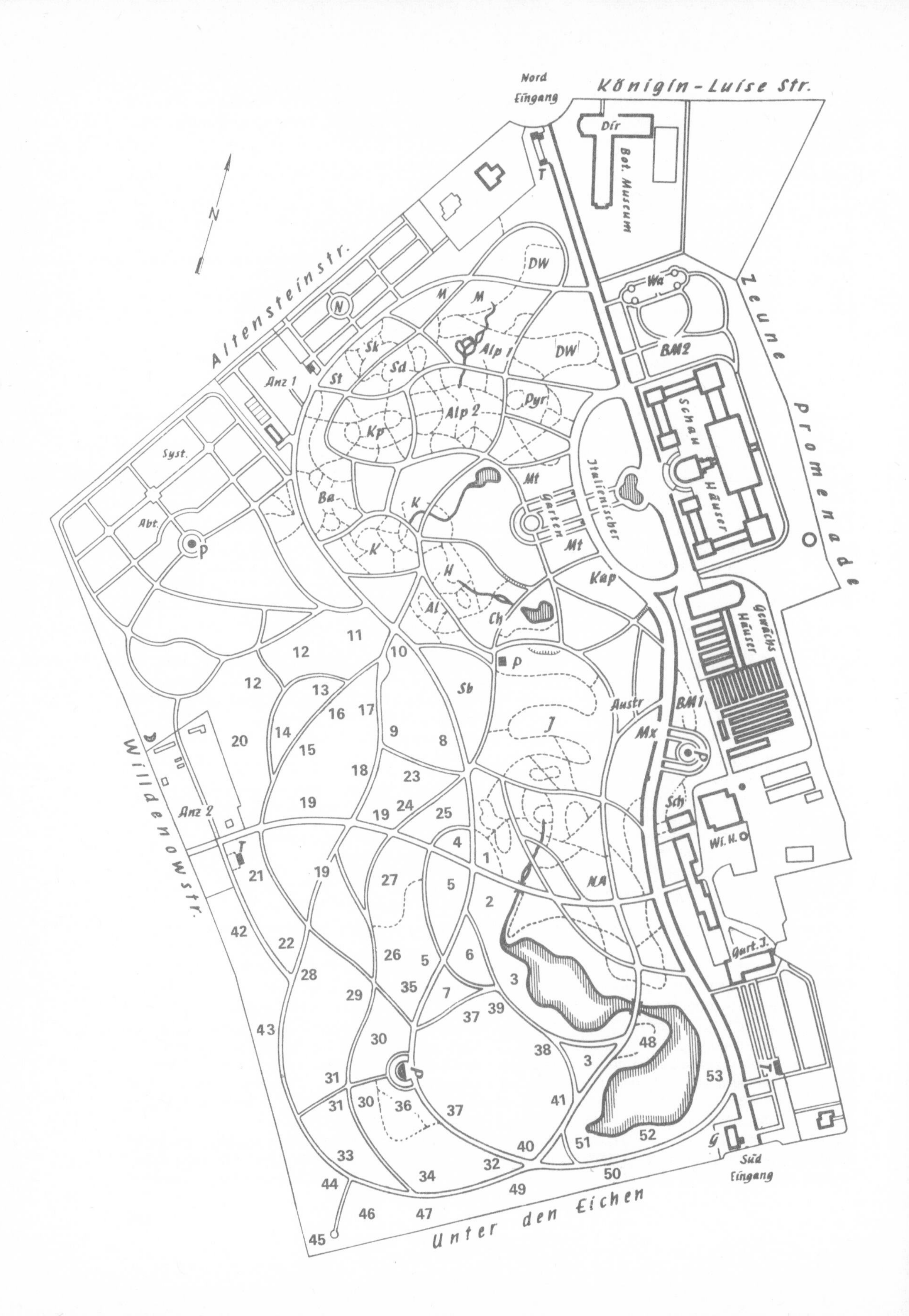

Nord Eingang
Königin-Luise Str.
Dir
Bot. Museum
Altensteinstr.
Zeune Promenade
Schau Häuser
Italienischer Garten
Gewächs Häuser
Wildenowstr.
Unter den Eichen
Süd Eingang
Syst.
Abt.
Anz 1
Anz 2
DW
Wa
BM2
BM1
Alp 1
Alp 2
Pyr
Kp
Ba
Mt
Kap
Sb
Austr
Mx
Sch
Wi. H.
Gart. J.
NA

Abbreviations used in the Map:

Al	Altai Mountains
Alp 1	Forest Regions of the Alps
Alp 2	Alps
Anz 1	Nursery for Alpine Plants
Anz 2	Nursery for Trees and Shrubs
Austr.	Australia
Ba	Balkans
BM 1	Biological-morphological Section 1
BM 2	Biological-morphological Section 2
Bot. Museum	Botanical Museum
Ch	China
Dir	Administrative Offices
DW	German Forest
G	Restaurant
Gart. I	Garden Superintendent
H	Himalayas
J	Japan
K	Caucasus
Kap	Cape Province, South Africa
Kp	Carpathians
M	Moor
Mt	Mediterranean Regions
Mx	Mexico
N	Industrial Plants (including Medicinal Plants)
NA	North America
P	Shelter
Pyr	Pyrenees
Sb	Siberia and Reaches of the Amur River
Sch	Show House
Sd	Sudeten
Sk	Scandinavia
St	Central Russian Steppes
Syst. Abt.	Taxonomical Section
T	Toilet
Wa	Aquatic and Swamp Plants
Wi. H.	Home Farm

Arboretum

1 Taxus, Ginkgo
2 Abies, Tsuga, Pseudotsuga
3 Picea
4 Larix, Cedrus
5 Pinus
6 Juniperus, Chamaecyparis
7 Thuja
8 Juglans
9 Carya
10 Pterocarya
11 Salix
12 Populus
13 Betula
14 Alnus
15 Corylus
16 Carpinus, Ostrya
17 Fagus
18 Castanea
19 Quercus
20 Ulmus, Morus, etc.
21 Magnolia, Liriodendron, etc.
22 Berberis
23 Deutzia, Philadelphus
24 Hydrangea
25 Ribes
26 Hamamelis, Plantanus, etc.
27 Spiraea, Sorbaria, Exochorda, etc.
28 Sydonia, Cotoneaster
29 Pyrus
30 Malus
31 Sorbus
32 Amelanchier
33 Crataegus
34 Mespilus
35 Rubus
36 Rosa
37 Prunus
38 Gymnocladus
39 Gleditsia
40 Sophora, Cladrastis, Laburnum, etc.
41 Robinia
42 Phellodendron, Ailanthus, Rhus, etc.
43 Acer
44 Aesculus
45 Rhamnus, Vitis, etc.
46 Tilia
47 Elaeagnus, Acanthopanax, Cornus, etc.
48 Ericaceae (Rhododendron, Erica, etc.)
49 Fraxinus
50 Ligustrum, Syringa, Forsythia, etc.
51 Catalpa, Paulownia
52 Sambucus, Viburnum
53 Lonicera

Botanischer Garten of the Technical High School Brunswick, Humboldtstrasse 1 (1840), 3½ acres (GH 625 sq. yds.)

RVS: May to July. Open, outdoors Monday to Friday 8 a.m. to 5 p.m., Saturdays and Sundays 8 a.m. to noon. Greenhouses, Tuesdays to Thursdays 1.30—4.30 p.m., closed during winter. SF: Orchids, Succulents, taxonomical section, ecological groups, small alpinum.

Botanischer Garten and Rhododendron Park Bremen, Marcusallee 60 (Rhododendron Park 1936, Botanical Gardens 1950), 86½ acres (GH for cultivation only)

RVS: May. SF: Rhododendron and evergreen leaf trees.

Rosengarten Coburg (1929), 20 acres

RVS: May to October. SF: Rosarium, sunk and rock gardens, water lily basin. Exotic plants. Iris garden, tulips, dahlias.

Botanischer Garten of the Technical High School Darmstadt, Rossdörfer Strasse 140 (1814), 15 acres (GH 1,495 sq. yds.)

RVS: Spring to autumn; open weekdays 9 a.m. to 8 p.m., Sundays 9 a.m. to noon. SF: Very extensive tree and shrub collections, plant-geographical arboretum. Collection of succulents containing very rare specimens, such as Idris columnaris, Ficus palmeri, Calibanus caespitosus, etc.

Botanischer Garten of the City of Dortmund (Romberg Park), D.-Brünninghausen (1930), 131 acres (GH 1,316 sq. yds.)

RVS: May to June, September to October. SF: Alpinum, very comprehensive tree and shrub collection. 15,000 rhododendrons, orchids, in the tropical greenhouses aquariums, terrariums and aviaries.

Westfalenpark Dortmund, Am Kaiserhain 25 (1959), 148 acres

RVS: March to October. SF: Botanical collections: rosarium, tropical water lilies, Victoria regia, shrub garden, heath garden, Rhododendron, Sun flowers, Dahlias, models of small gardens, Japanese garden, tree nurseries.

Städtische Schulgärten Düsseldorf, Räuscherweg 40 (1913), 6 acres

RVS: May to October.

Botanischer Garten Duisburg, Schweizer Strasse (1890), 5 acres

RVS: May to June. SF: Taxonomical and biological sections.

Botanischer Garten Duisburg-Hamborn, Hamborner Strasse (1905), 5 acres (GH 849 sq. yds.)

RVS: May to June. SF: Hothouse plants, Orchids, Succulents.

Botanischer Garten of the University of Erlangen-Nürnberg in Erlangen, Schlossgarten 4 (1825), 5 acres (GH 1,706 sq. yds.)

RVS: May to July. Open: Gardens on weekdays 8 a.m. to 5 p.m., Sundays and Holidays 10 a.m. to noon; GH, Saturdays, Sundays and Holidays 10 a.m. to noon, Tuesdays, Thursdays and the first Sunday in every month 2—4 p.m. SF: Alpinum, jura and keuper (plant societies of native flora), Orchids, Succulents, tropical and sub-tropical plant collections.

Botanischer Garten of the City of Essen, Külshammerweg 10 (adjoining the Gruga) (Hortus Botanicus Assindiensis) (1927), 37 acres (GH 2,392 sq. yds.)

RVS: Flowering seasons of Rhododendron, Roses, bulbs and alpinum: March to May; orchids throughout the year. Park open all year, greenhouses in summer, 10 a.m. to 7 p.m., from 1965 throughout the year. SF: Alpinum, shrubs, Rhododendron, roses, Westphalian cottage garden, mediaeval herb garden, greenhouse collection and orchids, aquarium, terrarium.

Gruga, Essen (1929), 49 acres (from 1965 Federal Flower Show), 180 acres, excluding the botanical gardens.

RVS: April to October. SF: Rhododendron, 500,000 bulbs, 500,000 summer flowers, Dahlias. Models of house gardens, models of small gardens. Rhododendron blossom in June.

Botanischer Garten of the Johann Wolfgang Goethe University, Frankfurt/Main, Siesmayerstrasse 72 (1763), 20 acres (GH 1,076 sq. yds.)

RVS: April to July. Open weekdays 9 a.m. to 6 p.m., Sundays and Holidays 9 a.m. to 1 p.m. SF: Alpinum and regional collections outdoors (ecological formations).

Städtischer Palmgarten Frankfurt/Main, Siesmayerstrasse 61 (1869), 49 acres (GH see article below)

RVS: March to November; at certain times special shows. SF: Tropical plants under glass, especially collections of Orchids, Cacti, Succulents, Bromeliaceae, plants with variegated foliage, insectivores, cold greenhouse plants, alpines, Calluna and Erica, etc.

The Palm Garden in Frankfurt/Main

The name "Frankfurt Palm Garden" has become famous as denoting an outstanding collection of tropical and exotic plants, a well-kept park with beautiful specialised gardens, good music and many opportunities for recreation.

Like many other institutions in Frankfurt, the Palm Garden owes its existence to the Frankfurters' sense of citizenship. In 1969 it will celebrate the 100th anniversary of its inception. The particular occasion for its foundation occurred when the famous plant collections of the Duke of Nassau at Bieberich on the Rhine were dissolved. In 1868 the entire collection—22,000 plants—was sold for 60,000 guilders to the newlyfounded palm garden society and formed the basis of their present-day collections. In the course of long years of varied history, the Palm Garden developed into a unique show piece. The Garden has never clung unnecessarily to tradition, but always aimed at a modern appearance. The only tradition which runs like a thread through the whole period from its inception to the present day lies in the ambition always to show the new and the latest alongside the proven old.

A walk through the Palm House, the show houses and the park is like a journey round the world in miniature. Plants from every continent and of every clime are represented. The greenhouses alone display over 5,000 tropical species from all over the world and in addition there are thousands of other plants in the open.

The great Palm House, built in 1869 and one of the largest in Europe, represents a tropical scene with giant palm trees, tree ferns, bamboos, banana trees, eucalyptus trees and many other tropical plants. Walking round the Palm House, the visitor encounters several other landscapes in which old Camellias,

Bird of Paradise flowers, Agaves and evergreen shrubs of New Zealand and Chile are especially spectacular. Further along he passes through a sub-tropical garden with heated water basin, containing water lilies and lotus flowers, and finally comes to the show houses. In Houses 1 and 2 there are insect-trapping plants, antler ferns, telegraph plants and an abundance of the rarest tropical plants. House 3 is devoted entirely to the marvellous family of orchids. It contains some 1,500 different species and represents one of the most valuable European Orchid collections. At any time of the year a great many flowering species are to be found, among them wholly unique rarities. The aquatic house accommodates the world's biggest aquatic plant, Victoria amazonica, whose leaves are up to 6½ feet in diameter and can easily carry a child of ten. At the sides of this house there are lotus, papyrus, tropical industrial plants, such as sugar cane, rice, cotton, giant gourds, etc., as well as the interesting Mimosa pudica, whose feathery leaves fold up at the slightest touch. Rare plants from South Africa, Australia, New Zealand and the Mediterranean region are contained in the next house. They spend the summer out of doors and are then replaced by various flowering plants, mainly members of the gorse family. The Cactus house depicts a Mexican landscape. Great numbers of thorny dwarfs, hiding behind a cloak of large flowers from early to late summer, stand side by side with giant globe and hedge cacti. At this time it would really be true to say that the 'desert blossoms.' What a contrast to the tropical desert scenery in the opposite house, in which moist hot air meets us, suitable for plants from tropical rain forests, especially lianas with their long aerial roots. The next house contains a collection of Begonias, some 150 species, together with a great number of variegated tropical leaf plants and the climbing Allamanda with large yellow trumpet-shaped flowers throughout the summer.

Bromeliaceae occupy the other show house—more than 500 species, among them the rootless Tillandsia usneoides which droops like long white beards from the glass roof. Here, as in their American habitat, most Bromeliaceae grow on trees and pieces of wood. Pretty tropical fish are contained in aquaria and basins and many aquatic plants, among them the famous Aponogetum fenestralis. Flowering plants in season attract the eye in House 10 all through the year. At the back of this house there is a large collection of insectivores (Sundew, Venus Fly Trap, Sarracenia, Drosophyllum, etc.). In the next house we find variegated tropical plants, in House 12 an unsurpassed collection of rare Succulents from the desert regions of the earth, among them 'living stones,' and finally in the last house, changing every month—a rich selection of flowering plants.

But not only the Palm House and the show houses contain beautiful and interesting specimens, the park also has much to offer. Proceeding on our walk, we come to the new rose garden with its fountains, a large selection of magnificent garden roses and many summer flowers, and there are seats of every shape and form for rest and enjoyment. Past the tennis courts we reach the children's playground. In the adjoining nurseries, open to visitors like the entire Palm Garden, we find a large range of annuals, shrubs, ericas and a big selection of rare alpines from all parts of the world.

The plant and garden lover will also be interested in the work of the gardeners in the nurseries, for here he can watch how every plant shown in the Palm Garden, from cuttings to mature plants, thrives under the careful hands of the gardeners. Needless to say, they will be ready and willing to answer all his questions.

Continuing our promenade, we see to the right and left extensive verdant meadows with magnificent trees whose foliage reaches down to the ground. If we climb through the big alpine garden to the top of the 'mountain,' we see the great lake below, where old and young enjoy themselves in rowing boats. If you do not like long walks, you will find much to interest you in the front part of the Palm Garden. There are the huge flower parterres in front of the assembly rooms with their conservatories and terraces, the music garden with the band stand and a large dance floor. Anyone staying in Frankfurt for any length of time or resident there, will be able to enjoy many special shows, the highlights of which are provided by the flower shows in the exhibition hall. The spring flower show, the azalea show and particularly the cut roses show are unforgettable occasions. *Fritz Encke*

Hauptschulgarten of the City of Frankfurt/Main, Ostparkstrasse (1906—1908), 9 acres
RVS: Spring and summer. SF: Extensive tree and shrub collections in the plant-geographical park.

Botanischer Garten of the University of Freiburg i. Br., Schänzlestrasse 9—11 (first founded during the Thirty Years War, the present BG in 1912), about 10 acres (GH 1,435 sq. yds.)
RVS: Throughout the year. SF: Palm and fern cupola, succulent cupola, Victoria House, densely planted arboretum (geographical), Coniferetum. In summer, geological groups outside.

Institut für gärtnerischen Pflanzenbau der Hessischen Lehr- und Forschungsanstalt für Wein-, Obst- und Gartenbau (Rheingau) (1872), 205 acres (GH for ornamental plants 1,794 sq. yds., a further

1,794 sq. yds. under construction); horticultural cultivations, no botanical collections. Park of 2½ acres as arboretum

Accessible from Wiesbaden down the Rhine by train or bus (Federal Highway No. 42) to two miles east of Rüdesheim on the right bank of the river; from the left bank, by ferry from Bingen to Rüdesheim, thence by train, bus or on foot.

Botanischer Garten of the Justus Liebig University, Giessen/Lahn (1609), 11 acres (GH 1,794 sq. yds.)

Open from 1st April to 30th September, Mondays to Fridays from 8 a.m. to noon and 2—5 p.m.; Saturdays, Sundays and Holidays 8 a.m. to noon. SF: Rare old trees: Nothofagus, Ginkgo, etc.

Botanischer Garten of the University of Göttingen, Untere Karspüle 1 (1736), 12 acres (GH 2,990 sq. yds.)

RVS: April to September. Open weekdays all day, GH 9 a.m. to noon and 2—4 p.m. Sundays and Holidays forenoon only. SF: Extensive alpinum, geographically arranged, historical collections, open-air ferns, African plants, Cacti, Orchids, Carnivores, etc.

Forstbotanischer Garten of the University of Göttingen in Hannoversch-Münden, Mitscherlichstrasse No. 5 (1871), 10 acres

RVS: Spring to autumn. SF: Dendrology.

Stadtpark der Freien und Hansestadt Hamburg, Kümmellstrasse 8, Horticultural Section (1912), 445 acres.

RVS: Late May to early October. SF: Rhododendrons, roses, summer flowers.

'Planten un Blomen'—Ausstellungspark der Freien und Hansestadt Hamburg, Am Dammtor (1935), 74 acres (GH 897 sq. yds.)

RVS: April to late October. SF: Tulips (about 250 varieties and novelties), summer flowers (particularly well stocked), bedding plants with all new varieties grown by G. Arends and K. Foerster, comparative shrub show with all novelties and plants not yet commercially available—shrub selection garden. Barbata Iris collection with about 1,000 varieties annually supplemented, Iris kaempferi collection annually supplemented; lily and Hemerocallis species and varieties. Rhododendron catawbiense location assortment, amateur assortment, Seidel's assortment. Rhododendron, botanical species and fortunei (R. repens) range. Roses with about 400 varieties in all categories and with all novelties and accompanying shrubs, trees and bulbs (show section), four rock gardens (specimen gardens with slate, limestone, Weser sandstone and scree).

Botanischer Garten Hamburg, Bei den Kirchhöfen No. 18 (Staatsinstitut für Allgemeine Botanik und Botanischer Garten, Hamburg 36, Jungiusstrasse 6) (1821), 24 acres (GH 5,143 sq. yds.)

RVS: April to October, show houses in winter also. SF: The 'system' as phylogenetic schema of relationships (evolutionary history of the plant world). Alpinum. Show houses with tropical house, subtropical house, palm fern and fern house, Succulents, Orchids, etc. Modern show house with interesting technical equipment.

Botanischer Sondergarten der Freien und Hansestadt Hamburg, Bezirksamt Wandsbek, Walddörferstrasse 273 (1927), 10 acres (GH 181 sq. yds.)

RVS: May to October. SF: 11,000 alpine shrubs (1,400 species), 22,000 ornamental shrubs (900 species), 7,000 botanical shrubs (500 species). 6,000 roses (210 species), 4,000 trees (500 species).
The 'Special Botanical Garden,' part of a public park covering an area of about 988 acres, was created in response to a desire that citizens and schoolchildren should be brought into closer contact with nature. It may well be said that the garden has something to offer to every lover of plants and gardens. It is divided into the following sections: shrubs, roses, summer flowers, plants demanding shade and ornamental shrubs. In addition there are pools, constructed and natural, with riparian and aquatic plants. Before the Second World War the accent was more on the botanical elements and at that time an extensive exchange of seeds took place with other well known botanical gardens.

Berggarten zu Hannover-Herrenhausen, Herrenhäuser Strasse 4 (1666), 31 acres (GH 4,355 sq. yds., of which 1,315 sq. yds. are taken up by modern show houses)

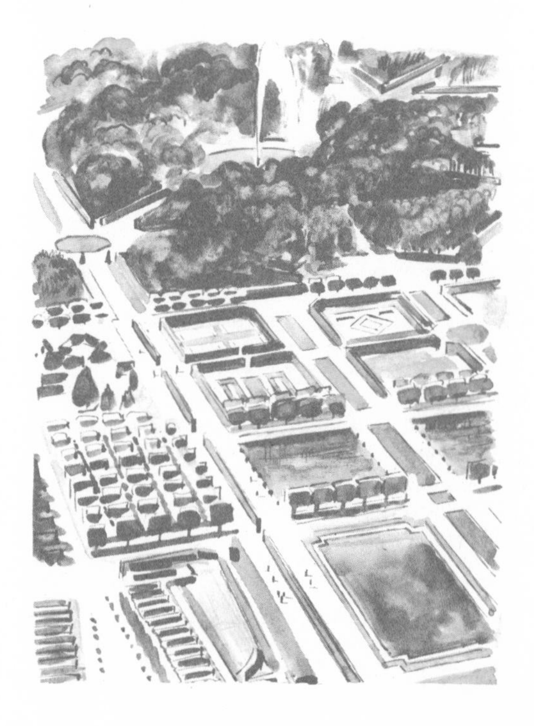

RVS: All the year. SF: Moor and moor bed plants, Orchids. The Great Garden of Herrenhausen was founded in 1666. It is a baroque garden of the first water.

Städtischer Botanischer Schulgarten Burg, Hannover-Herrenhausen, Brockenweg 5 A (1926), 19 acres (GH about 179 sq. yds.)

RVS: Spring to autumn. Open Mondays to Fridays, 7.30 a.m. to 4 p.m., Saturdays forenoon. SF: The lay-out is intended to serve educational purposes. Systematic section (1¼ acres), plant-sociological section with about 50 societies and many small sections devoted to flower ecology, genetics, apiculture, etc.

Botanischer Garten of the University of Heidelberg, Hofmeisterstrasse 4 (1593), 10 acres (GH about 3,598 sq. yds.)

RVS: May to September, Sundays and Holidays 9 a.m. to 1 p.m., otherwise closed to the public. SF: Succulents, Cacti, Orchids, Bromelias, Madagascar collection.

Botanischer Garten of the Technical High School Karlsruhe, Am Fasanengarten (1883, reconstruction and removal 1956), 5 acres (GH 1,434 sq. yds.)

RVS: May to June, November to January. Open Wednesdays and Saturdays, 1—6 p.m. SF: Orchids, Succulents, native lime-steppe flora. Tropical industrial plants.

Botanischer Garten of the City of Kassel, Bosestrasse 15 (1912), 11 acres (GH 1,435 sq. yds.)

RVS: May to August. SF: Alpinum, open-air ferns, Cyperaceae, especially genus Carex (over 300 different species).
An avenue connects Kassel with the important Hessian State Park 'Schlosspark Wilhelmshöhe' which merits attention on account of its 400 different species of trees.

Botanischer Garten of the Christian Albrechts University Kiel, Düsternbrookerweg 17 (entrance also Schwanenweg 13) (1635), 7½ acres (GH 1,555 sq. yds.)

RVS: April to October. Open Mondays to Fridays 9 a.m. to 5 p.m., Saturdays 9 a.m. to noon, Sundays and Holidays 9 a.m. to 1 p.m. Greenhouses, Tuesdays and Fridays 1—5 p.m.; by arrangement groups may be conducted at other times. SF: Famous collection of African Succulents, 500-year old Cissus species from South-West Africa. Comprehensive collection of Mesembryanthemaceae. Total number of succulent species about 2,000.

Gartenbauabteilung Dr. Madaus & Co., Köln-Merheim, Werksgärtnerei, 124 acres (GH 2,069 sq. yds.)

Visits by permission of the director. SF: Medicinal plants.

Botanischer Garten of the City of Cologne, Köln-Riehl, Amsterdamer Strasse 36 (1864), 25 acres (GH: show houses 3,588 sq. yds., cultivation houses 1,076 sq. yds.)

RVS: April to May, July to August. Open November to February 8 a.m. to 5 p.m., April to September 7 a.m. to 11 p.m., October and March 8 a.m. to 7 p.m.; show houses 10 a.m. to 4 p.m. SF: Alpinum, geographically arranged; lilies, irises, orchids, Succulents, tropical industrial plants; subtropical plant collection.

Botanischer Garten of the City of Krefeld, Im Schönwasserpark (1928), 12 acres, 6 acres of which were laid out in 1961 according to modern principles (GH are projected)

RVS: April to June. Open in summer 7 a.m. to 8 p.m., in winter 8 a.m. to 5 p.m. SF: Alpinum according to general considerations, arboretum systematically arranged, collection of conifers, plant taxonomy (herbaceous plants), collection of aquatic plants, rosarium, summer flower garden, cottage garden of the Lower Rhine.

Botanische Abteilung des Gartenamtes Landau in der Pfalz, Annweilerstrasse 8, about 100 acres (GH for cultivation and selection purposes, about 957 sq. yds.)

RVS: Late April, 100,000 tulips; in summer hundreds of thousands of bedding and grouping plants; from mid-August dahlia garden. SF: Seasonal flower shows in a glasshouse.

Park Lehmkuhlen near Preetz, Holstein, private grounds (1820), 123 acres, arboretum with about 1,000 tree species

RVS: June to July, September, October. The park is open to groups and societies only who will be conducted by Dr F. Glasau, Land Farmers Union, Kiel, or by Dr Jacobsen, Kiel, Martensdamm 27.

Schlossgarten Ludwigsburg—Flowering Baroque—Flower Show Ludwigsburg (1714), 74 acres

RVS: April to October. SF: Tulips (500,000 bulbs), rhododendron, rosarium, shrub collection, historic gardens, large pictorial designs with flowers and gravel.

National Park Lüneburger Heide (1909), 49,422 acres, 11,120 acres of which are the property of the Verein Naturschutzparke, Stuttgart

RVS: May to June, August, September. SF: Heather.
The use of motor vehicles of every description is strictly prohibited. There is sufficient parking space at Undeloh, Döhle and Niederhaverbeck. Access by train: Stations Hützel, Bispingen, Döhle of the East Hanover Railways on the line Lüneburg—Soltau. In addition several buses daily from Hamburg (ZOB) to Niederhaverbeck, and from Lüneburg to Undeloh at the border of the National Park. The centre of the park is marked by the village of Wilsede. Specially recommended: the Wilseder Berg (551 ft.), Totengrund, Steingrund, etc. Interesting and beautiful juniper landscapes. Wilseder Berg and Wilsede can be reached in an hour's walk from the places mentioned above.

Werner Harro König

Rhododendron-Waldpark Linswege via Westerstede/O. (1928), 160 acres

RVS: May to July. SF: Rhododendron, species and hybrids.

Schlosspark Insel Mainau/Lake Constance (1827), 74 acres (GH 4,186 sq.yds. for cultivation purposes only)

RVS: April to May: Tulips, Narcissi; mid-June to autumn, roses; September to October, Dahlias. Open from early April to late October. SF: Century-old arboretum, exotic plants, such as palms, banana trees, orange and lemon trees, fig trees, eucalyptus, etc. Access from the mainland via Konstanz and by boat from all lake-side resorts.

My Island Paradise

It was a hot day in the summer of 1916. My grandmother and my great-grandmother were standing close together on the sunlit terrace in front the Mainau Palace hiding something behind their backs. They looked down at me with laughing eyes and said they had a surprise for me. With a beating heart I tried to make out what it was and my curiosity was so intense that I felt quite dizzy. My joy knew no bounds when I was given a large, black box camera.

I remember that incident very clearly, for it was an event of decisive importance for my future life. To make the occasion even more solemn and exciting, the marble busts of Roman Caesars dotted about in the park looked at the scene like augurs, and the whole court, dressed as always in black, watched respectfully in the background. Who could have imagined that I would later become such an enthusiastic photographer as to be given the editorship of the leading Scandinavian photographic periodical on the strength of his amateur work, and would also be a film producer? Perhaps if they had had any suspicion they would have given me something else. But at that time neither I nor anyone else knew that the little boy in the white sailor suit, 15 years later and under very different circumstances, would make his home here on the Mainau.

In 1853 the Grand Duke Friedrich I of Baden, my great-grandfather, bought the Island of Mainau, where the Knights of the Teutonic Order had reigned for 500 years since 1272; and moved into the palace, built from 1739—1746 by the architect of the Order, Bagnato, in the baroque style. The magnificent situation in Lake Constance and the exceptionally mild climate must have suited the enthusiastic dendrologist very well. His joy in the property immediately found expression in an untiring desire to create. Thus an enchanting park was laid out and for countless summers, the Grand Duke and his wife returned to the island year after year. Their son, Grand Duke Friedrich II, left the Mainau to his sister Victoria, wife of King Gustav V of Sweden, on condition that it should be left to my father and his offspring. Queen Victoria of Sweden died in 1930 and I, her grandson, moved in with my bride.

The move to the south was accompanied by much heart-searching and caused many a sleepless night, for the famous and dendrologically valuable island park had turned into an impenetrable jungle, because since the death of Friedrich I in 1907 palace and gardens had been left untouched in accordance with the desire of the Grand Duchess. That meant that not a single tree had been felled.

I was much disturbed to find 25 years later that only the merest glimpse of Lake Constance could be had from the palace, except from two windows on the second floor. From the park, the rose garden, the palm grove and the Musa garden its blue surface was invisible and one hardly felt oneself to be on an island at all.

The park was urgently in need of re-arrangement. Our dear old park inspector Nohl co-operated magnificently. As a first step the palace court, divided up as it was by many flower beds and passages, was modernised. Large lawns were laid out to provide a calm and dignified frame for the splendid palace. The first trees were cut down on the east side towards the lake, to restore the building to its prominent position and make it visible again, but that operation had to be carried out while the inspector was away on holiday! On his return he was surprised at the magnificent view of the palace, which he thoroughly approved. But when he saw the fallen trees his conscience was troubled at the memory of the orders given by the late Grand Duchess. Nevertheless, he was content with what had been done, and I shall never forget his generous agreement.

No, it was not easy to make renovations. The common deciduous trees had almost managed to choke the beautiful foreign conifers which were fighting for their lives to get some light and air. Many mistakes had been made and they were obvious enough: the park had never been thinned out and cleaned up. The Grand Duchess Luise never realised that nature would not obey her command and that in the course of years the park was bound to change its appearance, though hardly to its advantage.

In these circumstances we had to tread warily and proceed carefully. It was impossible just to fell trees right and left, for many a splendid tree was already beginning to die off because its less interesting neigh-

bours were spreading themselves at its expense. Indiscriminate felling would have produced unsightly gaps. Thus we were forced in some cases to leave less valuable deciduous trees untouched and in close proximity to the conifers to prevent greater damage.
Sometimes we saved a single tree for years before we made up our minds finally to cut it down and it was never certain in advance whether the landscape gardener or the dendrologist would carry off the victory. There had to be a great deal of give and take on both sides.
Of course, the old folk round about took a keen interest in what was going on on the Island. At first they resented the new order and grumbled about 'vandalism.' Perhaps they thought the island would be restored to the condition in which it was at the time of the Swedish conquest in February 1647. In any event, they felt that the good old romantic island had been much, much prettier.
Whenever the talk turned to the Mainau someone was sure to say 'If the old Grand Duke knew...' I admit readily that during the interim period the scenery was not always perfect and unsightly gaps could not be avoided, although nature, with a climate as conducive to growth as it is in this part of the world, was always quick to close them. At any rate, my actions were guided always by the consideration that an island is surrounded by water and that water and wide vistas, therefore, are an integral part of its scenery.
Thus the new Mainau took shape during years of painstaking work. It acquired many new colourful clothes woven of tulips, iris and dahlias, in addition to its more sombre ones of cedars and sequoias and its lovely roses and abundant summer flowers.
From my earliest childhood we have been good friends, the Mainau and I, and any operations I undertook for the sake of perfecting and deepening its beauty, it has tolerated with true feminine patience and a girlish desire for charm. In the early summer mornings, when the sun rises above the hazy eastern shore of the lake, we commune secretly and undisturbed where land and water meet.
At these moments gentle and intimate pictures of its rich and varied history pass before my inner eye: The primeval stone age inhabitants of the lake shores paddle their dug-outs across the lake: Roman slaves build boats for the circumnavigators: the knights of the Teutonic Order come riding home from the crusades to the sound of hymns: and over there off Meersburg the Swedish fleet assembles to sail for the Mainau. Hammering sounds from the hill where the palace is being built. There comes the old Hungarian master-general of the ordnance, Count Esterházy. Look at the figure with the long, white beard, which appears among the tall trees by the shore! It is my great-grandfather and I am sure he wants someone to row him round the island to inspect the new work from the waterside. Behind him walk the two beloved women of my childhood, my great-grandmother and my grandmother...
But now someone really is coming down the path towards me. I am so deeply immersed in dreams of the past that I am almost frightened. No, it is no apparition or ghost, it is my wife, my dear companion, who has found the early summer morning too lovely for continued sleep.
Together we silently look across the deep blue lake before we return hand in hand through dew-fresh flowers to the house to begin our work.

Count Lennart Bernadotte

Botanischer Garten of the Johann Gutenberg University of Mainz, Saarstrasse 21 (1946), 20 acres (GH 1,794 sq. yds)

RVS: April to June. SF: Alpinum, arboretum, taxonomical section, rich orchid and succulents collection.

The Mainz Sands

West of Mainz, now immediately adjoining the city, there is a scenic feature of peculiar charm, the 'Mainz Sands.' It is an area of undulating dunes made up of chalky diluvial drift sand, which may be regarded as the northernmost part of the sandy stretches extending over the high terraces on both sides of the river in the plains of the Upper Rhine. Today these areas are largely covered by pine forests, with here and there a few pockets of woodless country. The largest of these open stretches is the Mainz Sands. Its many rare plants and animals have made it famous far beyond the German borders.
The area is one of the driest in Germany. The annual rainfall amounts to 20 inches but in particularly dry years may be as low as 16 inches. In addition, it is blessed with very favourable climatic conditions. Hot summers alternate with relatively mild winters. The mean temperature lies between 49° and 50° F. and thus resembles that of the South Russian steppes. Therefore, it is not surprising that the vegetation is not unlike that of the Eastern European steppes and actually comprises a number of species also to be

found in those regions. The steppe-like character of the Mainz Sands was described by Wilhelm Jännicke (1892), one of the first explorers of the region, who wrote, 'The barrenness of the ground in many places, the prevalence of few species for long stretches, the grey-green colour of many plants, the network of some Cladonia species are just as characteristic of the grass-steppes of Southern Russia as of the sand fields of the northern Rhine valley. A colourful plant carpet, typical also of the Russian herbaceous steppes, may be found in the Mainz Sands on clearings and along the edges of the forests, and in both cases we find identical species.' We may assume that these plants on the Mainz Sands represent pockets of a vegetation, the main distribution of which now lies further east. They are relics of a warm period after the ice ages.

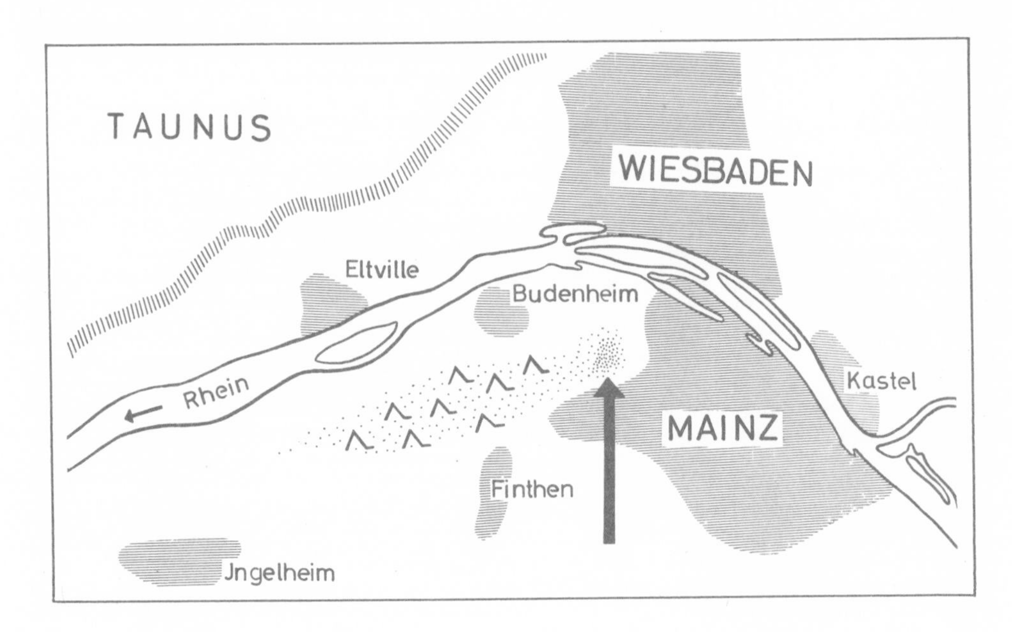

The vegetation offers very different aspects according to the season. In spring, for instance, there are large brilliant hummocks of yellow-flowering Potentilla arenaria. Anemone pulsatilla is very prevalent and Adonis vernalis still flowers in many places. Closer to the forest, Anemone sylvestris and Geranium sanguineum are to be seen. A rarity is Scorzonera purpurea, which also represents a typical element of steppe vegetation. In early summer other plants appear, in particular some characteristic grasses, such as the blue-green Koehleria glauca, which, as yet in single tufts on the otherwise open sand, marks the outskirts of a whole plant society. It is often interspersed with tall Euphorbia gerardiana. There are also Phleum boehmeri and arenarium and especially Stipa capillata and pennata, both of which are very rare elsewhere. Of umbeliferous plants, Peucedanum oreoselinum, Trinia glauca and Eryngium campestre should be mentioned, and, among the compositae, the rare Jurinea cyanoides. Gypsophila fastigiata, Anthericum liliago, A. ramosum, and Euphrasia lutea are now in flower. Onosma arenarium is to be found nowhere else in Germany and occurs otherwise only in the Rhone valley and in Moravia. Many other rare plants could be mentioned if there was room in this short description. It may be added, however, that Jännicke already listed 80 species, of which he classified 23 as of Southern European, 34 as of South-East European and 4 as of South-West European origin. The fauna also abounds in rare species. The special importance of the Mainz Sands in regard to its scenery and its unique and rich animal and plant life was recognised very early on and the area was declared a national park more than 100 years ago; a part of it was set aside in 1939 as a specially protected area in order to preserve its natural beauty. Its existence has nevertheless been very precarious and, in a constantly shrinking world, is still gravely endangered. Let us hope that this area, which is unique in Central Europe, will be preserved in spite of its situation in the midst of steadily growing development. Its destruction would be an irretrievable loss.

Professor Hans Weber

Botanischer Garten of the Philipps University, Marburg/Lahn, Pilgrimstein 4 (1810), 11 acres (GH 1,794 sq. yds.)

RVS: May to July.

Botanischer Garten München-Nymphenburg, Menzingerstrasse 65 (1914), 45 acres (GH 9,570 sq. yds.)

RVS: April to October. SF: Greenhouses: Orchids, succulents, bromelias, ferns, insectivores, Victoria regia; outdoors: Rhododendron grove, fern glen, heath and moor, ornamental court with flowering plants. The Botanical Alpine Garden on the Schachen Mountain is the property of the Botanical Garden München-Nymphenburg.

See also the article by Wilhelm Schacht 'Work and Pleasure in a Botanical Garden.'

Botanischer Garten of the University of Münster, Schlossgarten 3 (1804), 11 acres (GH 1,914 sq. yds.)

RVS: Spring. SF: Bromeliaceae (Tillandsias), ferns, cacti and other succulents.

Alpenpflanzengarten Neureuth near Tegernsee (Upper Bavaria) (1900), 4,145 ft. above sea level, 143 sq. yds.

SF: Native alpine flora and some examples of the flora of the West and South Alps—protected plants. Accessible in 1³/₄ hours' walk on good roads from Tegernsee.

Staatl. Botanischer Garten Oldenburg, Philosophenweg (1882), 9 acres

RVS: May to September; open Mondays to Fridays 8 a.m. to 6 p.m., Saturdays 8 a.m. to 1 p.m. and 3 p.m. to 6 p.m., Sundays 10 a.m. to 1 p.m., 3—6 p.m. SF: Complete collection of the wild plants of North-West Germany. Comprehensive tree and shrub collection, in particular evergreens, rhododendrons, medicinal plants, educational garden.

Botanischer Schulgarten Osnabrück, 2¹/₂ acres

SF: Native flora, medicinal and kitchen herbs. Azaleas, rhododendrons, evergreen trees.

Pforzheimer Alpengarten, Würm near Pforzheim, Northern Black Forest (1928), 2¹/₂ acres

RVS: April to June. Open from 1st April to 31st October. SF: Alpinum, alpine plants, rock garden shrubs, rhododendrons.

Botanischer Garten of the University of the Saarland, Saarbrücken, St. Johanner Stadtwald, 6 acres (in process of construction)

Deutsch-Französischer Garten, Saarbrücken 1, North Entrance, Im Deutschmühlental: South Entrance, Metzer Strasse (1960), 123 acres

RVS: Easter to September. SF: The park occupies the site of former fortifications of the Second World War. Remains of the blown-up fortifications are still visible. Roses grow among tank traps. The individual gardens have been laid out with particular care and skill. The park lies south of Saarbrücken in the wooded valley of a contributary to the River Saar. Valley of Flowers: flowering shrubs, evergreen plants; Grassland: a wide range of grasses and matching bulbs, shrubs and trees; Shady Grove: evergreens, shade-loving shrubs and perennials; Sunny Heath: heather exposed to the sun; Rose Garden: roses of German and French origin.

Botanischer Alpengarten on the Schachen (between Garmisch and Mittenwald) (1900), about 2¹/₂ acres

RVS: July to mid-August. Open 1st July to 15th September. SF: The gardens are arranged in plant-geographical order and in addition to an alpine flora section, contain separate beds and groups of alpine plants from all over the world and from the Arctic. The flora of the Himalayas is particularly well represented. The garden is the property of the Botanical Gardens of München-Nymphenburg. It is situated in the Wetterstein Range (6,151 ft. above sea level) near Garmisch-Partenkirchen and can be reached from the Partnach Gorge in 4—5 hours' walk via Schloss Elmau near Klais (between Garmisch and Mittenwald).

Botanischer Garten der Landwirtschaftlichen Hochschule Stuttgart-Hohenheim (1829), 11 acres (in process of being extended by a further 15 acres) (GH 718 sq. yds.)

RVS: May to October. SF: Dendrological section.

Botanischer Garten der Technischen Hochschule Stuttgart-Cannstatt, Neckartalstrasse (1923), 3 acres (GH 538 sq. yds.)

RVS: May. Open Mondays to Fridays from 7 a.m. to 5 p.m. SF: Alpinum.

Botanischer Garten Wilhelma, Stuttgart-Bad Cannstatt (1837), 30 acres (in process of being extended to 62 acres) (GH 7,180 sq. yds.)

RVS: All the year. The 'Wilhelma' is a biological garden. It combines a fairly large zoological garden with an important show garden and the largest stock of hundred-year old deciduous magnolias and a hundred-year old collection of azaleas and camellias, about 10,000 orchids and a heated water lily basin (1,196 sq. yds.) containing dozens of Victoria regia, Euryala and more than 100 tropical Nympheae, which are in flower throughout the summer. In addition there is an important collection of succulents.

Botanischer Garten of the University of Tübingen, Rümelinstrasse 32 (1805), 10 acres (GH 1,794 sq. yds.)

RVS: Outdoors, Spring to autumn; greenhouses, throughout the year. On Saturdays open till noon. Closed on Sundays and Holidays. SF: Orchids, especially Paphiopedilum, cacti, succulents, insectivores.

Norddeutsches Rosarium, Uetersen (1930—1934), 11 acres

RVS: Mid-June to late September. SF: Exhibition of trade and commercial assortment of Germany in about 700 varieties of roses of 24 species or classes, supplemented by international rose novelties suitable for the German climate.

Alpenpflanzengarten Wank near Garmisch-Partenkirchen/Upper Bavaria (1961, still under construction), 5,840 ft. above sea level, 100 sq. yds.

SF: Native alpine flora, several protected plants and some specimens from the South and West Alps. The garden adjoins the Wank Hut, Mountain Station 'Wank.'

Botanischer Garten of the University of Würzburg, Mittlerer Dallenbergweg 64 (old gardens: 1787, soon to be closed down; new gardens: 1959), about 15 acres (old GH about 2,154 sq. yds., new GH under construction). New gardens not yet open to the public.

SF: Collection of orchids by Professor Burgeff. New gardens: South-East European and Asian collection in the open.

Gartenanlagen of Veitshöchheim near Würzburg (1770)

SF: Baroque and rococo garden.

Botanischer Garten of the City of Wuppertal-Elberfeld, Elisenhöhe 5 (1910), 37 acres (3 GH, 718 sq. yds.)

Greece

Botanical Gardens of the University of Athens, 56 Odos Spiros Patsis (1835), 3 1/2 acres

Hungary

Region of Bátórliget

SF: Relic plants of the glacial eras: Trollius comarum, Angelica palustris, Ligularia sibirica.

Botanical Gardens of the Eőtvős-Lorand Training College, Illésutca 25, Budapest VIII.

Botanical Garden Debreczento of the Kossuth-Lajos University

Pécs and District

SF: Plants of the Mediterranean regions. Paeonia officinalis var. Banatica, Doronicum orientale, Colchicum hungaricum.

Botanical Gardens of the Pedagogic High School, Ifjuság, utca 6, Pécs

Hortus Botanicus Universitatis Soproniensis, Sopron (BG)

Hortus Botanicus Universitatis Tancis M., utca 2, Szeged (BG)

National Agraro-Botanical Institute, Tapioszele, 35 1/2 acres

SF: Cereals and other industrial plants.

Botanical Gardens and Geo-botanical Laboratory of the Hungarian Academy of Science, Vácrátót, 98 acres (GH 1,196 sq. yds.)

RVS: February, May, end-June, September, October. SF: Dendrological and systematical collections, Bromelias, trees and shrubs, perennial plants.

Hungarian Academy of Science, Botanical Research Institute, Vácrátót

Vértes Mountains

SF: Karst plants, especially Cotinus.

Iceland

Lystigardur Akureyrar, Public Park and Botanical Garden, Akureyri, 7 1/2 acres

Open May to October from 10 a.m. to noon. SF: Icelandic flora.

Ireland

Annesgrove Castletownroche, Co. Cork (1907), 7 acres (GH 2,631 sq. yds)

RVS: May, June, August. SF: Rhododendron, shrubs and summer flowers.

Botanic Gardens, Botany Department, University College Cork, 2 acres (3 GH)

Closed on Sundays and Holidays.

Trinity College Botanic Gardens, Shellbourne Road, Dublin, 2 1/2 acres (3 GH)

Visits by permission of the director. SF: Different species of Saxifraga.

National Botanic Gardens, Glasnevin, Dublin 9 (1790), 46 acres (GH 3 1/2 acres)

RVS: May to October. Open weekdays from March to end of October 9 a.m. to 6 p.m., November to February 10 a.m. to 4.30 p.m.; Sundays 11 a.m. to 4.30 p.m. in winter and 11 a.m. to 6 p.m. in summer. SF: Alpinum, orchids, conifers.

Garnish Island, 'The Italian Gardens,' Glengarriff, Co. Cork

SF: The whole island has been turned into a gem of a garden. Comprehensive collection of trees and shrubs.

Johnston Castle Gardens, Wexford, Co. Wexford

Open weekdays from 10 a.m. to 6 p.m. SF: Collections of rare trees and shrubs. Four miles from Wexford.

Mount Usher Gardens, Ashford, Co. Wicklow

Open Mondays to Fridays 9 a.m. to 6 p.m. SF: Botanical collections, interesting and rare trees and shrubs.

Muckross House Gardens, Killarney, Co. Kerry

SF: Sub-tropical gardens, woods.

Rowallane Saintfield, Co. Down, Northern Ireland, 210 1/2 acres

RVS: April to June, daily from 2—6 p.m.; July to October, Wednesdays, Saturdays, Sundays and Bank Holiday Mondays 2—6 p.m. SF: Rare trees and shrubs, especially rhododendron, bulbs, native wild flora.

Japanese Gardens, Tully, Co. Kildare (1910), 1 acre

RVS: May, September. Open from 1st April to 31st October 2 p.m. to 6 p.m. Visits in the forenoon by special arrangement.

Italy

Orto Botanico dell'Università, Bari, Via Amendola 173

Orto Botanico 'Antonio Bertoloni,' Bologna, Via Irnerio 42 (1568), about 5 acres (GH 358 sq. yds.)

Visits by permission of the director. SF: Succulents.

Giardino Alpino alle Viotte di Monte Bondone, c/o Museo Civico di Storia Naturale, Via Verdi, Trento, Casella Postale 95 (Trient) (1938)

RVS: April—September. SF: Alpine flora.

Orto Botanico dell'Università degli Studi, Cagliari, Viale Fra Ignazio da Laconi 13, Sardinia (1864), 11 acres (GH 119 sq. yds.)

RVS: April to June. Closed on Sundays and Holidays. SF: Succulents.

Orto Botanico dell'Università Camerino (1828), 1 1/4 acres (GH 96 sq. yds.)

RVS: June to September. SF: Ornamental plants.

Giardino all'Inglese, Caserta (1782), 81 acres (GH 861 sq. yds.)

RVS: April to September.

Orto Botanico dell'Università, Catania, Via Antonino Longo 19 (1858), 3 3/4 acres (2 GH)

RVS: April to June. Visits by permission of the director. SF: Sicilian flora.

Orto Botanico dell'Università, Ferrara, Via Scienze 17 (1771), 3/4 acres (GH 101 sq. yds.)

RVS: June and July.

Giardino dell'Iris, Florence, Piazzale Michelangelo (1955), 6 acres

RVS: 5th—20th May. Open from end of April to end of May. SF: The garden contains the most important and recent iris cultivars and shrubs from all over the world, with more than 1,000 varieties.

Orto Botanico dell'Università, Florence, Via Lamarmora 4 (1545), about 7 acres (GH 2,033 sq. yds.)

RVS: June to September. Open Thursdays 9 a.m. to noon and 3—5.30 p.m. SF: Collection of Cycadeae, palms, citrus trees (especially wild varieties), agaves and trees of the Mediterranean flora in old specimens.

Giardini di Marignolle, Florence, Via di Marignolle 65 (1950), about 10 acres (GH 837 sq. yds.). Owner: Marchese Pierro Grossi

RVS: May, June, September. Open 9 a.m. to noon and 2—6 p.m. SF: Aquatic plants, iris, orchids, Anthurium.

Giardino Dr. Hruska, Gardone, Lago di Garda (Lake Garda) (1907), 2½ acres (GH 144 sq. yds.), designed by Dr Hruska

SF: The alpinum is arranged in geological order. There are representatives of plants from all parts of the world. Over 2,000 plants of different ecological, sociological, plant-geographical and taxonomical position stand side by side. Dr Hruska himself says, 'I do not aim at possessing every plant there is. My main consideration is beauty. My garden is not really a botanical garden, just a beautiful piece of nature.'
Access: By train from Milano to Desenzano, thence by steamer along the southern shore of Lake Garda, a trip of 1½ hours; from the end of March onwards there is also an aquafoil (alisfaco) which covers the distance in half the time, or take a bus. Motorists on the 'autostrada' to Verona have to turn off. Visitors to the eastern shore of Lake Garda are recommended to park their cars and proceed by steamer or aquafoil.

Orto Botanico 'Hanbury' dell'Università Genova (Genoa), Corso Dogali 1c (1803), 2½ acres (GH 1,190 sq. yds.)

RVS: Spring. Open from 8.30 a.m. to noon and from 2.30—6 p.m. SF: Ferns and Cycadeae.

Giardino 'Isola Bella'—Lago Maggiore (Novara, administration Borromeo, Milano, Via Borromei 1 a) (1600), 7¼ acres (GH 239 sq. yds.)

RVS: April, September. Open from 9 a.m. to noon and 1.30 to 5 p.m. Closed from October to March. SF: Plants of tropical and Mediterranean regions, especially rhododendron. Accessible by steamer via Stresa—Baveno—Pallanza.

Giardino 'Isola Madre'—Lago Maggiore (Novara) (1500), 12½ acres

RVS: April to September; closed from October to March. SF: Sub-tropical plants. Magnificent rare trees, bamboo, rhododendron. Accessible by steamer via Stresa—Baveno—Pallanza.

'Alpinia,' Comune di Stresa, Lago Maggiore, Centro degli Studi, Torino (1934), 2¾ acres

RVS: May to September. SF: 2,000 herbaceous and woody species. Accessible from Stresa (motorway).

Villa Lante di Bagnaia, Lazio

SF: Artistically laid out park and gardens.

Orto Botanico di Messina, Via Pietro Castelli 2 (old botanical gardens, 1638; new gardens, 1881), 2½ acres

Orto Botanico dell'Università, Modena, Viale Cadutti in guerra 127 (1772), 3¾ acres

Visits by arrangement with the director.

Orto Botanico 'Hanbury,' La Mortola/Ventimiglia (founded 1867 by Sir Thomas Hanbury). Total area 45 acres, gardens 17½ acres (GH 122 sq. yds.)

'Villa Hanbury' is the largest acclimatisation park for exotic plants in Italy and one of the best known in the world. Sir Thomas Hanbury, after his return from China, founded an exotic garden in this climatically favoured area. In addition to typical plants of the Mediterranean regions, there are tropical species from different parts of the world, stone-pines, plants of the Ligurian coast, olive trees and citrus trees. Accessible by bus or car from Ventimiglia (towards Monaco).

Orto Botanico dell'Università, Via Foria 223, Naples, Campania

Orto Botanico di Portici-Napoli (Naples) (1872), 5 acres (GH 205 sq. yds.)

Visits by permission of the director only.

Orto Botanico dell'Università, Padua, Via Orto Botanico 15 (1545), 5 acres (GH 718 sq. yds.)

RVS: April to September; open daily from 9 a.m. to noon and from 2—6 p.m.; closed on Sundays and Holidays. SF: Iris, Alleum, aster, etc. This is the oldest of all botanical gardens to retain its original location and shape from its inception to this day and to serve science and education without interruption. In 1786 Johann Wolfgang Goethe visited the garden and described it in glowing terms. Two trees planted by the founders are still extant: the 'Goethe Palm' (Chamaerops humilis) and Vitex agnus castus. Other very old trees are Plantanus orientalis (1680) and Ginkgo biloba (1750). At present there are 6,000 species in the garden, a third of them under glass.

Orto Botanico dell'Università, Palermo, Via Lincoln (1795), 25 acres (GH 2,990 sq. yds.)

RVS: April to September. SF: Tropical and subtropical wild and industrial plants, especially trees and palms.

The Botanical Gardens of Padua and Palermo

Among Italy's many botanical gardens, those of the Universities of Padua and Palermo merit particular attention, the former for its unique historic significance, the latter for its exotic charm.
The Botanical Garden of Padua is one of the oldest in the world and the only one which has remained unchanged since its inception. It was laid out some 50 years after the discovery of America. Immediately adjoining the Antonius Basilica (1545), it has for centuries been the destination of travelling scientists as well as the first resting place of foreign plants on their introduction to Europe. Thus lilac was first cultivated in Europe in the Botanical Garden of Padua in 1565; in 1568 the sun flower and in 1590 the potato. Other familiar plants which came to Europe via Padua are rhubarb, the ornamental cyclamen, Virginia creeper, robinia, Ailantus, to name only a few.
The Gardens of Padua, with their strict division into geometrically shaped quarters, are intended mainly to serve as a monument. The visitor should walk in it as he would in the rooms of a museum. However, the garden lover perhaps coming from the lakes of Northern Italy or from the Riviera and accustomed to the splendour of parks and gardens in those blessed regions, is apt to be a little disappointed. He should go instead to see the Botanical Gardens of Palermo.
The sub-tropical and tropical flora is no where else in Europe as richly represented under the open sky as in Palermo. But the significance of the gardens does not lie exclusively in well-arranged collections of especially rare plants, although the lover of rarities will be richly rewarded. People from temperate zones will be far more impressed by the luxuriant wilderness of indiarubber trees, lianas, bamboo, the avenues of palm trees, the palm gardens, the barren hills with euphorbias, cacti, grass trees and thorny shrubs. Landscapes in miniature, characterised by strange plant shapes, excite our imagination and a walk through the gardens is like an expedition to distant lands.
The gardens are best entered from the old Botanical Institute on the Via Lincoln. From there a narrow path runs between two Chilian Livistona palms with ringed trunks and through a densely wooded grove; soon it crosses the date palm avenue. If you wish to see every kind of palm tree growing in the open in the Mediterranean regions—with the exception of Chamaerops humilis, they are all natives of other continents—you need only walk down the palm tree avenue. However, if we continue along the path we soon arrive at a large pond with water lilies, lotus and papyrus. Glancing to the right, we see spiky succulents, their arms raised to the sky, in front of a thatched hut in the Ethiopian style. Ahead of us a dense bamboo jungle forms a shallow arch round the pond. The narrow path winds among its spears and finally leads to the show piece of the gardens, the mighty Ficus magnolioides, more than a century old. Some 1,076 sq. yds. are shaded by its branches which rest on a forest of prop roots, once descended from the branches as aerial roots, until they developed into pillars capable of taking their weight. A network of broad roots with flattened sides spreads over the ground.
If we had taken a sharp right turn at the Institute, instead of walking straight ahead, we would have come to a less impressive part of the garden which, however, is most important from the point of view of science and economy. Here are the sections for industrial plants and the trial grounds. Almost every plant under cultivation for food and technical purposes in the temperate zone and particularly in the Mediterranean regions, and many plants from warmer climates, are being grown here. Particularly noteworthy are the banana and citrus plantations—an almost complete collection of the many species and varieties of the lemon-orange-grapefruit family. A row of trees with bulging stems and an armour of

pointed thorns appears to be marching in Indian file through the trial grounds. They are representatives of the pseudo-kapok tree (Chorisia insignis) from the tropical regions of the Southern hemisphere. Their cucumber-shaped fruits are stuffed with fine woolly hair. In the background, an avenue of tall Californian bog palms (Washingtonia filifera) with long beards of pendulous dry leaves attracts the attention. Following it we come to the new Botanical Institute from where, on the left-hand side, the large india-rubber tree is to be seen. We have come full circle. It was an excursion which not only introduced us to many different shapes and sizes in the plant world, but also gave us an insight into the vast sphere of botanical problems. *Dr Walter Larcher*

Orto Botanico 'Villa Taranto,' Pallanza, Lago Maggiore (1931), 42 acres (GH 781 sq. yds.)

RVS: April and May, July and August. Open from 10th April to the end of October. SF: 15,000 different plants, chiefly trees and shrubs. Lotus pond. The gardens are half and hour's drive from Locarno, one hour's drive from Milano. Simplon railway line.

Civico Orto Botanico, Parma (1599)

Orto Botanico dell'Università Parma (1770)

Orto Botanico dell'Università, Pavia, Via S. Epifanio 12 (general park, 1558; botanical gardens, 1763), 40½ acres (GH 562 sq. yds.)

RVS: Spring and autumn. Open on Sundays and Holidays from 9 a.m. to noon and 2—7 p.m. SF: Roses.

Orto Botanico dell'Università, Perugia (1811)

Orto Botanico dell'Università, Pisa, Via Luca Ghini 5 (1544), 7 acres (GH 1,214 sq. yds.)

RVS: May to June, September and October. Open from 8 a.m. to noon and 2—5 p.m. SF: Ferns, orchids, Nymphaeceae, Bromeliaceae.

Park Sammezzano, Comune di Regello

SF: Sequoia, different cypress species, cedars, Chamaecyparis.

Orto Botanico dell'Università di Roma, Via Corsini 24 (1883), 22 acres (GH 957 sq. yds.)

Not open to the public. Permission to view may be given in special circumstances. SF: Succulents and palms.

Giardino Vaticano, Rome, Città del Vaticano

SF: Artistically laid out park and gardens.

Rosarium, Roma, Via di Valle Murcia (1933, 1950), 3 acres

RVS: May and October. Open May—June 8.30 a.m.—7.30 p.m. October—November 8.30 a.m.—5 p.m. SF: One of the European rose trial gardens. The rose collection shows the development of roses over 150 years.

Stazione Sperimentale di Floricultura 'O. Raimondo', San Remo, Corso degli Inglesi 362 (1925), 5 acres (GH 598 sq. yds.)

Visits by permission of the director. SF: Alpinum, collection of native plants; orchids and succulents collection; industrial plants; ornamental: carnations, roses, lilies, pelargonias.

Orto Botanico dell'Università di Sassari/Sardinia (1888)

Villa 'La Gamberaia,' Settignano (Florence)

SF: Classic Italian gardens.

Orto Botanico dell'Università degli Studi di Siena, Via P. A. Mattioli 4 (1856), 2½ acres (GH 72 sq. yds.)

RVS: Spring. Visits by permission of the director. SF: Medicinal plants of Italy, cacti, lilies, euphorbia.

Villa Carlotta, Tremezzo, Lago di Como (1847), 5 acres (GH 358 sq. yds.)

RVS: April and May. SF: Azaleas, rhododendron, tropical plants. 'Villa Carlotta' is situated between Tremezzo and Cadenabbia. The park was first laid out in the early 18th century. During the last 30 years the artistic and botanical collections have been considerably extended. The large gardens with their important plant collections are the work of the Duke of Sachsen-Meiningen. Accessible from Como and Lugano by bus.

Civico Orto Botanico, Trieste, Via Marchesetti 2 (1828), 2½ acres (GH 120 sq. yds.)

RVS: April to June. Open Sundays from 9 a.m. to noon and 2—6 p.m. and on Holidays from 9 a.m. to 1 p.m. SF: Collections of plants of the Adriatic regions.

Orto Botanico dell'Università di Torino (Turin), Viale Mattioli 25 (1729), 74 acres (GH 478 sq. yds.)

RVS: May to September. Open from 9 a.m. to noon and 2—6 p.m. SF: About 3,000 different species of all regions.

'Paradisia'—Giardino Alpino del Parco Nazionale Gran Paradiso, Valnontey — Cogne (Aosta) (1955), 2½ acres

RVS: June and July. Open June—September 8 a.m. to 12.30 p.m. and 2—6.30 p.m. SF: Alpinum with various endemics of the Western Alps, especially Astragalus alopecuroides, Aethionema thomasianum, Potentilla pennsylvanica var. sanguisorbifolia, Aconitum burnati, Saxifraga florulenta, etc. Access: by train and bus to Cogne, thence on foot or by car to Valnontey (about 2 miles). 5,577 ft. above sea level.

Stazione Sperimentale di Selvicoltura di Vallombrosa, c/o Florence, Via delle Cascine 1 (East of Florence) (1880), 25 acres

RVS: May, June and October. SF: Castanetum, Fagetum, Alpinum. Small dendrological museum. Acer, Betula, Evonymus, Fraxinus, Ilex, Rhus, Chamaecyparis lawsoniana, Pseudo-Tsuga menziesii, Thuja plicata.

Civico Orto Botanico, Piazza Hortis 4, Trieste

Orto Botanico dell'Istituto Tecnico per Geometri, Piazza Cavedalis, Udine

Orto Botanico dell'Università, Via Bramante, Urbino

Civico Orto Botanico Urbino (1809)

Open from 8 a.m. to noon and 2—7 p.m. SF: Medicinal plants.

Malta

Argotti Botanic Gardens, Floriana (2 GH)

SF: Exotic flora, native flora, cacti, succulents.

Monaco

Jardin Exotique de Monte Carlo, Principality of Monaco (1913—1933), 2 1/2 acres (4 GH)

Open from 9 a.m. to noon and 2—6 p.m. SF: Succulents, cacti.

Jardins Publics du Casino de Monte Carlo (1873), 13 acres

SF: In 'Boulingrins' garden (French style) plants of the Mediterranean regions; in 'Petite-Afrique' garden (English style) exotic trees and shrubs from numerous sub-tropical regions; different species of palm, yucca, Ficus macrophylla, Musa, various Cycadea, Victoria cruziana, Euryale ferox.

Cultures des Jardins Publics du Casino de Monte Carlo, Principality of Monaco, Quartier du Ténao (GH 718 sq. yds.)

Visits by permission of the director. SF: Collection of tropical and equatorial plants; Anthurium, Pandanus, Bromelias, Platycerium grande, orchids, etc.

Jardins Publics du Gouvernment de la Principauté de Monaco (19th cent.), 11 acres

SF: Jardin St. Martin: Stone-pines and conifers. Jardin Testimonio: palms and Cycadeae. Jardin Princesse Antoinette: Olive trees, hardy shrubs and plants of the Mediterranean regions. The gardens are situated in different parts of the Principality.

Service de Botanique de la Principauté de Monaco, Travaux publics, Rue de la Poste, Monte Carlo, 371 acres (6 GH)

SF: Tropical plants: alpinum on Mount Agel (2,658 ft. above sea level).

Netherlands

Aalsmeer

SF: Centre of the cut flower industry; large halls for auctioning flowers.

Hortus Botanicus, Amsterdam C (1682), about 2 1/2 acres (GH)

SF: Encephalartos altensteinii, Bowenia spectabilis, Victoria amazonica, Selaginella grandis.

Hortus Botanicus 'Cantonspark,' Baarn (1920), 10 acres (1 GH)

SF: Arboretum (Fagus silvatica); tropical plants from West Africa. Himalayan plants. Alpinum.

'Linnaeushof,' Bennebroek/Haarlem (1956), 198 acres (GH)

RVS: June and July. Open from April to October. SF: Tulips, April and May; roses, July and August. Ornamental shrubs; dahlias in autumn; tropical plants; conifers; rhododendron, alpinum. This is the farm where Karl Linnaeus tested his theories (1735). Permanent show of flowers, plants, shrubs under glass. Access via Haarlem.

Extensive nurseries in Boskoop (centre of the tree and horticultural nurseries of Holland since the 17th century)

RVS: Spring and autumn. SF: Rhododendron, ilex, barberries, forsythia, magnolia, weigelia, deutzia, ligustrum, Picea pungens, lupinus, astilbe, Salvia superba. Boskoop is situated between Leiden and Rotterdam.

Botanical Test Institute, Boskoop

SF: Rhododendron, roses, Potentilla fruticosa, Acer palmatum, clematis, Cytisus, Chaenomeles, Hibiscus syriacus, conifers, etc.

Cultivation Gardens for Technical Plants, Delft, 1 Julianalaan 67 (1917), about 7 acres (5 GH)

SF: Cultivation of industrial plants.

Arboretum 'Poort Bulten,' De Lutte near Oldenzaal (1910), 21 acres

SF: Abietineae, Fagus, Quercus, Aceraceae, Leguminosae, roses, Oleaceae.

Zuiderpark, Den Haag (1930), about 401 acres

SF: 1,000 different tree and shrub species.

Rosarium Westbroekpark, Den Haag, Gaslaan 161 (1961), about 50 acres

RVS: Mid-June to mid-October. Open from 10 a.m. to 1 hour before sunset. From mid-April to mid-June admittance free. SF: 77 varieties of large-flowered roses, 154 varieties of floribunda roses, 27 varieties of park roses, 40 varieties of climbing roses, 42 varieties of dwarf roses. Total: 22,000 rose bushes. In addition, flowering trees, shrubs, bulbs and seed flowers according to season. International rose competition.

Von Gimborn Arboretum, Doorn, Dorpsstraat 75 (1924), about 50 acres

Visits by permission of the director. SF: Ericaceae, magnificent conifers, rare trees and shrubs.

Hortus Botanicus Groningen, Grote Rozenstraat 31 (1642), 3½ acres (10 GH)

Open from 9 a.m. to noon and 2—4 p.m. Closed on Sundays. SF: Platycerium.

Haarlem

SF: Important centre of bulb cultivation.

Hortus 'De Wolf,' Haren, Rijksstraatweg 74, about 34 acres

Pinetum Blijdenstein, Hilversum (1911), about 50 acres

SF: Conifers—pines.

'Keukenhof' (1949), 62 acres (GH 3,229 sq. yds.)

RVS: Mid-April to 10th May. Open from end of March to mid-May. SF: Tulips; hyacinths, narcissi, crocus, etc. Access: By train to Leiden or Haarlem, then change to N.Z.H.V.M. bus.

Hortus Botanicus Leiden (Botanical Gardens of the University of Leiden), Nonnensteeg 3 (1587), 5 acres (19 GH)

Open October to March from 9 a.m. to noon on weekdays, during the rest of the year from 9 a.m. to noon and 1.30—5 p.m. SF: Replica of the gardens of Charles l'Escluse (Clusius); orchids, Cycadeae, medicinal plants.

Lisse

SF: Important centre of bulb cultivation.

'De Dennenhorst,' Lunteren, about 25 acres (GH about 108 sq. yds.)

SF: Conifers.

Royal Deer Garden, Rotterdam (Botanical Section) (5 GH)

SF: Orchids, tropical and sub-tropical plants.

Stichting 'Arboretum Trompenburg,' Groene Westering 46 (1820), Rotterdam, 10 acres (GH 120 sq. yds.)

Open 9 a.m. to noon and 1—5 p.m. Closed on Sundays. SF: Quercus, Cedrus, Chamaecyparis, Fagus, Acer, Rhododendron, Liriodendron.

Hortus Botanicus, Utrecht, Lange Nieuwstraat 106 (17th/18th cent.), 2½ acres (5 GH)

The Garden is open to the public during office hours.

Botanical Museum and Herbarium 'Cantonspark' Lange Nieuwstraat 106, Utrecht, 11 acres (7 GH)

Open from 9 a.m. to noon and 1.30—5 p.m. Closed on Saturday and Sundays. SF: Orchids, alpinum.

Botanical Gardens and Belmonte Arboretum of the Agricultural High School, Wageningen, Foulkesweg 37 (1896), about 96 acres

Closed on Saturday afternoon and Sundays; open weekdays from 9 a.m. to noon and 2—5 p.m. SF: Crataegus, Forsythia, Lonicera, Malus, Prunus, Philadelphus, Hibiscus, rhododendron, Syringa, Rosa.

Institute of Horticultural Plant Breeding, Wageningen 15, Dr S. L. Manshaltlaan, 42 acres (GH)

Visits by permission of the director, Mondays to Fridays from 8 a.m. to noon and 1.30—5.30 p.m. SF: Trial grounds for the cultivation of garden plants. Succulents.

Norway

Botanical Gardens of the University of Bergen, J. Frieles gt. 1, Bergen, Muséplass 3 (1887), 4½ acres (GH 317 sq. yds.)

RVS: May and June. SF: Rhododendron, primula, alpinum, orchids, Gesneriaceae.

Botanical Gardens of the University of Oslo, Trondheimsveien 23 (1814), 32 acres (GH 837 sq. yds.)

RVS: May to August. Open: Greenhouses, from 1st May to 31st August—Sundays, Tuesdays and Fridays from noon to 3 p.m.; from 1st September to 30th April, Wednesdays from 6 p.m.—8 p.m.; the gardens, weekdays from 7 a.m. to 6 p.m., Sundays from 10 a.m. to 6 p.m. In Summer open daily till 10 p.m., Wednesdays from noon to 3 p.m. SF: Norwegian flora.

Kongsvoll Berggarten, 120 sq. yds., 2,952 ft. above sea level

RVS: Early June to second half of July. SF: Many interesting Norwegian plants and common alpines. Situated in the mountainous region of Dovre, Central Norway. The whole area of Dovre surrounding Kongsvoll is of botanical interest.
Access: Oslo—Trondheim road; about 8 hours' train journey from Oslo.

Nordreisa in Northern Norway

RVS: July, August. SF: Dyras octopetala, Cassiope tetragona, Armeria sibirica, Pedicularis flammea, Platanthera oligantha, Rhododendron lapponicum, Saxifraga hieracifolia, Campanula uniflora, Minuartia rubella, Erigeron unalaschkense, Pedicularis hirsuta, Ranunculus nivalis, R. sulphureus, Saxifraga foliolosa, Myricaria germanica, Polemonium acutiflorum, Melandrium augustifolium, Papaver radicatum ssp. hyperboreum. Access: By plane, Oslo—Bardufoss (4½ hours), thence by bus Bardufoss—Nordreisa (at least 4 hours); or by train from Oslo—Trondheim—Fauske (Bodo), 746 miles, thence by bus to Nordreisa, 186 miles; or by car, State Highway No. 50 from Oslo to Nordreisa, 1,056 miles (some poor roads).

Arboretum and Experimental Institute of the Agricultural High School of Norway, As, 36 acres

RVS: May, June, August, September. Arboretum open to the public throughout the summer. Conducted tours, weekdays from 9 a.m. to 3 p.m. SF: Arboretum; experimental grounds for flowers, fruit trees and vegetables. Access: State Highway No. 1 from Oslo, 18 miles, or by train.

State Horticultural School Ra Kvaefjord near Harstad, 93 miles south of Tromsö

SF: The northernmost horticultural school in the world.

Poland

Botanical Gardens, Bromberg, Bydgószcz, pl. Weyssenhoffa 11 (1946), 6 acres (GH 121 sq. yds.)

SF: Research into the acclimatisation of plants.

Botanical Gardens of the Medical Academy, Faculty of Botany, Al. K. Marksa 107, Danzig (Gdánsk) (BG)

Wyžsza Szkola Rolnicza w. Poznaniu (Posen), Arboretum Gołuchów, 390 acres (2 GH)

RVS: May to October. SF: Forest trees and ornamental shrubs.

Arboretum Kórnik of the Polish Academy of Science, Kórnik near Posen (1926), 124 acres (GH 1,196 sq. yds.)

SF: Syringa, Malus, Forsythia, Acer, Tilia, Populus, Betula, Magnolia, conifers.

Polish Academy of Science, Institute of Pharmacy, 16 Grzegórzecka Street, Krakow, 12½ acres (GH)

SF: Medicinal plants. Visits by permission of the director.

Botanical Gardens of the University Jagiellónskiego, Krakow, ul. Kopernika 27 (1783), 25 acres (9 GH)

RVS and open, May to October. SF: Cycadeae, orchids, bromelias.

Botanical Gardens of the Academy of Medicine, Lódž, Lindley 3 (BG)

Botanical Gardens of the University of Posen, ul. Dabrowskiego 165 (1923), 35 acres (GH 617 sq. yds.)

Arboretum of the Agricultural High School Rogow near Koluszek, 99 acres (1 GH)

Visits by permission of the director. SF: Conifers.

Botanical Gardens of the University of Warsaw, Al. Uljazdowskie 4, Warsaw (1818), about 12½ acres (GH 1,316 sq. yds.)

RVS: May, June, August, September. Open from the end of April to 15th October. SF: Sections: plant biology, protected plants, alpinum, arboretum (amongst others Metasequoia glyptostroboides), dahlias, hydrangeas, clematis, iris, fig trees, palm trees, begonias, Stangeria eriopus (S. paradoxa).

Botanical Gardens of the University of Breslau (Wrocław), Kanonia 6/8 (1811), 11 acres (GH 1,794 sq. yds.)

RVS and open, May to November. SF: Alpinum, succulents, aquatic plants, dahlias, roses, narcissi, liliaceae, tulips, crocus.

Garden Roslin Leczniczych Academy of Medicine, Breslau (Wrocław), ul. Kochanowskiego 10 (12 GH) (forest botanical garden)

Open on Sundays in the forenoon only. SF: Medicinal plants.

Portugal

Jardim e Museu Agrícola do Ultramar, Calçada do Galvao, Belem/Lisbon (1906), 17¼ acres (14 GH 1,076 sq. yds.)

RVS: Spring and autumn. SF: Tropical and subtropical plants; Arachis, Gossypium.

National Park of Serra de Bussaco (1268), northeast of Coimbra

SF: Cypressus lusitanica, Platanus acerifolia, P. orientalis, Pinus pinaster, Quercus ilex, Q. suber, Tilia spp. and Camellia japonica.

Jardim Botânico da Faculdade de Ciências da Universidade de Coimbra (1772), 33⅓ acres (3 GH)

SF: Tropical plants, succulents, Ornithogalum, Myrtaceae, narcissi and roses, conifers.

Estação de Melhoramento de Plantas, Elvas, 192¾ acres (2 GH)

SF: Industrial plants.

Jardim Botânico da Faculdade de Ciências, Rua da Escola Politécnica, Lisbon 2 (1858), 10 acres (GH 574 sq. yds.)

RVS: Spring and summer. SF: Cycadeae, palm trees, orchids, ferns.

Royal Park of Ajuda, Lisbon (1644) (GH)

SF: Sophora japonica, Dracaena draco, Fagus silvatica, Acacia armata, Nolina longifolia; Microlepia strigosa.

Jardim Botânico da Ajuda, Calçada da Ajuda, Lisbon, 11 acres (5 GH)

SF: Plants of the Mediterranean regions and the sub-tropics; industrial plants.

Estufa Fria, Lisbon (about 9,568 sq. yds.), private gardens

SF: Sub-tropical plants, ferns, begonias, lianas.

Crystal Palace Gardens, Oporto (1861), 17 acres (GH 718 sq. yds.)

Instituto de Botânica 'Dr. Gonçalo Sampaio,' R. do Campo Alegre 1191, Oporto, 11 acres (GH 933 sq. yds.)

SF: Orchids, cacti, rhododendron.

Jardim Botânico, Oporto (1940), about 30 acres

SF: Fagus silvatica, Camellia japonica and C. reticulata, Cytisus albus, Narcissus rupicola, Romulea bulbocodium.

Companhia Horticola, Oporto (1849). The oldest tree nurseries of Portugal

SF: Mahonia japonica, Ginkgo biloba, Camellia sasanqua.

Estação Agronómica Nacional, Sacavém

National Park of Montserrat/Sintra (1860), about 75 acres

SF: Agathis australis, Araucaria bidwilii, Magnolia grandiflora, Photinia serrulata; 25 palm species.

Park of Penha (1860). Sintra National Park

Admission by special permission of the director only. SF: Conifers. Trees of the northern and southern hemispheres.

Rumania

Grădina Botanică a Universitătii 'C. I. Parhon' Soseaua Cotroceni, 32 Raionul, Gh. Gheorgiu-Dej, Bucharest (BG)

Grădina Botanică a Universitătii 'Babes-Bolyai,' Strada Republicii 42, Cluj (BG)

Grădina Botanică a Institutului Agronomic 'Tudor Vladimirescu,' Strada Comuna din Paris 24, Craiova (BG)

Grădina Botanică a Universitătii 'Al. I. Cuza,' Iasi 1 (BG)

Grădina Botanică Institutul de Medicina si Farmacie, Strada Universitătii 38, Tirgu Mures, Regiúnea Autonómă Maghiáră (BG)

Scotland

Crathes Castle near Banchory, Kincardineshire (18th century)

SF: Noteworthy collection of British and foreign shrubs and hardy shrubs.

Younger Botanic Garden Benmore by Dunoon, Argyll, about 100 acres (4 GH)

RVS: April to September. SF: Conifers, rhododendron of rare size and beauty.

Botanic Garden Cruickshank, St. Machar Drive, Old Aberdeen, about 7 acres (7 GH)

SF: Alpinum.

Royal Botanic Garden Edinburgh (1670), about 79 acres (GH 1,196 sq. yds.)

RVS: April to June. Greenhouses open only from 1—5 p.m. SF: Flora of the Himalayan regions and of China. Arboretum, rhododendron, primula, lilies, Meconopsis. One of the largest rock gardens in the world.

Achamore Gardens, Isle of Gigha, Argyll

Open April to September. SF: Azaleas, rhododendron, flowering trees, aquatic plants, roses, delicate plants from New Zealand and Chile.

Botanic Gardens Glasgow, Great Westend Road, Glasgow W. (1817), 42 acres (GH 5,860 sq. yds).

RVS: Spring and summer. The greenhouses are open only in the afternoons. SF: Orchids, tropical plants, ferns, industrial plants.

Inverewe Poolewe Wester Ross, Ross & Cromarty

Closed in the forenoon on Sundays. SF: Open-air park on rocky peninsula. Exotic plants from all over the world. Special trees, rhododendron, azalea, magnolia, rock garden, aquatic garden.

Kennedy Castle Gardens, Lochinch near Stranraer, Wigtownshire

RVS: April to June. Open 11th April to 8th August, Wednesdays and Sundays 2—5 p.m. SF: Rhododendron and azalea collections, magnolias, camellias.

Keillour Castle, Methven, Perthshire. Owner: Major Knox Finlay

SF: Natural park with rich collection of Chinese plants: primula, Nomocharis, Lilium, Corydalis cashmeriana, Meconopsis, etc.

Logan Gardens, near Stranraer, Wigtownshire

Open from 2nd April to 29th September 10 a.m. to 6 p.m. Closed on Sundays. SF: Many rare and sub-tropical plants, tree ferns, rhododendron, Cordyline australis.

Culzean Castle near Maybole, Ayrshire

Closed from December to February. SF: Special trees, hothouse plants.

The University Botanical Garden, St. Andrews, 5 acres (3 GH)

Closed on Saturday afternoons and Sundays. SF: Plants of the Alps and Himalayas, cacti, succulents.

Spain

Royal Gardens de la Isla, Aranjuez (16th century)

SF: Arboretum; Park in the style of the Italian Renaissance; Magnolia, Lagerstroemia, Fraxinus, Taxus, etc.

Botanical Garden Barcelona, 10 acres

Open daily from 10 a.m. to 2 p.m. SF: Arboretum with Sophora japonica, plants of the Balearic Islands, North Africa and Morocco.

Acclimatisation Garden 'Pinya de Rosa,' Blanes-Gerona, Costa Brava (1940), about 60 acres (9 GH)

RVS: July. Visits by permission of the director. SF: Succulents, large collection of Opuntia and other cacti; Alpinum; Convolvulus mauritanica, Pelargonium acetosa; Aloe, orchids, agave. Especially the flora of Catalonia.

Botanical Gardens 'Mar y Murtra,' Fundacion Carlos Faust, Blanes/Gerona, Costa Brava (1918), 35 acres (GH 120 sq. yds.)

RVS: End of April to mid-June. SF: Succulents, especially cacti.

Botanical Gardens Madrid, Plaza de Murillo 2 (1781), 20 acres (5 GH)

RVS: April to July. SF: Dahlias (first introduced to Europe in 1789), plants of Central and South America.

Acclimatisation Gardens de la Orotava, Tenerife (Canary Islands) (1788), 5 acres (4 GH)

SF: 80 plant families with more than 220 species, 30 of which are various palm trees. Aristolochia, Ceropegia, Stapelia.

Botanical Gardens Valencia (17th century), 20 acres

Access via Calle de Cuarte.

Sweden

Norrvikens Trädgårdar—Båstad (1906), 12 acres

RVS: Mid-May to mid-September. SF: Every known conifer. Access: Situated in the southernmost province of Sweden, in Skåne, about 2 miles from Båstad. By car: Europe Road 'E 6' to Östra Karup, then road 115 through Båstad to Norrviken. By train: Hälsingborg—Göteborg line to Båstad, thence by bus. By plane: Ängelholm, 15¹/₂ miles.

Botaniska Trädgården Göteborg SV, Frölundagatan 22 (1923), 370 acres (GH 629 sq. yds.)

RVS: May, June, September. SF: Large alpinum, rhododendron, Japanese and other Asian plants. Arboretum, orchids from South-East Asia and South Africa (Disa uniflora).

Botaniska Trädgården Hälsingborg, Hunnetorpsvägen (1936), about 15 acres

SF: The flora of Southern Sweden in plant-sociological groupings.

Arboretum Drafle, Hultom

Botaniska Trädgården Lund, Ö. Vallgatan 18 (1862), 19¹/₂ acres (GH 1,495 sq. yds.)

RVS: August for open-air plants.

König-Gustav-Adolf-Rhododendron-Park Sofiero, Southern Sweden (1865). Summer residence of the Swedish royal family

SF: Azalea and rhododendron species from America, Asia, many European species.

Bergianska Trädgården (Hortus Botanicus Bergianus), Stockholm 50, Freskati (1791), 20 acres (GH 867 sq. yds.)

RVS: May-June. SF: Asian plants, especially from China. Conifers (Podocarpaceae in hothouse).

Sällskapet DBV: s Trädgård (1855)

RVS: May to September. SF: 330 trees and shrubs.

Linnés Hammarby near Uppsala. Country residence purchased in 1758 by Linnaeus; charming old garden of the great naturalist

Botanical Gardens of the University of Uppsala (1653), 35 acres (GH 2,165 sq. yds.)

RVS: July to September. SF: Hosta, Sorbus-hybrids, viola (all Scandinavian species), Scandinavian flora. Very comprehensive taxonomical collections.

Switzerland

Alp Grüm (Alpine Garden, in process of being extended since 1962), 2¹/₂ acres, 7,750 ft. above sea level

RVS: June to August. SF: Alpine plants, natives of the Bernina Pass region. Alp Grüm is on the Bernina line of the Rhaetian Railways.

Botanical Gardens of the University of Basle, Schönbeinstrasse 6 (1588—1898), 3³/₄ acres (GH about 957 sq. yds.)

RVS: May to June. SF: Orchids, Araceae, succulents, alpinum.

Botanical Gardens Bern, Altenbergrain 21 (1860), about 6 acres (GH about 1,316 sq. yds.)

RVS: June to September. SF: Alpinum with several geographical sections.

Florealpe, Alpine Garden, Champex (Vallais) (1930), about 2¹/₂ acres, 4,921 ft. above sea level, in the Mont Blanc Massif

RVS: June to July. Open from 1st May to 31st October from 11 a.m. to noon, except Sundays. SF: About 5,000 alpine plants from all over the world. On the road Martigny—St. Bernhard (40 minutes by car from Martigny). Railway line Paris—Lausanne—Milano.

Acclimatisation Gardens 'Floraire,' Correvon Fils & Cie., 50, Avenue Petit-Senn, Chêne-Bourg (Geneva) (1902), 3³/₄ acres (1 GH)

RVS: 15th March to June. SF: Alpine plants for alpinum, dry walls. Primularium, aquatic plants.

Botanical Gardens of the University of Fribourg (1936), 3¹/₂ acres (GH 299 sq. yds.)

RVS: June to July. SF: Alpinum (lime, granite, etc.).

Botanical Gardens and 'Conservatoire botanique' of the City of Geneva, 192, Route de Lausanne (1817), 25 acres (GH 1,200 sq. yds.)

RVS: April to June, Greenhouses, closed on Fridays. SF: Alpinum and greenhouses with subtropical and tropical flora, rare aquatic plants. Arboretum, Herbarium de Candolle.

Botanical Gardens of the Canton of Ticino, Isole di Brissago (1950), 7¹/₄ acres (small open GH)

RVS: April to May and throughout the summer. Flowers as late as November. Open from 15th March to 15th November. Scientific direction by Professor Dr Markgraf of the University of Zürich. SF: Sub-tropical species in the open, Taxodium in the lake, bamboo and palms, Camellia sasanqua, Metasequoia, Citrus species, tropical and industrial plants. Mediterranean scented plants, Maquis shrubs, rhododendron and eucalyptus, ornamental banana trees. Accessible by steamer or boat from Porto Ronco.

Jardin Botanique de l'Université de Lausanne, Palais de Rumine (1892), 5 acres

RVS: April to June. Open daily from 1st April to 31st October, except Mondays. SF: Alpinum and medicinal plants.

Jardin Alpin 'Rambertia,' Montreux, aux Rochers de Naye, Waadt

Private garden, open to the public from June to October daily. SF: Various acclimatised and native plants.

Montreux and surrounding country

RVS: May to June. SF: Flowering daffodils in the meadows.

Jardin Botanique de l'Université Neuenburg (Neuchâtel) (1955), 3³/₄ acres (GH 72 sq. yds.)

RVS: May to August (open from 1st April to 1st November). SF: Veronica, Caryophyllaceae, Sempervivum, Androsace, 'chromosome strains.'

La Thomasia, Botanical Alpine Gardens at Pont de Nant sur Bex (1891), 15,000 acres

RVS: June to July (open from 1st May to 31st October). SF: Alpine botanical garden. Accessible by car via Pont de Nant.

Jardin Botanique Ecole Cantonale, Porrentruy, Jura Bernois (1795), 17,798 acres (GH 295 sq. yds.)

RVS: According to the collections. Open daily from Mondays to Saturdays.

Swiss National Park (1914), 62 sq. miles, Graubünden. To be entered from Bad Scuol, Tarasp, Vulpera, Scarl, Scanfs, Zernez

RVS: Mid-June to mid-July, September. SF: All plants are protected. Very rich flora on account of variation in altitude by 5,906 ft. and the mineral contents of the soil which provides favourable conditions for lime-loving as well as lime-hating plants. Numerous alpine plant societies are represented: mixed coniferous forests, stone-pines, larches, firs, mountain firs, alpine alders and Rhododendron ferrugineum, dwarf shrub heather, trained fruit trees, various types of alpine meadow, extensive scree areas, etc. The incomparable splendour of the flowering season reaches its height in the second half of June.

Botanical Gardens St. Gallen, Brauerstrasse 69 (1945), 3¹/₂ acres (GH 777 sq. yds.)

RVS: Throughout the year. SF: Alpinum of the Cantons of St. Gallen/Appenzell; alpine house with 400 species, 700 orchids, 800 cacti and other succulents, mutations, insectivores, garden plants. See the following article.

The Botanical Gardens of St. Gallen

The Gardens were founded in 1945. They are owned by the City of St. Gallen and run at the expense of the City and the Canton.

The founders stated that the gardens were intended for the education, enjoyment and recreation of all schools, the inhabitants of the city and countryside, plant and garden lovers as well as botanical experts. They do not serve any botanical university institute.

Because no one is obliged to visit the gardens, they had to be laid out in such a way as to attract every type of person. The shapes, the personalities and the beauty of plants with their differing needs and habits, their different relations, problems and life cycles are to be brought to the knowledge of as many people as possible. The difference between visitors in regard to age, knowledge, education and interests should be no obstacle to such a meeting. A botanical garden should be beautiful and attractive. The Gardens of St. Gallen represent a synthesis between show and comparative plantations, with a chiefly aesthetic effect and an arrangement of the collection material according to purely scientific considerations. No plant is placed indiscriminately. In regarding a plant, the visitor should be impressed by its beauty and individuality. He finds identical plants in different relations to others according to origin, kinship, genetics, outward shape and form, common needs, manifestations of life, chemical elements, etc. There are the following sections:

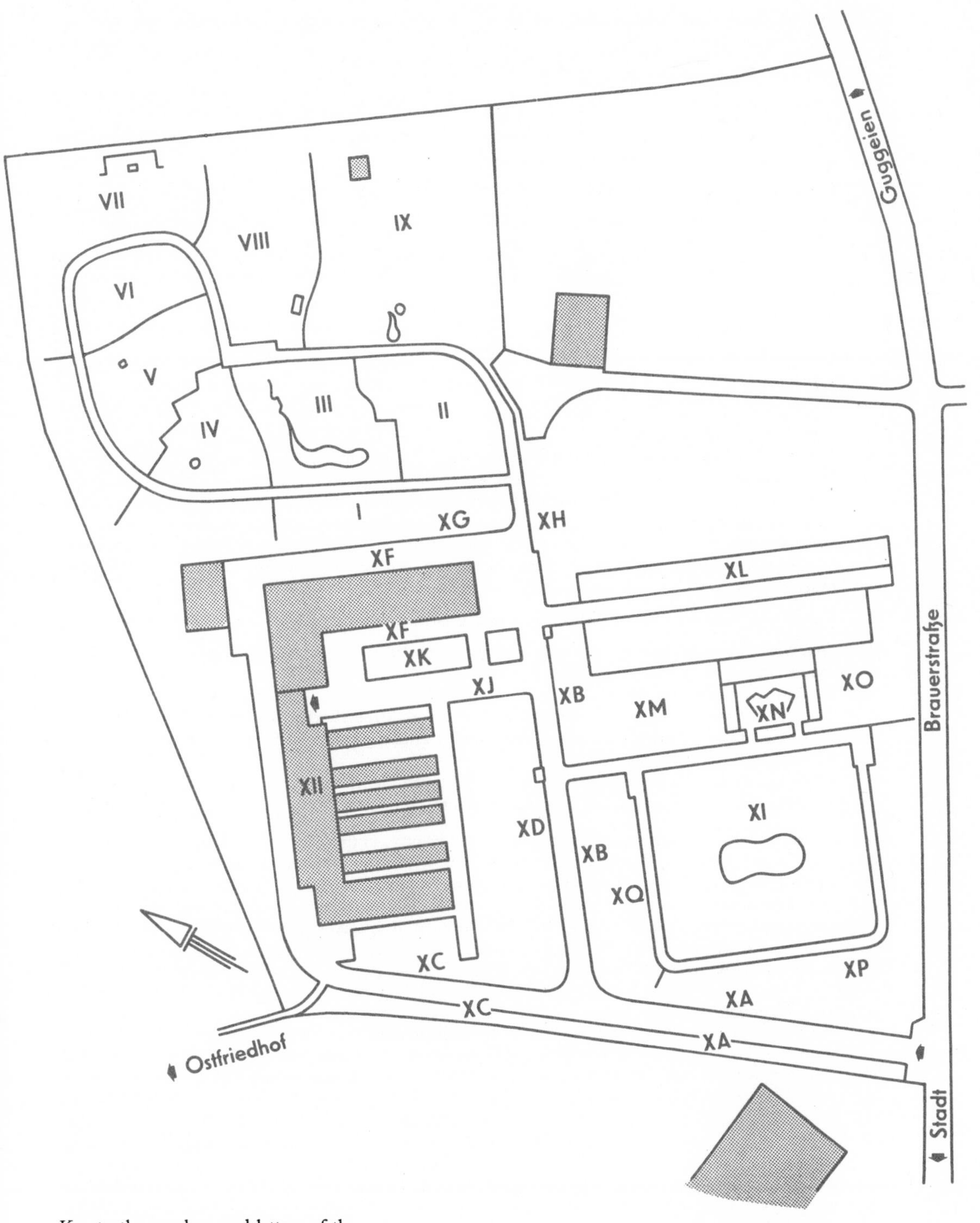

Key to the numbers and letters of the Botanical Gardens in St. Gallen on Page 212

I	*Industrial plants of Switzerland,* such as cereals, fibre, oil and important fodder plants.
II	*Poisonous and medicinal plants* according to chemical elements: volatile oils, glycosides, alkaloids, bitter principles, tannic acid, gummy substances, etc., wild fruit, kitchen herbs.
III	*Alpinum* with native plants of the Cantons of St. Gallen and Appenzell.
IV	*Ornamental plants of Europe:* perennial, herbaceous and woody plants of Europe arranged according to ecological-aesthetic considerations.
V	*Ornamental plants of America:* as for IV, with plants chiefly from North America.
VI	*Morphology:* Comparison between shapes of leaf and bud in relation to their particular functions.
VII	*Genetics:* Heredity in the plant world demonstrated by simple hybrids. Collection of plants (mutations) with abnormal growth, forms and colours of foliage and flowers. Famous plants of hereditary science.
VIII	*Biology:* Various incidents in the life of a plant, such as pollination, the distribution of sexual organs, spreading of seeds, symbiosis, semiparasites, parasites, insectivores.
IX	*Ornamental plants of Asia:* as for IV, with plants from Asia. Small Japanese garden.
X	*Assortments of ornamental plants in sub-groups:* A. Herbaceous border—B. Lily beds (lilies, narcissi, Japanese ornamental cherry)—C. Dwarf conifers—D. Rock garden (species from all over the world)—E. Little treasury (with noteworthy plants at eye level)—F. Climbers—G. Bush roses—H. Barberries—J. Tub plants, sub-tropical with lemons, figs, palms, etc.—K. Comparisons, changing themes—L. Comparisons, changing flowers—M. Primula garden—N. Aquatic garden (collection of aquatic plants)—O. Changing themes—P. Fern corner—Q. Iris garden. Plants which tend to be overlooked in the garden are raised to eye level in small 'treasuries' with explanatory text 'à la bijouterie' for the benefit of interested visitors. Tub plants, sub-tropical, Mediterranean and other species.
XI	*Taxonomy:* Classification of flower and seed plants according to genealogical considerations.
XII	*Greenhouses:* At present the plant collections in the show houses are arranged under the following headings: 1. Attractive plants of the season. 2. Tropical rain forest with bog and marginal plants, Bromeliaceae, climbers. 3. Cacti and other succulents, plants from chiefly American and African dry regions. 4.a Tropical industrial plants. 4.b and c. Tropical and sub-tropical orchids and green plants. 7.a Tropical 'specialists,' pitcher plants, ant plants, etc.

We are always anxious to introduce our visitors to the beauty, individuality and mystery of plants. To this end all plants are carefully labelled, in some cases with supplementary text; we have panels with constantly changing explanatory descriptions, monthly conducted tours at 10 a.m. and 3 p.m. every first Sunday, usually under a particular heading, many conducted tours and demonstrations for schools and groups of visitors, illustrated articles in the daily press and specialised periodicals, competitions and observation tests with raffles and encouraging prizes. From time to time temporary shows take place in the plant hall to draw attention to the various activities in the gardens and behind the scenes.

Species and Varieties:

Greenhouses:	Cacti and Succulents	800	
	Orchids	700	
	Alpine House	400	
	Others	500	2,400
In the open			5,100
	Total		7,500

Insectivores—Orchids—Mutations—Garden Plants—Alpine House.

Admission is free and the Gardens are open throughout the year daily from 8 a.m. to noon and from 1.30—6 p.m., the show houses daily from 9.30 a.m. to noon and from 2—5 p.m.

P. Zülli

Alpine Garden Schynige Platte, 6,576 ft. above sea level (1928), 2 1/2 acres

RVS: Late June to early July: Spring flowers. July to mid-September: tall perennials. (Open from mid-June to end of September.) SF: The Garden shows plants of the alpine and sub-alpine regions growing wild in Switzerland. Representations of plant societies. Access by rack-railway from Station Wilderswil near Interlaken. Incomparable panorama of the Bern Alps (Eiger, Jungfrau, Mönch).

Botanical Gardens of the University of Zürich, Pelikanstrasse 40 (1837, in another location, 1556), 3 3/4 acres (GH 203 sq. yds.)

RVS: May and August to September. SF: Plants of the Mediterranean regions, the Canary Islands, New Zealand, Xantorrhoea, Davidia.

Municipal Collection of Succulents, Zürich 2, Mythenquai 88 (protective collection and herbarium of the International Succulents Research Organisation, IOS), 6 show houses, 1 cultivation house, 13 tall show cases in the open (GH 971 sq. yds.)

RVS: Throughout the year. Main flowering season, March to September. SF: Exclusively succulents from all over the world and of 30 families. Most comprehensive collection of mimicry plants of the family of Mesembryanthemaceae (Lithops, Titanopsis, Argyroderma, etc.)

USSR

Botanical Gardens of the Academy of Science, Kazakh, Alma-Ata, Kazakh SSR, 272 acres (1 GH)

Open Tuesdays and Fridays from 9 a.m. to 3 p.m.

Botanical Gardens S. M. Kirov of the Kazakh State University, Kirov Street 136, Alma-Ata, Kazakh

Dendrological Gardens of V. V. Kuybyshev, Stalin Quay 17, Archangel.

Botanical Gardens of the Academy of Science, Ashkhabad, Keshi, Turkmenistan SSR, 44 acres (1 GH)

Open Mondays to Fridays from 10 a.m. to 6 p.m. SF: Native and acclimatised species, especially trees and shrubs.

Botanical Gardens of the Science Research Institute for Cattle Breeding of the Ukraine, Askania Nova, Region Khersonsky, Novo Troitsky, Ukraine, 168 acres

Dendropark, 26 Comissarov Street 89, Baku 44, Mardakyany, Azerbaijan SSR, 20 acres (1 GH)

Open three times a week. SF: Punica granatum, Olea europea, Ficus carica, Vitis vinifera, Eucalyptus. Vine and sub-tropical cultures.

Botanical Gardens of the Botanical Institute Komarov of the Academy of Science of Azerbaijan, Lokbatanskoechaussée, Baku, Azerbaijan SSR, 117 acres (2 GH)

Closed on Sundays.

Dendropark of the Fruit and Berry Experimental Institute of Altai, Barnaul 20, Smeinogorskytrakt 25, Altai, 22 acres

Open June to September.

Botanical Gardens of the Academy of Science of Georgia, Batumi, Zeleny mis., Georgia SSR (1912), 267 acres (5 GH)

SF: Collection of sub-tropical plants with about 4,000 main and sub-species. The Botanical Gardens consist of a park, plant-geographical sections, commercial and trial plantations, greenhouses and conservancy area.

Dendrological Park 'Alexandria' of the Academy of Science of the Ukraine, Belaya Tserkov, Region Kiev, Ukraine, 498 sq. yds. (2 GH)

SF: Populus, ornamental shrubs, flowering plants.

Botanical Gardens of the Pedagogic Institute, Cherkassy, Gromov Street 26, Ukraine, 25 acres

Open May to October. SF: Dahlias, gladiolas, asters.

Botanical Gardens Chernigov, Projectnaya Street 4, Ukraine, 225 acres (GH 60 sq. yds.)

SF: Arboretum, dahlia garden, hardy-ornamental plants, bulbs, annuals, orchards.

Botanical Gardens of the University of Chernovtsy, Fedkovich Street 11, Ukraine, 17 acres (4 GH)

SF: Botanical Museum.

Botanical Gardens of the University of Dnjepropetrowsk, 10, Shinnaya 4, Ukraine, 161 acres (GH 896 sq. yds.)

The Greenhouses are open daily. SF: Ornamental shrubs, gladiolas, chrysanthemums.

Botanical Gardens of the Botanical Institute of the Academy of Science of Tadzhikistan, Düschambe 17, Karamow Street 19, Tadzhik SSR, 99 acres (GH under construction)

Visits by permission of the director. SF: Maple, oak, ash, conifers, evergreen leaf plants (trees and shrubs), roses, lilies, Eremurus, tulips, chrysanthemums, phlox, narcissi.

Botanical Gardens of the University of Düschambe, Lenin Street 17, Tadzhik SSR, 99 acres

Open from 8 a.m. to 1 p.m. SF: Figs, almond, pomegranate, apricot, apple, mulberry trees.

Botanical Gardens Dzhezkazgan, 1, Karaganda Region, Kazakh SSR, 32 acres

Agro-botanical Gardens of the University of Frunse, Belinsky Street 100, Kirghizia SSR, 5 acres

Open to experts and students only. SF: Agricultural plants, such as fruit trees, vine, berries, cereals, etc.

Botanical Gardens of the Kirghizian Academy of Science, Frunse, Volgogradskaya 100, Kirghizia SSR, 297 acres (GH 718 sq. yds.)

Botanical Gardens of the White Russian Agricultural Academy Gorki, Mogilev Region, White Russia SSR, 38 acres (GH for exotic plants)

SF: Dahlias, gladiolas, tulips.

Botanical Garden of the State University of Gorkij, 9, P. O. 62, 25 acres

SF: Populus, drupe cultivations.

Botanical Gardens of the University of Gorkij, 62, 173 acres (2 GH)

Open July to September from 7 a.m. to 3 p.m. SF: Conifers, Crataegus, Centaurea, gladiolas, dahlias, Fragaria, Rubus.

Dendrological Park 'Trostyanets,' Ischma, Tschernigov Region, Ukraine, 497 acres

Botanical Gardens of the University of Irkutsk, Vuzovskaya Quay 20, Irkutsk, 75 acres (2 GH)

SF: Medicinal and industrial plants.

Botanical Gardens 'Nikita,' Yalta/Crimea, Ukraine (1812), 2,265 acres (27 GH)

SF: Drupes, figs, pomegranates, almonds, olives, roses, chrysanthemums, lavender, rosemary. See articles by Nina Pavlovna Nikolajenko, 'Botanical Gardens and Parks in the Soviet Union,' and by Professor Dr H. Walter, 'The Southern Crimea—The Riviera of Eastern Europe, and Nikita Gardens.'

Botanical Gardens of Kaliningrad, Belomorskaya 20, 40 acres (8 GH)

Closed on Saturdays and Sundays in the forenoon. SF: Arboretum, rosarium, bulbs.

Botanical Gardens Kamenets-Podolsky, Leningradskaya 78, Khmelnitzky Region, Ukraine, 3¾ acres (2 GH)

Open May to February. SF: Vine, roses, gladiolas, tulips, hyacinths, dahlias, native plants.

Botanical Gardens of Karaganda, Kazakh SSR, 112 acres (2 GH)

Open Wednesdays and Fridays from noon to 4 p.m. SF: Ornamental plants, berries, industrial plants, flora of Central Kazakhstan.

Botanical Gardens of the Botanical Institute of the Academy of Science of Lithuania, Kaunas, P. O. 19, Botanikosprospect 1, Lithuania SSR, 188 acres (8 GH)

Closed on Saturdays. SF: Alpinum, peonies, climbers, roses.

Botanical Gardens of Kazan, Khadi-Taktash Street 112, Kazan, Tartarian Autonomy, 6 acres (2 GH)

Botanical Gardens of the University of Kharkov, Klochkovskaya 52, Kharkov, 20 acres (10 GH)

Botanical Gardens of the Academy of Science of the Tadzshikian SSR, Khorog, 230 acres

SF: Plants of Central Asia.

Botanical Gardens of the Academy of Science of the Ukraine. Timirjazevskaya 1, Kiev 14, Ukraine, 445 acres (GH 2,904 sq. yds.)

SF: Liliaceae, deutzia, weigelia, clematis, Philadelphus, medicinal and industrial plants, orchards.

Botanical Gardens of the Ukrainian Academy of Science, Timirjazevskaya, Kiev 14

Botanical Gardens of the University, Komintern Street 1, Kiev, Ukraine, 56 acres (2 GH)

SF: Arboretum, rosarium, palms, cacti.

Botanical Gardens of the Pedagogic Institute, Kirov, Karl Marx Street 95, 8 acres (2 GH)

SF: Dendrological collection, bulbs.

Botanical Gardens of the Armenian Academy of Science, Kirovakan, Vanadzorskoye Ushchelis, Armenia SSR, 34 acres

SF: Ornamental plants (trees and shrubs).

Polar and Alpine Botanical Gardens of the Academy of Science, Kirovsk (Kola Peninsula), Kirov Street 9 a, Murmansk Region (1931), 865 acres (GH 478 sq. yds.)

SF: Breeding of new varieties suitable for northern regions.

Botanical Gardens of the Academy of Science of the Moldavia SSR, Kishinev, Dunaevsky Street 5, Moldavia, 182 acres

SF: Ornamental plants, shrubs, trees. Oil plants, medicinal and industrial plants.

Botanical Gardens of Kremenez, Krupskaya 1, Ternopol Region, Ukraine, 30 acres (1 GH)

Botanical Gardens of Kuibishev, Ovrag Podpolshikov, P. O. 24, 98 acres (1 GH)

Closed on Sundays. SF: Liliaceae, tulips, irises, succulents, poplars.

Botanical Gardens of Leninabad, Pravyi bereg, P. O. 6, Tadzhik SSR, 173 acres (3 GH)

Botanical Gardens of the Botanical Institute Komarov of the Academy of Science, Leningrad 22, Professor Popov Street 2 (1714), 55 acres (24 GH)

The greenhouses are closed on Sundays. SF: tropical and sub-tropical plants, arboretum, medicinal plants, hardy grasses. See also the article by Nina P. Nikolayenko.

Botanical Gardens of the University of Leningrad, Universitetskaya 7—9, Leningrad V, 164 (1712), 6 acres (1 GH)

Visits by experts and students by permission of the director. SF: Ornamental and medicinal plants.

Arboretum of S. M. Kirov Academy of Forestry, Institutsky Street 5, Leningrad 18, 27½ acres

Visits by permission of the director. SF: Azaleas, Betula, Populus, Ulmus, Sorbus.

Altai Botanical Gardens Leninogorsk, East Kazakhstan, Kazakh SSR, 445 acres (1 GH)

SF: Ornamental plants, trees and shrubs. Native medicinal plants, sub-tropical and tropical plants.

Forest-Steppe-Experimental Station for Ornamental Trees and Shrubs, Post Meshcherskoe, Lipetsk, 447 acres (1 GH)

SF: Syringa, Philodelphus, Spiraea, Crataegus.

Botanical Gardens of the University of Lvov, Marc Cheremshina Street 44 and Lomonosov Street 4, Lvov, Ukraine, 11 acres (1 GH)

Open Tuesdays and Fridays. SF: Tulips, dahlias, gladiolas, hyacinths, lilies, peonies, roses, native apple trees and vines.

Arboretum of the Institute of Forestry, Lvov, Pushkin Street 103, Ukraine, 15 acres

Central Botanical Gardens of the White Russian Academy of Science, Minsk, 13, Akademie Street 31, 237 acres (GH 1,837 sq. yds.)

Closed on Mondays. SF: Arboretum, lilies, tulips, roses, gladiolas.

Botanical Gardens of the White Russian University, Minsk, White Russian SSR, 6 acres

Botanical Gardens for Medicinal Plants of the First Medical Institute, Moscow D-100, 4, Krasnogvardeisky Proezd 20, 11 acres (GH 327 sq. yds.)

SF: Medicinal Plants.

Main Botanical Gardens of the Academy of Science of the USSR, Moscow, Botanicheskaya 4, Moscow I-276, 998 acres (GH 1¼ acres)

Open: Greenhouses, June to September, Tuesdays to Sundays from 10 a.m. to 6 p.m.; gardens, May to September daily from 10 a.m. to 8 p.m. SF: Native flora; trees and shrubs; narcissi, tulips, gladiolas, dahlias, roses, Liliaceae, irises, medicinal and industrial plants (more than 1,000 species). See article by N. P. Nikolayenko, 'Botanical Gardens and Parks in the Soviet Union.'

Botanical Garden and Schreder's Dendrarium of the Academy of Agriculture Timirjazev, Moscow A-8, Prjanishnikov Street 1, 2½ Acres (GH 120 sq. yds.)

SF: Systematic collections, dendrological collections of Crataegus, Euonymus, Quercus, Salix, Amelanchier, Rhododendron, Roses, Spiraea, Cornus, Syringa, Philadelphus.

Botanical Gardens of the Lomonosov University, Lenin Hill, Moscow V-234, 100 acres, 15 of which are occupied by a shrub garden (GH 2,213 sq. yds.)

Open: main gardens by permission of the director. Shrub garden, daily except Mondays. SF: Trees and shrubs, alpine and steppe flora, industrial plants, taxonomical collections, ornamental plants, orchards and berry fruit cultivation, hothouse plants.

Botanical Gardens of Kabardino-Balkar; Nalchik-Dolinsk, Kabardino, Balkaria SSR, 124 acres (GH under construction)

SF: Flora of Kabardino-Balkaria and North Caucasian regions and mountain flora of the Elbrus region.

Botanical Gardens of the Institute of Agriculture of Novosibirsk, Dobrolubov Street 289, 40 acres

SF: Fruit and berry cultivation.

Central Siberian Botanical Gardens of the Academy of Science, Novosibirsk, 553 acres (2 GH)

SF: Industrial and ornamental plants, dahlia garden, rosarium, hardy trees and shrubs, fruit and berry cultivation.

Botanical Gardens of the Academy of Science, Nukus, Karl Marx Street 2, Uzbek SSR, 124 acres (GH under construction)

Botanical Gardens of the Mechnikov University, Odessa, Proletarskyboulevard 48—50, Ukraine, 40 acres (7 GH)

Open Wednesdays and Fridays from 8 a.m. to 4 p.m.

Botanical Gardens of the Institute of Agriculture, Omsk, $3\frac{3}{4}$ acres

Open from June to August. Visits by permission of the director.

Botanical Gardens of the Pedagogic Institute, Penza, Karl Marx Street 4, $17\frac{1}{2}$ acres (1 GH)

Closed on Sundays. SF: Medicinal plants, ornamental plants, plants containing volatile oils.

Botanical Gardens of the University of Perm, Genkel Street 1, Perm 5, Zaimka, 15 acres (2 GH)

SF: Agricultural plants, medicinal plants, ornamental plants.

Botanical Gardens of the University of Petrosavodsk, Solomennoje, 348 acres (GH 287 sq. yds.)

SF: Medicinal plants, rock garden.

Botanical Gardens of the Agricultural-Biological Station of the Pedagogic Institute, Poltava, Ostrogradsky Street 2, Ukraine, 13 acres (GH 96 sq. yds.)

SF: Succulents.

Experimental Station of the Research Institute for Medicinal and Aromatic Plants, Przhevalsk, Kirghizian SSR, $2\frac{1}{2}$ acres

SF: Medicinal plants and herb garden.

Botanical Garden of the Institute of Pharmacy, Pyatigorsk, Kirov Avenue 33, $20\frac{1}{2}$ acres (GH 120 sq. yds.)

Open to students only. SF: Medicinal plants, poisonous plants.

Botanical Gardens of the Latvian Academy of Science, Riga, Salaspils, Latvian SSR, 327 acres (GH 2,870 sq. yds.)

SF: Native flora, annual and perennial plants, bulbs, roses, hothouse plants.

Botanical Gardens of the Latvian University, Riga, L. Kandavas Street 2, Latvia, 39 acres (GH 715 sq. yds.)

Open June to September from 10 a.m. to 8 p.m.; October to May from 8 a.m. to 3 p.m. daily except Saturdays and Mondays. SF: Arboretum, taxonomical groups, biological and morphological groups, decorative plants, hothouse plants.

Botanical Gardens of the University of Rostov/Don, P.O. 2, 494 acres

Closed Saturday afternoons and all day Sundays. SF: Fruit and berry cultivation, nuts, medicinal plants.

Botanical Gardens of the University of Samarkand, Gorkijboulevard 2, Uzbekian SSR, 50 acres (GH)

Botanical Gardens of the Institute of Agriculture, Schitomir, Stalin Street 9, Ukraine, 18 acres

Visits by permission of the director.

Botanical Gardens of the Armenian Academy of Science, Sevan, Armenia SSR, 10 acres

SF: Trees and shrubs, ornamental plants, fruit and berry cultivation.

Arboretum of the Scientific Research Institute for Sub-Tropical Forest and Park Cultivation, Kurortny Avenue 74, Sotshi (1910), 150 acres (GH 1,555 sq. yds.)

SF: Sub-tropical trees and shrubs, hothouse plants, flora of the Caucasus. Park of fabulous beauty.

Botanical Gardens of the Pedagogic Institute, Stavropol, Pushkin Street 1, Caucasus, $1\frac{3}{4}$ acres (1 GH)

SF: Agricultural plants of the Northern Caucasus.

Botanical Gardens of Stavropol, Caucasus, 1,203 acres

SF: Trees and shrubs, hardy bulbs.

Botanical Gardens of the Academy of Science, Sukhumi, Chavchavadze Street 18, Georgia SSR, 30 acres (1 GH)

SF: Sub-tropical plants, aquatic plants, chrysanthemums. The garden is one of the sights of the Caucasian Black Sea coast.

Botanical Gardens of the Biological Institute of the Academy of Science in the Urals, Sverdlovsk 8, 8th March Street 102, 120 acres (GH 418 sq. yds.)

Visits by permission of the director. SF: Trees and shrubs, hybrids of local origin.

Botanical Gardens of Tallin, Kloostrimetsa Street 44, Estonia, 313 acres (14 GH)

SF: Roses, carnations, begonias, succulents, irises.

Botanical Gardens of the University of Tartu, Michurin Street 40, Estonia, 7 acres (5 GH)

Botanical Gardens of the Academy of Science of Uzbekistan, Tashkent, Karamurtskaya 272, 198 acres (3 GH)

Closed on Tuesdays; visits at other times by permission of the director. SF: Dendrological park of the flora of Central Asia, Europe, the Caucasus, the Far East, China and North America. Tulips and other bulbs of Central Asia, plants of the Pamir Plateau, Allium, grass-like plants of Central Asia, ornamental plants, conifers, plants with technical uses, medicinal plants. This is the most interesting garden in Central Asia. See also article by N. P. Nikolayenko.

Central Botanical Gardens of Tiflis, 316 acres (GH 144 sq. yds.)

SF: Native species of vine and orchards. Interesting park with rich garden flora.

Botanical Gardens of the University of Tomsk, Lenin Street 36, Siberia (1885), 371 acres (4 GH)
Open Tuesdays, Thursdays and Sundays from 9 a.m. to 4.30 p.m. SF: Greenhouse plants, ornamental plants (trees and shrubs), flora of Siberia, fruit and berry cultivations. See also article by N. P. Nikolayenko.

Botanical Gardens of the Academy of Science of Bashkir, Ufa, Polarnaya Street 8, 299 acres (1 GH)
SF: Ornamental plants (trees and shrubs), greenhouse plants, fruit and berry cultivation, grasses.

Dendrological Park 'Sofievka,' Uman, Cherkessian Region, Ukraine, 319 acres

Botanical Gardens of the University of Ushgorod, Oktyabrskaya 60, Zakarpatskaja Region, Ukraine, 63 acres (1 GH)
SF: Bulbs.

Botanical Gardens of the Research Institute for Medicinal and Aromatic Plants, Vilar, Moscow Region, 105 acres (8 GH)
SF: Pharmaceutical plants.

Botanical Gardens of the University of Vilnius, Churlionio 110, Lithuania SSR, 15 acres (2 GH)
SF: Taxonomical collection, medicinal plants, plants with technical uses, vegetables.

Botanical Gardens of the Medical Institute of Witebsk, Frunse Avenue 7, White Russian SSR, 50 acres (1 GH)
SF: Medicinal plants, taxonomical section.

Botanical Gardens of the Far Eastern Department of the Academy of Science of Siberia, Vladivostock, Makovsky Street 27, 443 acres (GH 239 sq. yds.)

Botanical Gardens of the University of Woronesh, P. O. 12, 178 acres

Botanical Gardens of the Pedagogic Institute, Yaroslavl, Republikanskaya 108, Yaroslavl, about 7½ acres (GH 120 sq. yds.)
Closed on Sundays. SF: Medicinal plants, industrial plants, oil-bearing plants, gladioli, dahlias, phlox. Taxonomical collections, cacti.

Botanical Gardens of the Armenian Academy of Science, Yerevan, Kanaker, Armenian SSR, 247 acres (GH 957 sq. yds.)
SF: Trees and shrubs, ornamental plants, greenhouse plants, medicinal plants.

Africa

Algeria

Service Botanique Expérimentale Hamma, Rue de Lyon, Hamma, Algeria, 153 acres (GH 598 sq. yds.)
Closed from 11.30 a.m. to 2 p.m. SF: Ornamental shrubs and trees, Cycadeae, palms, Ficus, exotic fruit, flora of Algeria.

Station Botanique de Maison-Carrée, Maison Carrée near Algiers

Cameroons

Victoria Botanic Gardens, Victoria (1892), 119 acres (1 GH)
SF: Plants formerly of commercial value.

Congo (formerly Belgian Congo)

Jardin Botanique Eala (near Coquilhatville), Equator

Arboretum du Comité Spécial du Katanga, Route de l'Étoile, Elisabethville, Katanga

Jardin Gillet, Kisantu, Congo, 319 acres (1 GH)
SF: Orchids, ornamental and medicinal plants, palms, native trees.

Jardin Botanique, Institut National pour l'Étude Agronomique du Congo, Yangambi, Orientale

Congo (formerly French Congo)

Jardin d'Essais, Brazzaville

Jardin d'Essais, M'Boko

Jardin d'Essais, Mindouli

Jardin d'Essais, Pointe Noire

Egypt

Botanic Gardens of the University of Alexandria, Moharram Bey, 3 acres (4 GH)
Visits by permission of the director. SF: Cacti, palms, begonias, ferns, Croton.

Botanical Gardens of Assuan, 16 acres
SF: Tropical industrial plants.

Botanic Gardens of Giza-Orman, Cairo, 30 acres
SF: Conifers, palms, cacti, succulents.

Zohariya Trial Gardens, Gezira, Cairo, 15 acres (5 GH)
Open daily from 8 a.m. to 2 p.m. SF: Ferns, greenhouse plants.

Botanical Gardens, Section of Desert Institute, Rue Sultan Hussein, Cairo

Botanic Garden, Faculty of Sciences, Department of Botany, A'in Shams University, Abbassiya, Cairo

Middle Egypt Botanic Station, El Saff

Ghana

Botanic Garden Aburi

Botanic Garden, University College of Ghana, P.O. Box 25, Accra Legon

Kenya

East Africa Agriculture and Forestry Research Organisation Kikuyu, P.O. Box 21, 1,582 acres
Open weekdays. SF: Eucalyptus, Callitris, Latin-American Pinus species.

Forest Arboretum, Nairobi, Kenya, East Africa, 100 acres
SF: Native hard woods, aloe, euphorbia.

Libya

Sidi Mesri Experimental Station, Tripoli, Libya, 198 acres (1 GH)
SF: Palms.

Madagascar

Jardin Botanique de Tsimbazaza, Tananarive, Post Box 434 (1927), 57 acres
SF: Succulents, aloe, euphorbia, Kalanchoë, Pachypodium, orchids, begonias, native plants.

Mali

Parc Botanique et Zoologique, Bamako

Mauretania

Royal Botanic Gardens, Pamplemousses, Mauritius (1735), 66 acres
SF: Palms

Morocco

Jardin Botanique, Avenue Biarnay, Rabat, 887 sq. yds.
Visits by permission of the director. SF: Native plants.

Pepinières Générales, Rabat, Route de Rabat No. 1 (1921), 36 acres (GH 1,316 sq. yds.)
Open daily from 9 a.m. to noon and 2—6 p.m. SF: Cacti collection and collection of evergreen shrubs, Philodendron, Ficus decora.

Jardins Exotiques, Kénitra, Sidi Bouknadel
RVS: April to end of May. Open daily from 10 a.m. to 11.30 a.m. and 2—7 p.m. SF: Victoria regia, water lilies, calendula, violets, poppy, marguerites, palms. Tropical trees, roses, plants from Brazil, Mexico, Peru, the Cape Province, Australian flora. On the Route de Rabat.

Jardins du 'Dar Es-Salaam' (Palace gardens of the Kings in Rabat), at 8 km. (5 miles), exit towards Qued-Zem
Open Fridays and Sundays afternoons.

Jardins de la Chella, Rabat
SF: Carnations, blossoms and fruit of the cedar.

'Les Jardins d'Essais,' Meknes
SF: Trial grounds near the ruins of the palace of Meknes.

Le Jardin Majorell, Marrakesh
SF: Exotic garden.

La Rosairie, Marrakesh
SF: Rosarium.

Mozambique—Portuguese East Africa

Jardim Botânico Vasco da Gama, Laurenço Marques
SF: Collection of rare tropical plants.

Nigeria

Botanical Garden of University College, Ibadan, 40 acres
SF: Native Plants.

Réunion

Jardin Botanique, Saint Denis

Rhodesia

Federal Botanic Garden, Causeway, Salisbury, P.O. Box 8100, 119 acres
Visits by permission of the director. SF: The garden is still in process of extension.

Senegal

Jardin Botanique—Institut Français d'Afrique Noire, Dakar, B.P. 206, 2 acres
Open weekdays. SF: Native and acclimatised trees and shrubs.

Jardin Botanique de la Faculté des Sciences, P.O. Box 6049, Dakar, 10 acres (2 GH)

Parc Forestier de Hann (1903), 131 acres
SF: Tropical, sub-tropical and Mediterranean plants, orchids, cacti, Aralias, Arboretum. Access via Dakar, road to Rufisque, 3¾ miles.

South Africa

Harold Porter Botanic Reserve, Betty's Bay (near False Bay)—37 miles from Cape Town (1959), 988 acres

RVS: Winter and spring. SF: Proteaceae, Erica species, bulbs, flora of the winter rain region.

Caledon Wild Flower Garden (1927), 25 acres

RVS: August to October. SF: Shrubby and annual Mesembryanthemum, Compositae, Erica, Protea; shrubs and trees; e.g. Nymania capensis, Alberta magna, Podalyria, etc. About 68 miles from Cape Town on the National Road to Garden Route.

Cape Flats Flora Reserve (1957), 15 acres

RVS: Winter and spring. SF: Bog plants and flora of the Cape Flats.

Claremont Public Garden, Cape Town (about 1900), 10 acres

SF: Collection of Araucarias. Tall rhododendrons, copper beeches, birches, conifers, Japanese garden. Native and foreign trees and shrubs.

Public Garden Cape Town (1652), 12 acres (GH 1¼ acres)

Closed on Good Friday and Christmas. SF: Orchids, hothouse plants, ferns, roses, rock gardens, succulents, native and foreign trees and shrubs.

Darling Flora Reserve Yzerfontain, Darling (about 31 miles from Cape Town) (1957), 124 acres

RVS: Spring only. SF: Flora of the sand veld and bulbs.

Museum Gardens of East London

SF: Cycadeae collection.

Grahamstown Municipal Botanical Gardens, Grahamstown, 40 acres (2 GH)

SF: Native plants and trees.

Succulenta Nurseries, Hout Bay, Cape (1953), 20 acres (GH 1¼ acres)

RVS: October to April. To view make appointment by telephone; Tel.: 705,135. SF: South African succulents and cacti.

Durban Botanical Garden, Durban (1851), 50 acres

SF: Collection of orchids (a total of 3,000 plants) with specimens from Brazil, America and other parts of the world. Palms. Large collection of exotic plants.

'The Wilds' Garden of the City of Johannesburg (1932), 45 acres

SF: Transvaal and Cape Proteaceae, Ericaceae, Cycadeae. A total of 325 different species, of which 120 are aloes, 17 gladiolas, 40 ericas.

National Botanic Gardens of South Africa, Kirstenbosch, Newlands, Cape Province (7½ miles from Cape Town) (1913), 1,086 acres (6 GH)

RVS: August to November. The annual flower shows take place on 23rd and 24th September. SF: Cycadeae and proteaceae. The famous silver tree (Leucadendron argenteum). Collection of South African bog plants, trees and shrubs, succulents, annuals, collection of Ericaceae, etc., in magnificent surroundings.

Nursery 'Sheilam' (M. Malherbe), Klaasvoogds near Robertson, about 75 miles from Cape Town

SF: Beautiful specimens of cacti in the open, latest discoveries from South America, Mexico, etc. Excellent South African succulent cultivations, especially Fockea and other Asclepiadaceae. Euphorbias, Pleiospilos, Argyroderma, Lithops and many other species.

The Harvey Nature Reserve, Linksfield (1952), 7 acres

SF: Aloe and Protea species.

Melville-Koppies Nature Reserve (1959), 140 acres

SF: Interesting native plants.

Paarl Mountain Flower Reserve, Paarl, 32¼ miles from Cape Town

RVS: September to November. SF: Protea, heathers, native shrubs and trees in attractive surroundings.

Botanic Gardens Pietermaritzburg, Natal, 140 acres (3 GH)

SF: Azaleas.

Prince Alfred Park, Port Elisabeth, about 100 acres (GH)

SF: Succulents.

Botanic Garden of the University of Pretoria, Pretoria (1934), 5 acres (GH 178 sq. yds.)

Visits by flower lovers and students by permission of the director. SF: Aloe, euphorbias, South African succulents and ferns.

Pretoria National Botanic Garden, National Herbarium, Division of Botany, Department of Agriculture, P. O. Box 994, Pretoria (1955), 173 acres (GH 957 sq. yds.)

RVS: January to March (summer); July (aloe in flower), September (Proteaceae and erica in flower). FS: One of the largest collection of greenhouse succulents in South Africa. Aloe garden (contains the best part of all South African, including some tropical species), Encephalartos collection, including all South African species (with one exception); special collection of Cape Proteaceae and Erica species. The Garden contains chiefly South African flora, but also some plants from other parts of Africa, e.g. Madagascar. There are no plants from other countries.

Steenbras Reservoir. 40 miles from Cape Town

Open: weekdays from 8.30 a.m. to 4 p.m.; Saturdays from 8.30 a.m. to noon. Application for admission to Central Booking Office, City Hall, Corporation Street. SF: Wild flower gardens in the Hottentot-Holland Mountains on the road to Caledon. In high summer the famous red Disa uniflora, a large flowering ground orchid, flowers here as in its natural habitat. At about the same time the ground is red with the flowers of Rochea coccinea which is a native of that region. Access: On the road leading over the mountain beyond Gordon's Bay, or from the summit of Sir Lowry Pass.

Protea Heights Wild Flower Garden, Devon Valley, Stellenbosch, 148 acres

Open: August to October, Wednesdays, Saturdays, Sundays, Tuesdays and Holidays from 10 a.m. to noon and from 3—5 p.m. SF: Various Proteaceae and flora of South Africa. About 25 miles from Cape Town, via Bellville and Kuils River, then along the road to Stellenbosch, bear left at the far end of the General Box Factory, signpost to garden.

Botanical Garden, University of Stellenbosch, Stellenbosch, 3 acres (GH 436 sq. yds.)

RVS: August to November. Open 8 a.m. to noon and 2—5 p.m., Saturdays 8 a.m. to noon; closed on Sundays. SF: One of the most beautiful collections of succulents, especially Mesembryanthemaceae, Asclepiadaceae, Apocynaceae, Liliaceae, Portulacaceae; Welwitschia, which flowers and fruits regularly. Insectivores. Tropical in-

dustrial plants: cocoa, coffee, pepper, rice, cotton, etc. Tree ferns of South Africa and New Zealand. Proteaceae and Ericaceae of South Africa. Small arboretum of native trees and shrubs. Orchids, Cattleya, Cymbidium, Paphiopedilum, Phalaenopsis and native species, e.g. Disa uniflora among others, as well as Satyrium, Schizodium.

Karoo Garden in Worcester (about 75 miles from Cape Town). The Garden is administered in conjunction with the Kirstenbosch Garden (1946), 269 acres

RVS: September and October (spring). Closed on Sundays. SF: One of the best collections of South African succulents.

Tunis

Service Botanique et Agronomique de Tunisie, Ariana, 370 acres

Open daily from 8.30 a.m. to noon and from 12.40—4 p.m.

Uganda

Botanic Garden, Entebbe, P. O. Box 40 (1898), 69 acres

SF: Tropical industrial plants.

Asia

Burma

The Agri-Horticultural Society of Burma (Kandawgalay), Rangoon (2 GH)

Open from 7 a.m. to 11 a.m. and 2—5.30 p.m.

Botanical Gardens, Maymyo

Ceylon

Botanic Garden, Heneratgoda, Gampaha, Colombo District (1878), 34 acres

SF: Rubber, natural jungle, cocoa palms. Access: 25 miles north-east of Colombo. Good road. Also direct by train.

Botanic Gardens, Hakgala, Newara Eliya District (1861), 64 acres (GH 178 sq. yds.)

RVS: April. SF: Tree ferns, trial grounds for Chichona. Plants of temperate and sub-tropical climates. Access: 114 miles from Colombo and 3 miles from Newara Eliya. 5,480 ft. above sea level. To be reached by car or train.

Royal Botanic Gardens, Peradeniya, Kandy District (1821), 145 acres (5 GH)

RVS: January to April. SF: Collections of Anthurium, orchids, palms. Access: 67 miles from Colombo, 4 miles from Kandy. Good road. Also direct by train.

China

Canton Botanical Garden, Canton, Kwantung, 2,471 acres

Hainan Botanical Garden, Hainan, Island of Hainan (under construction)

Hangchow Botanical Garden, Hangchow, Chekiang (under construction)

Wuhan Botanical Garden, Hupei, 445 acres

Kunming Botanical Garden, Kunming, Yunnan, 87 acres

SF: Rare camellia and rhododendron species, plants cultivated for the extraction of volatile oils (camphor, etc.).

Lushan Botanical Garden, Lushan, Kiangsi, 692 acres

SF: Alpine plants and trees.

Nanking Sun Yat-Sen Botanical Garden, Nanking, Kiangsu, 544 acres

SF: Medicinal plants (500 different species).

Peking Botanical Garden, Peking Hopei, 1,236 acres (GH)

Botanical Garden Si-Shan, Shanghai

Formosa

Heng-Chun Tropical Forest Botanical Garden, Heng-Chun, Pingtung, Taiwan, 124 acres

SF: Industrial plants (trees and shrubs).

Taiwan Forestry Research Institute Botanical Garden, Po-Ai Road, Taipei, Taiwan, 26 acres (3 GH)

Hong Kong

Botanic Gardens, West-Wing, Central District, Garden Road, Hong Kong (1871), 16 acres (GH 211 sq. yds.)

RVS: March to May and October. SF: Rhododendron and chrysanthemums.

India

Experimental Garden, Central Botanical Laboratory, 10 Chatham Lines, Allahabad, 3 acres (3 GH)

Visits by permission of the director between 10 a.m. and 5 p.m. SF: Indian industrial plants, orchids, Dioscorea.

Botanic Garden 'Lal-Bagh,' Bangalore 4, South India (1856), 237 acres

RVS: January to March, July to September. SF: Bougainvillea, Hibiscus, magnificent flowering tropical trees, climbers and shrubs, Croton. Access: 4 miles from railway station and 8 miles from airport.

Botanical Garden of Benares Hindu University, Benares 5, Uttar Pradesh

Victoria Garden, Bombay

Kamala Nehru Garden, Bombay

Botanic Gardens, Agricultural College and Research Institute, Coimbatore, Madras State

Botanic Gardens Calcutta, Howrah District, West Bengal (1787), 269 acres (GH 2 acres, one large and one small palm house, one fern house, one cactus house and one orchid house)

RVS: October to March. SF: Palms (about 250 species), Pandanetum (8 species), bamboo collections (28 species), collections of Adiantum and cacti; Metasequoia and other conifers, Ginkgo, ornamental plants, aquatic plants and many exotic plants, some of them extremely rare; industrial plants.

Botanic Garden, Darjeeling

Botanic Garden of the Forest Research Institute, New Forest, Dehra-Dun, 18 acres

SF: Timber trees and other industrial plants.

Botanic Garden, Osmania University, Botany Department, Hyderabad-Deccan, 2 acres (2 GH)

Visits by permission of the director. SF: Ferns, cacti, succulents, Codiaeum, Coleus, ornamental plants, tropical trees and shrubs.

National Botanic Gardens, Lucknow, 75 acres (5 GH)

SF: Numerous collections of ornamental and industrial plants, hibiscus, canna, Ixora, citrus, vitis, roses, climbers, Indian medicinal plants.

Botanic Gardens, Madras

Bryant Park, Kadai Canal, Madurai

Division of Botany, Indian Agricultural Research Institute, New Delhi, 49½ acres (3 GH)

Visits by permission of the director.

Botanic Gardens Ootacamund, Nilgiris (1847), 54 acres (GH 400 sq. yds.)

RVS: April, May and September. SF: Cacti, ferns and orchids.

Sim's Park, Coonor, Nilgiris (1873), 30 acres

RVS: April to June, August and September. SF: Roses.

Experimental Garden, Botanical Survey of India, Western Circle, 7 Koregaon Road, Poona 1, 49½ acres (1 GH)

Visits by permission of the director. SF: Orchids, Indian medicinal plants.

Governmental Horticultural Research Institute, Saharanpur, Uttar Pradesh, 125 acres (2 GH)

Open daily from 5 a.m. to 7 a.m. and from 5—7 p.m. SF: Tropical and sub-tropical fruit and ornamental plants.

Shalimar Gardens, Srinagar, Kashmir

Botanic Garden, Maharana Bhupal College, Udaipur, Rajasthan

Indonesia

Indonesian Botanical Garden, Bogor (1817), 198 acres (GH 1½ acres)

SF: Palms, bamboo, cacti, orchids, ornamental plants.

Purwodadi Botanic Garden, Lawang, Java, 210 acres

SF: Palms. Trial grounds for plants not native to tropical climate.

Setia Mulia Botanic Garden, near Pedang, Sumatra Indonesia Botanical Garden Tjibodas, Bogor, Indonesia (1817), 87 acres (GH 2,392 sq. yds.)

SF: Tropical rock garden.

Iran

Botanical Garden, Agricultural College, University of Teheran, Karadj (1930), 7 acres (GH 143 sq. yds.)

Open from 8 a.m. to noon and 2—5 p.m., except Fridays. SF: Arboretum.

Iraq

Zaafaraniyah Arboretum, Zaafaraniyah, Horticultural Experimental Station, Bagdad, 11 acres (2 GH)

Open 8 a.m. to 2 p.m. SF: Acacia, eucalyptus, Callistemon, Phoenix, Washingtonia, Sabal, Nerium, Platanus, Fraxinus, Schinus, Populus, Catalpa, Rosa, Morus, Lantana, Vitex.

Israel

Botanical Garden 'Mikveh-Israel,' Holon, 20 acres (GH)

SF: Annual flowers, conifers, Quercetum, palms, bamboo, climbers.

The Botanic Garden of the Hebrew University, Jerusalem, 20 acres

Botanic Garden Ilanoth, P. O. Box 88, Nathanya, 30 acres

Open from 8 a.m. to 4 p.m. SF: Acacia (70 species), eucalyptus (180 species).

Botanic Garden of Tel-Aviv University, 155 Herzl Street, Tel-Aviv, 4 acres

Visits by permission of the director for experts and students. SF: Bulbs and corms native to Israel.

Japan

Botanic Garden of Hiroshima University, Higashisenda-machi, Hiroshima

Botanic Garden of the Tohoku University, Kawauchi, Sendai-shi, Miyagi-ken

Botanic Garden Kanagawa, 1018 Okamoto, Kamakura-shi, Kanagawa-ken (1962), 17 acres (GH 654 sq. yds.)

RVS: May, June. Open throughout the year (except 28th Dezember to 4th January, Mondays and days following national holidays). SF: Peonies (perennials and shrubs), Japanese iris, Liliaceae.

Botanic Garden of the Faculty of Science, University of Kanazawa, Isikawa-ken, 7 acres (1 GH)

Visits by permission of the director. SF: Orchids and Liliaceae.

Saitama Botanical Garden, Angyo Kawaguchi-shi, Saitama-ken

Experimental Station of Medicinal Plants, 30 Kasukabe-shi, Saitama-ken, 6 acres (1 GH)

Open weekdays from 8.30 a.m. to 5 p.m.; Saturdays from 8.30 a.m. to 12.30 p.m. SF: Aloe, Artemisia, Gentiana, Rauwolfia.

Kobe Municipal Arboretum, 4-1 Nakaichiri-ya, Shimotanigami, Yammada-cho, Hyogo-ku, Kobe-shi, 244 1/2 acres (1 GH)

Open 4th January to 28th December from 9 a.m. to 4.30 p.m. SF: Conifers.

Kyoto Botanical Garden, Shimogamo, Sakyo-ku, Kyoto-shi

Kyoto Takeda Herbal Garden, Ichijoji, Sakyo-ku, Kyoto-shi, 17 acres

Visits by permission of the director on weekdays between 8 a.m. and 4.30 p.m. SF: Digitalis (foxglove), Allium (Leek) species.

The Botanical Garden of Osaka City University, Kisaichi, Katano-cho, Kitakawochi-gun, Osaka-fu, 75 acres (GH 837 sq. yds.)

SF: Hibiscus, succulents, tropical ornamental and industrial plants, perennials of Japan and Japanese garden plants.

The Botanic Garden, Faculty of Agriculture, Hokkaido University, Sapporo, 34 acres (GH 1,196 sq. yds.)

Open May to October from 8.30 a.m. to 4.30 p.m. November to April on Saturdays, Sundays, Wednesdays and Holidays only. SF: Alpinum, especially plants of Northern Japan.

Botanical Garden Tohoku University, Sendai, 4 sq. miles (GH under construction)

Visits by permission of the director.

Botanic Garden Koishikawa 106, Hakusan-Godenmachi, Bunkyo-ku, Tokyo (1877), 40 acres (GH 568 sq. yds.)

SF: Japanese ornamental cherry trees, Prunus mume, Japanese Primulae, barberries, Cotoneaster. The oldest botanical garden in Japan with a rich variety of plants.

Nagoya Higashiyama Botanical Garden, Tashiro-cho, Chigusa-ku, Nagoya-shi

Botanic Garden of the Agricultural Academy of Tottori

Botanic Garden Miye University, Kamihama-cho, Tsu-shi, Miye-ken

North Korea

Botanical Garden, Pyongyang

Lebanon

Jardin d'Acclimatation, Beirut

Malaya

Forest Research Institute, Kepong, Selangor, 1,285 acres

Visits by permission of the director. SF: Various families of the woody plants of East Asia.

Botanic Gardens Penang, George Town, Waterfall Road (1884), 71 acres

RVS: January to April. SF: Malayan orchids in the open.

Seremban Lake Gardens, Negri Sembilan, Malaya (1946), 26 acres (4 GH)

Botanic Gardens, Singapore 10 (1859), 80.5 acres

SF: Orchids, palms, bamboo, ferns. Access: 4 miles from the centre of Singapore.

Lake Gardens Taiping, Perak (1897), 180 3/4 acres

RVS: January, March, November, December. SF: Spathoglottis, Gerbera, Xanthosoma, Pentas, begonia, hydrangea, Barleria, Gardenia, Kopsia, Nerium (oleander), Allamanda, Bignonia, Bougainvillea, Lantana, Canna, Ixora, Croton. Access by Simpang and Kota roads from the Main Trunk road.

Pakistan

M. Gandhi Garden, Burns Garden and Frère Hall Gardens, Karachi, 45 1/2 acres (1 GH)

Botanic Garden of Punjab University, Lahore, West Pakistan

Philippines

Makiling National Park, College of Forestry, University of the Philippines, Laguna, 9,637 1/4 acres (5 GH)

Open Mondays to Fridays from 8 a.m. to 4 p.m. SF: Bamboo, palms, exotic plants.

Arboretum Los Baños, College of Agriculture, Laguna, 39 sq. miles (GH)

Open Mondays to Saturdays from 7 a.m. to noon and 1—4 p.m. SF: Ferns, Ficus, palms.

Botanic Garden, Manila, Rizal

Thailand

Phu Khae-Botanic Garden, Saraburi near Bangkok (1940), 3/4 sq. mile

RVS: May. SF: The arboretum of Thailand.

Turkey

Botanical Garden of the University of Istanbul, Süleymaniye, Istanbul (1935), 2 1/2 acres (GH 776 sq. yds.)

RVS: Spring and winter. SF: Plants of the Anatolian highlands, tropical and sub-tropical plants.

North Vietnam

Jardin Botanique et d'Acclimatation de Hanoi, Hanoi

South Vietnam

Huyul Van-Tung, Jardin Botanique, Saigon

Australia, New Zealand, Oceania

Australia

Waite Agricultural Research Institute, Private Mail Bag 1, Adelaide, South Australia, 54 acres

SF: Eucalyptus.

Botanic Gardens, North Terrace, Adelaide, South Australia (1855), 257 acres (148 of which on Mount Lofty, east of Adelaide) (GH 925 sq. yds.)

RVS: September, October, December, January, March, April. SF: Roses, wisteria, dahlia garden, collection of cacti and succulents, water lilies (under glass and in the open), especially Victoria species, Platanus and Ficus, native plants of Australia.

Botanic Garden Brisbane, Queensland (1855), 47 acres (GH 359 sq. yds.)

RVS: October to May. SF: Palms, succulents, leaf plants, native plants, tropical trees.

Sherwood Arboretum, Sherwood, Brisbane, Queensland, 32 acres

SF: Eucalyptus.

Canberra Botanic Gardens, Canberra. A.C.T., 86 1/2 acres (GH under construction)

Visits by permission of the director. SF: Eucalyptus, acacia, Grevillea.

Plant Introduction Section, Division of Plant Industry, C.S.J.R.O., P.O. Box 109, Canberra, 10 acres (4 GH)

Visits by permission of the director.

Botanical Gardens of North Territory, Darwin, North Territory

Tasmanian Botanical Gardens, Queen's Domain, Hobart, Tasmania (1818), 27 1/2 acres (GH 718 sq. yds.)

RVS: December to April. SF: Various collections. Conifers, oak trees, eucalyptus.

Royal Botanic Garden and National Herbarium, South Yarra, S.E. 1, Birdwood Avenue, Melbourne, Victoria (1846), 87 acres (GH 47 acres)

RVS: April to October. Open all day weekdays. SF: Flora of Australia, rhododendron, camellia, Quercus, cacti, succulents (interesting collections).

'King's Park' Botanic Gardens, Perth, Western Australia (1961), 25 acres (GH 178 sq. yds.)

RVS: September and October. SF: Flora of Western Australia, palm collection in the open.

Botanic Gardens, Rockhampton, Queensland

Royal Botanic Gardens, Sydney, New South Wales (1816), 64 acres (GH 1,196 sq. yds.)

RVS: September and October. SF: Palm collection in the open. Native trees.

Toowomba Botanical Gardens, Queensland, 44 sq. miles (3 GH)

Botanic Gardens Townsville, North Queensland, 10 acres

SF: Hibiscus, Codiaeum, Acalypha.

Fiji Islands

Suva—Botanical Gardens, Queen Elizabeth Drive, Suva, 10 acres

SF: Tropical palms and flowering shrubs.

New Guinea

Botanic Gardens (Division of Botany Department), Lae, 100 acres and 138 acres (3 GH)

Botanic Gardens, Department of Agriculture, Rabaul, Bismarck Archipelago, New Britain (Birara)

New Zealand

Auckland Domain—Address: Town Hall, Auckland, C 1 (1893), 139 acres (GH)

RVS: January to March. Greenhouses open from 10 a.m. to 4 p.m. SF: Native and exotic plants. Victoria amazonica. Comprehensive collection of wild roses.

Mrs. Nancy Steen, 30 Upland Road, Auckland, S.E. 2

SF: Complete collection of wild roses.

Brooklands Park, Brooklands Drive (N.P.C.C.) (1843), 54 acres

RVS: January to February, September and October. SF: Flora of Taranaki.

Christchurch Botanic Gardens, C 1 (1863), 75 acres (GH about 1,675 sq. yds.)

RVS: September to November, January to May. SF: Collection of New Zealand plants divided into alpine, cultivated species of native plants, shrubs and perennials. Collection of exotic trees and shrubs. Cacti, ferns, large rock garden, primula garden and flower beds with the most beautiful flowers of the season. Succulent house, fern house, house with tropical plants.

Otari Open-air Native Plant Museum, 160 Wilton Road, Wilton, Wellington (1927), 158 acres

RVS: September to March. SF: Alpinum, ferns, native bush vegetation, taxonomical collections of Hebe, Coprosma, Olearia, Pittosporum, Carmichaelia.

Pukekura Park, New Plymouth, City Council, Cnr. Liardet and Filis Streets (1875), 53 acres (GH about 720 sq. yds.)

RVS: October, January, February. SF: Native flora, rhododendron, begonias, collection of New Zealand ferns.

Pukeiti Rhododendron Trust Garden, Upper Carrington Road, Okato, Taranaki (1951), 890 acres

RVS: September, October, November. Always open to members. SF: Exotic rhododendrons, camellia, magnolia, sub-tropical rain forest.

Truby King Dell, Brooklands Road (N.P.C.C.) (1954), 4 acres

RVS: October and April. SF: Conifers, azaleas, summer and autumn flowers, deciduous trees.

Waiwaka Reserve, Waiwaka Terrace (N.P.C.C.) (1961), 6 acres

RVS: August and September, April. SF: Camellias, deciduous trees, hydrangeas.

'Iris Place,' Bastia Hill, Wanganui

SF: Internationally famous iris garden.

Wellington City Botanic Gardens, Glenmore Street, Wellington (1869), 62 acres (GH 977 sq. yds.)

Open in summer 10 a.m. to 4.30 p.m. and on Tuesdays, Thursdays, Saturdays and Sundays from 7 a.m. to 9 p.m.; in winter 10 a.m. to 4.30 p.m. SF: Alpinum, collections of native plants.

South and Central America

Argentina

Botanical Garden, Agricultural and Veterinary Faculty, Avenue San Martin 4453, Buenos Aires, 3³/₄ acres (1 GH)

Open daily from 7 a.m. to 1 p.m.

Botanical Garden 'Carlos Thays,' Municipal Institute of Botany, Santa Fé 3951, Buenos Aires (1892), 20 acres (4 GH)

SF: Plants of the sub-tropical regions of Argentina.

Institute of Botanical Agriculture—I.N.T.A.—Araoz 2875, Buenos Aires, 25 acres (2 GH)

Open Mondays to Fridays from 9 a.m. to 5 p.m. SF: Salicaceae.

Botanical Garden, Castelar, Province of Buenos Aires

Botanical Garden of the Faculty of Natural Science and Museum of La Plata, La Plata, Province of Buenos Aires

Agro-Botanical Garden Santa Catalina, Institute of Technology of Santa Catalina, Llavallol, FNGR, 30 acres (GH projected)

Institute of Botany Darwinion Lavardén y Del Campo (affiliated to the Academy of Science, Physics and Natural Science, Buenos Aires), San Isidro, Province of Buenos Aires, 2,392 acres

Visits by permission of the director. SF: Ornamental plants and flora of Argentina.

Botanical Garden of the National University del Litoral, Santa Fé, Province of Santa Fé

Acclimatisation Garden Yeruá, Experimental Sub-Station of Colonia Yeruá, Yeruá, Entre Rios Province

National Park, Nahuel-Huapi

Barbados

Andromeda Gardens, St. Joseph, Barbados (1948), 5 acres

Open daily from 10 a.m., except Sundays. SF: Bougainvillea, Philodendron, Heliconia, Oleander, Hibiscus, palms, ferns.

Welchman Hall Gulley, St. Thomas, Barbados (1958), 10 acres

Open Mondays, Wednesdays and Fridays from 9.30 a.m. to noon. SF: Industrial plants (trees and shrubs).

Brazil

Museu Paraense 'Emilio Goeldi,' Post Box 399, Belém, Para, 10 acres

Open daily from 7 a.m. to 11 a.m. and from 1—5 p.m.; Closed on Saturday afternoons. SF: Flora of the Amazon region.

Botanical Garden Belo Horizonte, Belo Horizonte, Minas Gerais

Botanical and Horticultural Gardens, Experimental and Cultivation Service for Vegetable Produce, Florianópolis, Est. Santa Catarina

Botanical Garden, School of Pharmacy, Ouro Prêto, Est. Minas Gerais

Zoological and Botanical Park, Dois Irmãos, Recife, Pernambuco

Park of Ribeirão Prêto, Ribeirão Prêto, Minas Gerais

Botanical Garden 'Kurt Klagebrunn,' Rio de Janeiro, Rua Moura Brasil 40 a, Laranjeiras, Est. da Guanabara

Division of Botany of the National Museum—Botanical Garden, Quinta de Boa Vista, Rio de Janeiro, Guanabara, 8 1/2 acres (1 GH)
Visits by permission of the director. SF: Flowering trees, Heliconia, Scitaminae, medicinal plants, aquatic plants.

Botanical Gardens of Rio de Janeiro, Rua Jardim Botânico, 1008 Gavea GB-ZC-20, Rio de Janeiro, Guanabara (1808), 133 acres (7 GH)
RVS: Spring and autumn. Open Mondays to Fridays from 11 a.m. to 5 p.m. SF: Orchids, Araceae, cacti, palms, Marantaceae, Musaceae, Filicales.

Ondina Park, Rio Vermelho, Salvador, Bahia

Botanical Garden of São Paulo, Post Box 4005, 592 acres (2 GH)
Closed on Mondays. SF: Orchids, begonias.

British Guiana

Botanic Garden, Georgetown, 355 acres (GH)

Botanic Gardens New Amsterdam

British West Indies

St. Vincent Botanic Gardens, Kingstown, 30 acres
SF: Hibiscus, Bougainvillea, Ixora.

Botanic Gardens Roseau, Dominica, 44 acres
SF: Roses, flowering shrubs, palms; arboretum.

Botanic Gardens, St. Georges, Grenada, 12 acres (GH 55 sq. yds.)

Botanic Garden, Scarborough, Tobago, West Indies (1899), 2,153 sq. yds. (GH 60 sq. yds.)
RVS: January to July. SF: Palms. Tropical fruit trees, flowering shrubs.

Royal Botanic Garden, Trinidad (1818), 60 acres (GH 215 sq. yds)
RVS: December to May. SF: Palms, tropical trees, flowering shrubs.

Chile

Botanical Institute and Botanical Garden, Austral University, Valdivia (1958), 12 acres
RVS: December to March; open weekdays from 8 a.m. to noon and 2—6 p.m. SF: Flora of Southern Chile, Oenotheraceae.

National Botanical Gardens of Chile, Valparaiso, Viña del Mar (1898 and 1957), 3,707 acres
RVS: September to December. Open from 9 a.m. to noon and 2—6 p.m. SF: Flora of Central Chile, succulents. Access: 10 minutes from railways station Viña del Mar by car or bus.

Columbia

Botanical Garden 'José C. Mútis,' Carrera 58, Calle 65, Bogotá (1955), 66 acres (GH 1 1/4 acres, under construction)
Not yet open to the general public. SF: Alpine flora, flora of the Andes, orchids, 'Bosques subandinos.'

Gardens of the Faculty of Agronomy, University of Caldas, Manizales, 1 1/4 acres (1 GH)

National Botanical Gardens, Cali, Valle

Cuba

Atkins Garden and Research Laboratory, Apartado 414, Cienfuegos, 25 acres (3 GH)
SF: Palms, leguminous plants.

Botanic Garden, Santiago de las Vegas, Havana, 12 acres
SF: Industrial plants.

Arboretum, Experimental Agricultural Station, Medicinal and Aromatic Plants, Santiago de las Vegas

Guatemala

Botanic Gardens of Guatemala, Avenida de la Reform 0-42, Zona 10, Guatemala City, affiliated to the University of San Carlos, 62 acres (2 GH)
SF: Native orchids, mosses, begonias, Cryptogams.

Botanical Gardens, 30 Boulevard de Junio, Guatemala de Nueva

Guadeloupe

Botanical Gardens of the Agricultural Service, Trial Grounds, Point-à-Pitre, Guadeloupe, West Indies

Honduras

Botanical Gardens, Perez Estrada, San Pedro Sula, 2 1/2 acres

SF: Tropical fruit trees, begonias.

Botanical Gardens, Comayagula, Patuco

Jamaica

Bath Garden, St. Thomas, Bath, 1 acre (2 GH)

SF: Plants introduced by Capt. Wm. Bligh.

Castleton Gardens, St. Mary, Castleton, 45 acres

SF: Plants of the tropical rain forest, especially palms, collection of aromatic plants and fruit trees.

'The Hill Gardens,' Cinchona, Hall's Delight, St. Andrew, 33 1/2 acres

SF: Pinus species, orchids of the temperate zone.

Royal Botanic Garden (Hope), Kingston 6 (1873), 85 acres under cultivation, a further 119 acres of hilly country not yet under cultivation

RVS: June to December. Open October to January 7 a.m. to 5.30 p.m.; February to April and September 7 a.m. to 6 p.m.; May to August 7 a.m. to 6.30 p.m. SF: Cacti, beautifully flowering trees and shrubs, tropical plants. Accessible by car or bus. Situated in the north-eastern part of the Liguanea Plain, 7 1/2 miles from Palisadoes Airport and 4 1/2 miles from the centre of Kingston.

Martinique

Botanical Garden, St. Pierre

Peru

'Club de Plantas,' Teruel 325, Miraflores/Lima (1957)

Open from 8.30 a.m. to 12.30 p.m. and from 3—7 p.m. SF: Orchids.

Puerto Rico

Plant Collection, Federal Experimental Station, Mayaguez, 232 acres (5 GH)

Open Mondays 7.30 a.m. to noon and 1—4.30 p.m. SF: Tropical ornamental and industrial plants.

Arboretum and Casa Maria Gardens of the Inter-American University, San German, 20 acres (1 GH)

SF: Native forest plants.

Uruguay

Botanical Garden, Faculty of Agriculture, Avenue Garzón 780, Montevideo, 5 acres (1 GH)

Visits by permission of the director. SF: Grasses and leguminous plants.

Botanical Garden del Prado, Avenida Reyes 1155-1179, Montevideo

Venezuela

Botanical Gardens of the Central University, Carácas (1945), 166 acres (GH 1,137 sq. yds.)

RVS: May to September. Open from 8—11.30 a.m. and 2—5 p.m. SF: Palms, bromelias, orchids, Araceae, cacti, Euphorbiaceae.

National Park del Este, Carácas (near La Carlota Airport)

SF: Artistically laid out park and gardens.

Places where wild-growing Venezuelan orchids are to be found—according to G. C. K. Dunsterville and Professor Dr W. Volkmar Vareschi, 'Die Welt der Orchideen' (The World of Orchids)

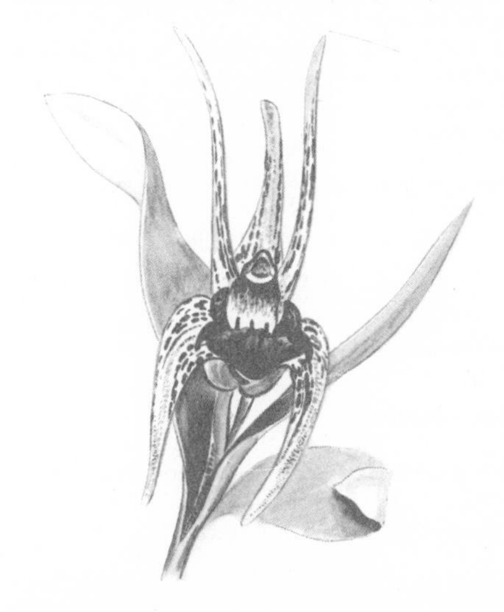

Formerly about 160 species of orchids grew in the valley of Carácas. More than a third of these are now extinct. A rich orchid flora is still to be found in the 'Selva de Guatopo,' a forest area covering about 772 sq. miles, about 50 miles south-east of Carácas, e.g. Platystele ornata, Huntleya lucida and Paphinia cristata.

Many orchid species—mostly those living on trees—are to be found on the oceanside of the coastal Cordillera. A single tree once yielded 50 different epiphytic species.

The Andes have their particular orchid flora as far up as the mountain forest which reaches an altitude of 13,800 ft.

South of the Orinoco River

The region of the source of the Orinoco, close to the Brazilian border, is still largely unknown. Some important discoveries, however, have been made in this area, e.g. Catasetum pileatum.
From Carácas it is possible to spend a weekend in the 'Forest of Guatopo' or in the 'Cloud Forest of Rancho Grande' and to see the most magnificent orchids of the northern forest region. They are protected. Venezuela, the land of orchids, offers many opportunities for more or less difficult orchid hunting. In the West of the country, for instance, the Transandina Road leads through the Andes, where the lover of orchids can indulge his passion at almost any altitude.

Botanical Garden of the University of Mérida.

North America

Canada

Alberta

Botanic Gardens and Field Laboratory, Department of Botany, University of Edmonton, 79 acres

Waterton Lakes National Park (1895), 200 acres
RVS: May to September. SF: Prairie plants, as well as mountain flora. Wild roses, asters, geraniums, aquilegias, Liliaceae, juniperus and evergreen trees.

Banff National Park (1887), 2,435 sq. miles. 75 miles west of Calgary
RVS: June to October. SF: Arctic, alpine and subalpine flora. Conifers, wild roses, orchids, Liliaceae, arnica and many other species growing wild in the region.

Jasper National Park (1907), 3,989 sq. miles, 235 miles west of Edmonton
RVS: May to September. SF: Characteristic plants of prairie and mountains, especially Liliaceae, species of violet, anemones, gentians, asters, arnica, Ledum groenlandicum, dog-roses, alders, Juniper, Rhododendrons.

British Columbia

Queen Elizabeth Arboretum, Vancouver (1949), 50 acres
SF: Evergreen plants, trees and shrubs.

Botanical Garden, University of British Columbia, Vancouver 8, 593 acres (3 GH)
RVS: Open from Mondays to Fridays from 8 a.m. to 5 p.m. Closed on Saturday afternoons and Sundays. SF: Rhododendron; native trees and shrubs; Japanese garden; roses.

Yoho National Park (1886), 482½ sq. miles
RVS: May to October. SF: 600 different plants. Alpine and sub-alpine vegetations with their characteristic plants. Situated on the western slope of the Canadian Rocky Mountains.

Kootenay National Park (1920), 513¼ sq. miles, 106 miles north of Cranbrook
SF: Evergreen forests, ornamental plants.

Manitoba

Experimental Farm, Research Branch, Canadian Department of Agriculture, Morden (1924), 618 acres (3 GH)
SF: Syringa, Malus, Prunus, roses and chrysanthemums.

Riding Mountain National Park (1930), 1,090½ sq. miles, 164 miles north-west of Winnipeg
RVS: May to September. SF: Mixed forests of tundra-like expansion, native flora of all seasons.

New Brunswick

Fundy National Park (1948), 75 sq. miles, 49¾ miles south-west of Moncton
RVS: May to September. SF: Mixed forests, evergreen plants, conifers; typical flora of the region, all growing outdoors. Accessible by Provincial Highway No. 14.

Newfoundland

Terra Nova National Park (1957), 132¾ sq. miles, on the eastern coast of Newfoundland, southern section of Bonavista Bay
RVS: Beginning of May to end of October. SF: Young woods, firs, pines, blueberries, rhododendron, Canadian azaleas.

Nova Scotia

Cape Breton Highlands National Park (1936), 374 sq. miles. Between the Atlantic Ocean and the Gulf of St. Lawrence
RVS: May to October. SF: 'Acadian Forest,' firs, pines, junipers, maples, birches, oaks, evergreen plants, etc.

Ontario

Royal Botanical Gardens, Burlington

Royal Botanical Gardens, Hamilton (1941), 3⅓ acres
RVS: May to September. SF: Rock garden, iris, peonies, Hemerocallis, arboretum, trial grounds for summer flowers.

'The Niagara Park Commission,' Niagara Falls (1936), 99 acres

RVS: Spring and summer. SF: Tulips, Liliaceae, Japanese cherries, peonies, roses, rhododendron, dahlias, chrysanthemums, rock garden, Oriental rock garden, oak arboretum, cyclamen, cinerarias, ferns, etc. About 5 miles north of the City of Niagara Falls.

Dominion Arboretum and Botanic Garden, Plant Research Institute, Central Experimental Station, Ottawa (Arboretum, 1887, Botanic Garden, 1959), 198 acres (GH 4,784 sq. yds.)

RVS: May to October. Open, gardens daily, greenhouses Mondays to Fridays from 8.30 a.m. to 5 p.m. SF: Wintergreen trees and shrubs, Liliaceae.

High Park, Toronto (1873), 383 acres

RVS: April to September. SF: Hanging gardens.

Point Pelee National Park, 4½ sq. miles, south-west of Ontario, about 3¾ miles south of Leamington

RVS: May to September. SF: Maples, mulberry trees, hickories, chestnut trees, firs. Virginia creeper and other liana-like plants. Forest flora, black walnut, etc.

Quebec

Botanic Garden, 4,101 Sherbrooke Street, Montreal (1936), 198 acres (GH 2½ acres)

RVS: May to September. SF: Begonias, bromelias, ferns, succulents, Gesneriaceae, tropical orchids.

Morgan Arboretum, P. O. Box 240, Macdonald College (1946), 594 acres

Open for drivers of motor vehicles 9 a.m. to 5 p.m.; for visitors on foot at any time. SF: Native trees, especially Betula species.

Saskatchewan

Forest Nursery Station, Indian Head (2 GH)

Prince Albert National Park (1927), 1,421 sq. miles, 36 miles north of the City of Prince Albert

RVS: May to September. SF: Evergreen forests, wild roses, Viburnum and other flowering shrubs. Anemones, asters, aquilegias, Ledum groenlandicum, etc.

United States of America

Alabama

The Camellia Arboretum—Bellingrath Gardens, near Mobile (Gulf of Mexico), 7 acres (1 GH)

RVS: February to April (azaleas); end of September (camellias). SF: More than 2,000 camellias, more than 250,000 azaleas; hydrangeas, gardenias, mighty oak trees. Access by US 90, 18½ miles south-west of Mobile.

Arboretum of the University of Alabama, P. O. Box 1927, University (Tuscaloosa), 59 acres (1 GH)

SF: Plants of the south-eastern USA.

Arizona

Organ Pipe National Monument, Administration Ajo (1937), 516½ sq. miles

RVS: May to July. SF: Lemairocereus thurberi (organ pipe cactus), flowers at night; Saguaros, many other cacti flowering from April to June. Shrubs and spring flowers. Cereus greggii (Queen of the Night), flowers at night, very strong scent, relatively rare. Yucca, golden poppy, Encelia, Palo Verde, Ocotillo, the small Baeria covers the ground. Geraea, etc. Situated in South Arizona at the US border.

Apache Trail, no administration, no fencing. One of the best areas for the magnificent desert flora

RVS: End of April and May. Golden poppy, large expanses below the rocks. Saguaro, yucca, Sotol, Palo Verde, Mesquite, Opuntia basilaris, desert calendula, Mariposa lily, Sego lily, Layia. Fouqueria splendens, Ocotillo with red flower spikes at the end of thin branches. Access: State Highway 88. Beautiful road between Apache Junction and Globe; passes a series of artificial lakes of the Salt River and leads up to the Superstition Mountains.

Boyce Thompson SW Arboretum (1924), 59 acres under cultivation (a total of 1,186 acres) (4 GH)

SF: Succulents, evergreen plants, woody plants, eucalyptus, Melaleuca, acacia. 60 miles from Phoenix.

Desert Botanical Garden of Arizona—Papago Park, Tempe (1937), 150 acres (GH 502 sq. yds.)

RVS: April, May. SF: Desert flora of all regions of the world, trees, shrubs, succulents, flowers. East of Phoenix in Papago Park.

Saguaro National Monument—Administration Tucson (1933), 91 sq. miles

RVS: April to June. SF: Splendid specimens of Saguaro (Carnegia gigantea). Flowering season (flowering depends on the rainy season): May, June. Edible fruit, the plant may reach a weight of up to 10 tons. Large selection of annual flowers, flowering shrubs and trees. Cacti, opuntia, etc. Palo Verde tree (official state emblem)—luxuriant yellow flowers in May. Access: 16 miles east of Tucson on Broadway or Speedway.

California

Arboretum Arcadia (1947), 123 acres (13 GH)

SF: Eucalyptus, plants from Australia, sub-tropical plants, flora of the Mediterranean regions, acacia, Myrtaceae, Proteaceae.

Regional Parks Botanic Garden, Tilden Regional Park, Berkeley 8 (1940), 20 acres (1 GH)

SF: Native plants, about 600 species.

University of California, Botanical Garden, Berkeley (1928), 20 acres (8 GH)

SF: Succulents, rhododendron, orchids, Pteridophytes, cacti, Crassulaceae, Aizoaceae, woody plants. South American collection.

'Rancho Santa Ana'—Botanic Gardens, 1500 North College, Claremont (1927), 79 acres (3 GH)

RVS: March to July. SF: Collection 'The Californian Flora,' iris, Arctostaphylos. 35 miles from Los Angeles, access by US Highway 66.

Colorado Desert

Desert without clearly defined borders and without administration. From February to May it is clothed in glowing colours (depending on the rainy season). The sand dunes near Palm Springs are famous for their flowers. Lavender-coloured sand Verbenas mixed with white evening primrose. Apricot-coloured hollyhocks grow by the side of the roads.

Arboretum of the University of California, Davis (1936), 19 acres (1 GH)

SF: Local plants and plants from Australia, especially Ceanothus, Eriogonum, Penstemon, Pinus, Prunus, Quercus, acacia, eucalyptus.

Humboldt State Redwood Park, 36½ sq. miles

RVS: Spring. SF: Sequoia sempervirens, one of the tallest trees in the world. Trunks may reach heights of more than 328 ft. Spring flowers in the meadows, in the canyons, in the woods, between the tall trees. Particularly noteworthy are blue iris, oxalis, Clintonias, etc. Access: By Redwood Highway US 101 north of San Francisco along the Pacific coast.

Yosemite National Park—Administration Yosemite National Park (1890), 1,189 sq. miles

RVS: May, July. SF: Very varied vegetation is to be found from the Yosemite valley (3,937 ft. above sea level) to the higher regions of the Sierra Nevada (8,202 ft. above sea level). Azaleas, dogwood flower in the valley (May), the splendid Sarcodes sanguinea—an inhabitant of humus without any green foliage—as high up as 8,202 ft. Penstemon and primula flower in the mountains.

Joshua Tree National Monument. Administration Twenty Nine Palms (1936), 880 sq. miles

RVS: March to May. SF: The Joshua tree is a member of the Agave family (Yucca brevifolia), it grows to about 39 feet and flowers in April and May. Typical desert flowers: Wild leek, desert lilies (Ajo), sand Verbenas, evening primrose, thorn apple, creosote bush, Californian poppy, lupins and many others. Access: 100 miles from Los Angeles. By US 60, 70 and 99 to Twenty Nine Palms Highway. Turn off south of the city.

Kings Canyon and Sequoia National Park, Common administration Three Rivers

Sequoia National Park (1890), 504 sq. miles

SF: Magnificent giant mammoth trees, many native wild flowers, Sequoiadendron giganteum on the western slopes of the Sierra Nevada. Vegetation resembling that of Yosemite National Park.

Kings Canyon (1940), 710 sq. miles

The high altitude Sierra regions can be reached only on foot.

Descanso Gardens, La Canada (1942), 140 acres (GH 36 sq. yds.)

RVS: February to May. SF: 100,000 camellias, 10,000 roses, 10,000 azaleas, 100 different native species; liliaceae, orchids, rhododendron, etc. 5 miles north-west of Pasadena.

Exposition Park, Figuero Street, Los Angeles, 7 acres

SF: 15,000 different rose trees.

Botanical Gardens University of California, Westwood Village, Los Angeles (1929), 8 acres (GH 36 sq. yds.)

RVS: Late winter and spring (camellias and acacias). SF: Australian plants, eucalyptus, acacias, Melaleuca and Callistemon, succulents.

Mojave Desert

The region below Yellow Pine on the lower slopes of the Sierra Nevada south of Little San Bernardino and Eagle Mountain. No administration, no fencing. Antelope Valley, north of Palmdale and Lancaster, is resplendent with many colours in April. Giant patches of Californian poppy (State emblem), combine with lupins and many other annual flowers to form a wonderful carpet. The Joshua tree also grows here.

Knowland State Arboretum and Park, 98th Avenue & Mountain Boulevard, Oakland (1935/1950), 499 acres (GH 6 acres)

RVS: Spring, especially April. SF: Plants of the southern hemisphere, grouped according to continents, plants of the northern hemisphere grouped according to families. Tropical plants.

Botanic Garden, Pacific Grove (1935)

RVS: April to June. Closed on Mondays. SF: Flora of the Monterey County region.

'Eddy Arboretum,' Placerville (1925), 185 acres (5 GH)

RVS: Mondays to Fridays from 8 a.m. to 4.30 p.m. (closed on Holidays). SF: The world's largest collection of firs.

Point Lobos Reserve and State Park, 356 acres

RVS: May. SF: One of the only two remaining woods of the Monterey cypress on the rugged coast. Spring flowers in May, including the yellow lupin, Californian poppy, Mesembryanthemum cristallinum. 4 miles south of Carmel, off State Highway 1.

C. M. Goethe Arboretum, Sacramento State College, Sacramento, 7 acres (1 GH)

Visits by permission of the director. SF: Native trees and shrubs.

Golden Gate Park, San Francisco (1868), 1,018 acres

SF: Japanese tea gardens, roses, rhododendrons and azaleas.

'The Strybing Arboretum' and Botanic Garden, 9th Avenue and Lincoln Way, San Francisco (1937), 43 1/2 acres (1 GH)

RVS: March to May. SF: Magnolias, rhododendron, native plants of California, special plants of Australia, New Zealand and South Africa.

Botanic Gardens 'Huntington,' 1151 Oxford Road, San Marino (1912), 204 acres (2 GH)

RVS: Tuesdays to Sundays from 1—4.30 p.m. SF: Cycadeae, palms, cacti, camellias, roses.

Botanic Garden 'Santa Barbara,' 1212 Mission Canyon Road (1926), 51 acres

RVS: March to June. SF: Californian flora, especially shrubs and ornamental plants: Ceanothus, Arctostaphylos, Eriogonum. 1 1/2 miles beyond Old Mission Santa Barbara.

North and South Carolina

Cocker Arboretum, University of North Carolina, Chapel Hill (1903), 5 1/2 acres (1 GH)

SF: Woody plants from the south-east of the USA.

Sarah P. Duke Garden, Durham, North Carolina (1934), 55 acres (2 GH)

SF: Prunus, malus, hemerocallis, iris, lilies and decorative flowers.

Cypress-Garden near Charleston, South Carolina (1840), 250.2 acres

RVS: May; open from 15th February to end of May. SF: Evergreen plants, shrubs and trees, camellias, azaleas, magnolias, cypresses. 20 miles north of the town, 4 miles east of US Highway 52.

Brookgreen Gardens, Murrells Inlet, Georgetown (Pawleys Island), South Carolina (1931), 15 acres

RVS: April, May; closed on Mondays and at Christmas. SF: Native flora of the south-east USA.

Middleton Gardens near Charleston, South Carolina (1741)

RVS: Camellias: December to March; azaleas: March to April. SF: Camellias and azaleas. Northwest of the town, 13 1/2 miles from junction of State 61 with US 17.

Magnolia Gardens near Charleston, South Carolina (1880), 64 1/2 acres

RVS: Mid-March to mid-April; open from 15th February to 1st May. SF: 700 varieties of Camellia japonica; Magnolia grandiflora, Azalea indica. These are among the world's most beautiful magnolias. 'Magnolia on the Ashley' lies northwest of the city on State 61.

Colorado

Denver Botanic Gardens, 909 York Street, Denver 6 (1951), 77 1/2 acres

Open daily during the growing season from 8 a.m. to 5 p.m. SF: Evergreen plants, roses, irises, lilies, tulips, petunias, alpine flora on the slopes of Mount Goliath.

Rocky Mountain National Park—Administration Estes Park (1915), 405 sq. miles

RVS: June, July. SF: An excellent area for the wild and alpine flora of Colorado, e.g. the blue Colorado aquilegia (Aquilegia coerulea) (state emblem). At altitudes of 8,202 up to 11,483 ft. several delphiniums, aconites, silvery lupins, violets, fringed Rocky Mountain gentians, Polemonias and grape hyacinths. Accessible by Continental Divide between Estes Park and Grand Lake.

District of Columbia

National Arboretum of the United States, Washington 25, D.C. (1927), 410 acres (10 GH)

RVS: April, May, October; open Mondays to Fridays from 8 a.m. to 4.30 p.m., in the flowering season also at weekends. SF: Camellias, clematis, hibiscus, ilex, Lagerstroemia, magnolia, Malus, Pyracantha, rhododendron, azaleas, viburnum, evergreen plants.

Connecticut

Marsh Botanical Garden, 277 Mansfield Street, New Haven 11 (1900), 5 acres (3 GH)

SF: Azaleas, oaks, hemlock pines.

Connecticut Arboretum, New London (1931), 282 acres

SF: Woody plants.

Estate of Frank G. Shinn, Woodbury, 65 acres, preserve for wild growing flowers, with meadow, bog, woods and rocks

SF: Native flora. Aquatic plants, shrubs and trees.

Elizabeth Park, Hartford, 915 Prospect Avenue (1897)

RVS: June, July. SF: World famous state rose garden, 500 varieties and more than 10,000 plants.

Delaware

Orton Plantation near Wilmington (1725)

RVS: End of December to beginning of April. SF: Azaleas, mossy trees. 19¼ miles south of the town, by US 17 and State 133.

Winterthur Gardens, Winterthur (1917), 100 acres

Open: last week of April, May, Tuesdays 10 a.m. to 4.30 p.m.; Sundays 1—4.30 p.m. Visits at other times by permission of the director. SF: Azaleas, rhododendrons, conifers, narcissi, evergreen plants.

Florida

Everglades Wondergarden, Bonita Springs

SF: Ornamental garden, laid out as 'jungles' among the remains of natural sub-tropical jungle vegetation.

Flamingo Groves Tropical Botanic Garden, Fort Lauderdale/Davie (1927), 7 acres

RVS: June to September. SF: Various species of tropical trees; special sections for different citrus species. Access: From Fort Lauderdale westward by Route 84 to Route 823, about 3 miles further south.

Botanic Garden 'Thomas A. Edison,' Mr. Gregor Boulevard, Fort Myers (1885), 13½ acres

RVS: December to March. SF: Tropical and subtropical palms, flowering trees, orchids, ornamental shrubs.

'Wilmot Memorial Garden,' University of Florida, Gainesville (1952), 2 acres

SF: Rare camellias, azaleas and ilex.

Monkey Jungle, Goulds

SF: Ornamental garden laid out among the remains of natural sub-tropical jungle vegetation.

Orchid Jungle, Fennel Orchid Company, 26,715 SW 157 Avenue, Homestead, 25 acres (9 GH)

SF: Orchids, bromelias, Philodendron, Anthurium. Access: By car south of Miami by US 1, about 25 miles, thence 1 mile, signposted.

Sub-tropical Experiment Station, Route 1, Box 560, Homestead (1930), 119 acres (3 GH)

Visits by permission of the director. SF: Tropical industrial plants, evergreen plants.

Fairchild Tropical Garden, 10,901 Old Cutler Road, Miami 56 (1935), 80¼ acres (GH 360 sq. yds.)

SF: Palms, Cycadeae, tropical trees and shrubs. Famous tropical garden.

Parrot Jungle, Miami

SF: Ornamental garden laid out among remains of natural sub-tropical jungle vegetation.

Caribbean Gardens, Naples (3 GH)

SF: Bromelias, orchids, tropical leaf plants.

Jungle Gardens, Sarasota

SF: Ornamental gardens in remains of natural subtropical jungle-vegetation.

Sub-tropical Botanic Gardens, St. Petersburg

SF: Ornamental gardens in remains of natural subtropical jungle-vegetation.

Sunken Gardens St. Petersburg

SF: Ornamental gardens in remains of natural subtropical jungle-vegetation.

McKee Jungle Gardens, Vero Beach (1930), 80 acres (GH 897 sq. yds.)

RVS: Spring, summer. SF: Orchids, tropical and sub-tropical plants.

Cypress Gardens, Winter Haven

SF: Ornamental gardens in remains of natural subtropical jungle-vegetation.

Georgia

Ida Cason Callaway Gardens, Pine Mountains (1949), 2,148 acres (GH 2)

SF: Hollies, azaleas, quinces, crabapples, magnolias.

Hawaii

Kapiolani Hibiscus Garden, 3,620 Leaki Avenue, Honolulu, 2 acres

SF: Endemic hibiscus species of Hawaii; native flora.

Botanic Garden 'Foster,' 50 N. Vineyard Street, Honolulu 17, 17 acres (5 GH), affiliated to Lyon Botanical Garden, 297 acres

SF: Orchids, palms, tropical ornamental plants.

Haleakala National Park

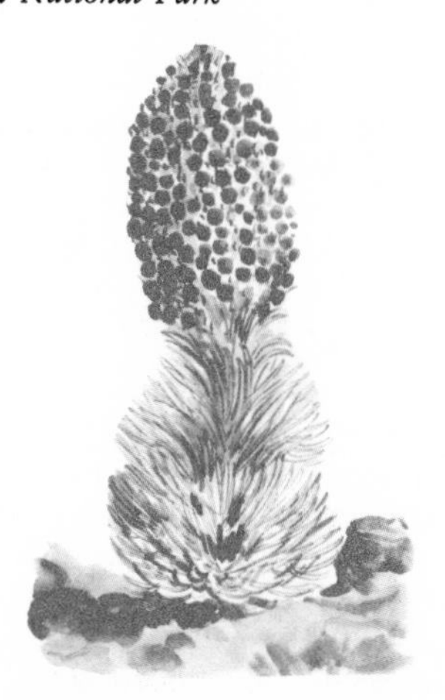

SF: Endemic flora of Hawaii, Argyroxiphium, Dubautia, Raillardia, Hillebrandia, Neurophylloides, Clermontia.

Botanic Garden Wahiawa, 1,396 California Avenue, Oahu, 27 acres

SF: Orchids and decorative plants.

Idaho

Charles Houston Shattuck Arboretum, College of Forestry University of Idaho, Moscow, 7 acres

SF: Native flora of the Northern Rocky Mountains.

Illinois

Garfield Park Conservatory, 300 N. Central Park Avenue, Chicago (1907), 4 1/2 acres (GH about 2 1/2 acres)

RVS: July, August, September. SF: Ferns, palms, cacti and succulents, orchids.

Botanical Garden, University of Chicago, Chicago 37, about 4,785 sq. yds.

Visits by permission of the director. SF: Cycadeae, trial grounds.

The Morton Arboretum, Lisle (1922), 1,360 acres (1 GH)

SF: Lilies, conifers, hedges, avenue trees, evergreen plants.

Ernest H. Wilson Garden, Peoria

SF: 1,000 plants, including Lilium elegans (introduced from West China by H. Wilson).

Hazelwood Dixon, Property of Charles R. Walgreen

SF: Ornamental plants growing wild: Narcissi, tulips, irises, chrysanthemums, hellebores; tree peonies, oaks and acacias, hickory, stone-pine and spruce.

Indiana

Botanic Garden 'James Irving Holcomb,' Indianapolis (1930), 15 acres

SF: Woody plants.

Christy Woods (Arboretum), Ball State Teachers College, Muncie, 17 acres (1 GH)

Open: Mondays to Fridays all day; Saturdays to 11.30 a.m. SF: Native spring flora; peonies, iris, chrysanthemums.

International Friendship Garden, Michigan City, 100 acres

RVS: May to October. SF: Many nations helped to stock the garden. 500 different rose varieties, 500 different tulips, shrubs and trees. 1 1/2 miles east of Michigan City. Access: by US Highway 12.

Iowa

Iowa State Teachers College Garden, Cedar Falls, 15 acres

SF: Arboretum, prairie flora.

Kentucky

General Electric Appliance Park, Louisville (1953), 50 acres (1 GH)

SF: About 1,100 trees and shrubs.

Bernheim Forest Arboretum, Clermont

Open from 15th March to 15th November. SF: Nut trees, maples, crabapple trees.

Louisiana

Jungle Gardens, Avery Island, 300 acres

RVS: November to March (camellias); end of February to end of April (azaleas); March to June (iris). SF: Camellias, azaleas, iris.

Hodges Gardens, P. O. Box 921, Many (1959), 7¼ acres (GH 3,588 sq. yds.)

RVS: March to May, July to October. SF: Rhododendron, roses, camellias, ilex, iris, water lilies, tropical leaf plants, orchids, anthurias, begonias, Gesneriaceae. Access by Highway 171.

Maine

Botanical Plantations of the University of Maine, 203 Deering Hall, Orono (1934), 4¾ acres

SF: Native flora.

Maryland

Sherwood Gardens, Highfield Street, East of North Charles Street, Baltimore, 7 acres

RVS: April to beginning of May. SF: 100,000 tulips and other bulbs, 5,000 azaleas, cherry trees, crabapple trees, box, pansies.

Massachusetts

Botanical Museum of Harvard University, Cambridge, Massachusetts

Arnold Arboretum of Harvard University, Jamaica Plain 30 (1872), 282 acres (3 GH)

SF: Malus, forsythia, syringa, Chaenomeles, Lonicera, Quercus, Acer, Ulmus, rhododendron, conifers, evergreen dwarf shrubs.

The Botanic Garden of Smith College, Northampton (1893), 148 acres (GH 960 sq. yds.)

SF: Tropical plants, trees, shrubs, rock gardens.

'Garden in the Woods,' South Sudbury (1930), 30 acres (GH 63 sq. yds.)

RVS: April to June. Closed on Sundays and Holidays. SF: Plants of North America, including alpines. Accessible by Route 20 from Boston to South Sudbury, thence turn off on to Raymond Road, 1½ miles.

Berkshire Garden Centre, Stockbridge (1934) 7½ acres (2 GH)

RVS: July, August. Open from March to November. SF: Primulas, iris, tulips, peonies, roses, begonias, ornamental shrubs and trees. Alpinum, orchards and vineyards. At junction of Routes 102 and 183.

'Alexandra' Botanic Garden and Arboretum, Wellesley (1923), 23½ acres (6 GH)

SF: Woody plants.

Walter Hunnewell Arboretum, 845 Washington Street, Wellesley (1852), 40 acres

RVS: Open weekdays. SF: Conifers, rhododendron, evergreen plants.

Michigan

Botanic Garden and Nichols Arboretum, University of Michigan, Ann Arbor (1907, Botanic Garden, 1917, arboretum), 153 acres

SF: Peonies, lilac, Liliaceae, rare trees and shrubs.

Botanic Garden, Michigan University, Beal-Garfield, East Lansing (1873), 7½ acres (3 GH)

SF: Rare trees and shrubs.

Campus, Michigan State University, East Lansing (1855), 624 acres

SF: Evergreen plants, rare trees and shrubs.

Slayton Arboretum of Hillsdale College, Hillsdale (1922), 75 acres

SF: Lilac, crabapple trees, evergreen plants, especially trees and shrubs.

Holland Garden (1847)

RVS: May. SF: Tulip centre of America; in parks and public gardens.

Minnesota

Hormel Foundation Arboretum, Austin (1927), 240 acres

Visits by permission of the director. SF: Evergreen plants, especially trees and shrubs.

Eloise Butler Wild-Flower Garden, Minneapolis (1907), 12½ acres

RVS: 1st April to 1st November. SF: Many native plants as well as some from other States.

Greenhouse of the College of Pharmacy, University of Minnesota, Minneapolis (1913), 2,631 sq. yds. (GH 225 sq. yds.)

Visits by prior arrangement. SF: Medicinal plants.

University of Minnesota, Landscape Arboretum, St. Paul (1958), 158 acres

RVS: Open 15th April to 1st November. SF: Azaleas, lilac, philodelphus, evergreen plants.

Mississippi

Botanic Garden, Natchez, Mississippi (19th century)
RVS: March.

Missouri

Botanic Garden, 2315 Tower Grove Avenue, St. Louis 10 (1959), 67 acres (25 GH). Fully air-conditioned greenhouse ('climatron')
SF: Tropical plants, orchids, bromelias, water lilies, succulents.

Ozark Mountains. Many parks in lake and forest area, no administration
RVS: Spring, early summer and autumn. SF: Judas tree, wild verbenas, dwarf delphinium, hepatica, violets. Many herbaceous plants in the shade of oak and hickory forests on the limestone clearings of the south-west slopes. In spring the large flowers of the Missouri primula and delphinium; in autumn asters (Aster anomalus), etc.

Montana

Glacier National Park, Northern Montana, Administration West Glacier (1910), 1,583½ sq. miles
RVS: From thaw to first frost. SF: Many alpine flowers, Erythronium parviflorum, Western pulsatilla, Xerophyllum tenax. Accessible by US 2 which runs along the border. US 89 leads to the east entrance.

Nebraska

'Arbor Lodge State Historical Park,' Nebraska City (1903), 64½ acres (1 GH)
RVS: 15th April to 1st November. SF: Castanea dentata (rare American chestnut), Liriodendron tulipifera, Ginkgo biloba.

New Hampshire

Lost river Nature Gardens, Kinsman Notch
RVS: June to September. SF: 300 species of native flora, especially ferns and mosses. In White Mountains, west of North Woodstock.

New Mexico

Leding Desert Garden of the New Mexico State University Museum (1936), 1 acre
RVS: April, May. SF: Chiefly cacti of North America and other desert plants.

New Jersey

'Rutgers Display Gardens,' Department of Horticulture, College of Agriculture, Rutgers University, New Brunswick (1929), 50 acres (GH about 600 sq. yds.)
SF: Ilex, yew trees, iris, rhododendron, azalea, chrysanthemums.

Presbey Memorial Iris Garden, Upper Montclair
SF: One of the world's most complete iris collections. Old and new varieties. Access by US 40, State 3 or by Garden State Parkway to Montclair.

Cedar Brook Park, Plainfield (1927), 100 acres
SF: Iris, Liliaceae, narcissi.

Gotelli Arboretum, South Orange (1941), 2 acres
SF: Evergreen plants, conifers, rhododendron, azalea.

New York

Brooklyn Botanic Gardens and Arboretum, Washington Avenue, Brooklyn 25 (1910), 50 acres (several show and greenhouses)

RVS: End of April to beginning of May (flowering shrubs and trees); June (roses). Open daily till sunset; Sundays and Holidays from 10 a.m. to 4 p.m. SF: Orchids, cacti, bromelias, tropical industrial plants, ferns, roses, water lilies. Japanese garden, evergreen shrubs, dwarf shrubs, native flora, rock garden, rare trees, twice yearly flowering cherry trees.

Botanic Garden, Buffalo (1901), 115 acres (16 GH)

George Landis Arboretum, Esperance (1950), 40 acres
SF: Spring bulbs, rhododendron, oriental and North American conifers, Malus, Viburnum, native flora, alpinum, moss garden.

The New York State Agricultural Experimental Station, Geneva (1882), 50 acres

SF: Vegetable and fruit cultivations, Malus, Pyrus, Prunus, Vitis, Rubus.

Cornelle Plantation, Ithaca (1928), 1,483 acres

SF: Evergreen plants, rare shrubs and trees.

Thomas C. Desmond Arboretum, R. D. 1, Newburgh (1939), 50 acres

Open Mondays to Saturdays 10 a.m. to 4 p.m. Closed on Sundays. SF: Collection of almost every North American tree and shrub.

Sterling Forest Gardens, Rt. 210 off Rt. 17, North of Tuxedo, 124 acres

RVS: May to October. Open from 11 a.m. till dusk. SF: Tulips (142 species), more than a million narcissi, hyacinths, 25 different native ferns, Liliaceae, 'hanging gardens,' Japanese garden, oriental garden, roses, 80,000 begonias, chrysanthemums, rhododendrons, dahlias, shrubs and rare trees.

'The New York Botanical Garden,' Bronx Park, New York 58 (1895), 237 acres

SF: Conifers (Montgomery), collection of Liliaceae (Havemeyer), magnolias, rhododendrons, azaleas, firs and native flora.

Bayard Cutting Arboretum, Oakdale, Long Island (1887), 636 acres

SF: Rhododendron, conifers: Abies, Picea, Chamaecyparis, Cedrus, Pinus, Taxus, Tsuga.

Planting Fields Arboretum Oyster Bay, Long Island (1920), 119 acres (GH about 3,468 sq. yds.)

Visits by prior arrangement. SF: Rhododendron, camellias, succulents, evergreen plants.

Highland and Durand Eastman Park, 5 Castle Park, Rochester 20 (1890), 594 acres (9 GH)

SF: Syringa, Malus, magnolias, Acer, conifers, Picea, Pinus.

Jackson's Garden, Union College Campus, Schenectady, 16¹/₄ acres

RVS: Open from 15th April to 15th October. SF: Some very old peonies, evergreen plants.

Hammond Museum Stroll Gardens, North Salem, Westchester (1961), 2¹/₂ acres

RVS: May, June, October. Open from 22nd May to 25th October on Fridays, Saturdays and Sundays from 1—5 p.m. SF: Oriental gardens and plants.

Ohio

Eden Park Conservatory, Park Board, 950 Eden Park Drive, Cincinnati 2 (1933), 2,617 sq. yds. (GH 2,518 sq. yds.)

RVS: April and May, autumn. Open daily from 10 a.m. SF: Ferns, orchid collection, palms, cacti, succulents, chrysanthemums.

Mt. Airy Arboretum, 5083 Colerian Avenue, Cincinnati 23 (1932), 120 acres

RVS: April to November. SF: Evergreen plants, Liliaceae, rhododendron, azaleas.

Ault Park Municipal Rose and Dahlia Gardens, 950 Eden Park Drive, Cincinnati 2 (1958), 4 acres

RVS: June to mid October. SF: Roses, dahlias.

The Stanley M. Rowe Arboretum, 4500 Muchmore Road, Cincinnati 43 (1928), 168 acres

SF: Evergreen plants, Liliaceae.

'The Garden Center of Greater Cleveland,' 11190 East Boulevard, Cleveland 6 (1939), 10 acres

RVS: June. Open Mondays to Fridays from 9 a.m. to 5 p.m., Sundays from 2—6 p.m. Closed on Saturdays. SF: Cherry and apple trees, some rare trees.

Kingwood Center, Mansfield, 900 Park Avenue West (1953), 46¹/₂ acres (GH 837 sq. yds.)

Open: Gardens from April to November; greenhouses throughout the year. SF: Tuberous plants, roses, native flora.

'The Holden Arboretum,' Sperry Road, Mentor (1930), 1,772¹/₃ acres (1 GH)

RVS: April to July, October. Closed on Mondays. SF: Syringa, Acer, Malus, Ilex, Viburnum, native flora.

'The Dawes Arboretum,' Newark (1929), 520 acres (1 GH)

SF: Beeches, rhododendrons, azaleas, hawthorn species.

Secrest Arboretum, Ohio Agricultural Experiment Station, Wooster (1906), 55 acres (1 GH)

SF: Conifers: Taxus, Juniperus, Picea.

Oregon

Azalea State Park, 26 acres

RVS: May and August. SF: Five varieties of wild azaleas. Access by US 101—Oregon Coast Highway near Brookings.

Botanic Garden Jan de Graaffs, Sandy River, George

RVS: Spring and July/August. SF: Narcissi, Liliaceae.

Crater Lake National Park—Administration Medford (1902), 251¹/₂ sq. miles

RVS: July, August. SF: Wild flowers of every description surround a deep lake. Especially noteworthy the Castle Crest wild flower garden. Access by State Routes 62, 230, 232, off US Highways 97 and 99.

Lambert Gardens, Portland (altogether 10 gardens)

RVS: Spring, June. Open from April to November. SF: Japanese cherry trees, crabapple trees, plum trees, roses, annual garden flowers. About 1 mile east of US 99 E.

Rose Gardens, Portland

RVS: June. SF: 10,000 roses of 520 varieties, distributed over different parks in the city.

Hoyt Arboretum, 4000 SW Fairview Boulevard, Portland 1 (1930), 217 acres

SF: One of the largest conifer collections in the USA.

Petersens Rock Garden, Redmund

SF: Mountain Garden. 7½ miles south-east of US 97.

Thule Lake—National Nature Reservation, 35 sq. miles

RVS: Spring to autumn. SF: The area is brimful with various wild flowers. Situated in the Klamath Basin on the borders of California and Oregon. Access: About 15 miles south of US 97.

Pennsylvania

Taylor Memorial Arboretum, 10 Ridley Drive, Garden City, Chester (1951), 36½ acres (1 GH)

SF: Ericaceae, trees and shrubs.

Masonic Homes Arboretum, Elizabethtown (1910), 3 acres

SF: Evergreen plants, woody plants.

Haverford College Arboretum, Haverford, 43½ acres

SF: Firs, native trees.

Hershey Gardens, Hershey, US 322 (1937), 21 acres

RVS: April to October. Open from April to November. SF: 30,000 tulips (flowering season late April to early May), 42,000 roses (about 1,200 varieties, flowering season from June to first frost), more than 25,000 specimens of annual plants (flowering season June to first frost).

Rose Garden, Breezehill, Harrisburg

SF: Trial grounds for all American roses.

Longwood Gardens, Kennet Square (1921), 1,000 acres (GH 3¾ acres)

Open daily from 11 a.m. to 5 p.m.; cold greenhouses and hothouses, November to May; open-air, summer (especially tropical water lilies). SF: Tropical and sub-tropical ornamental plants, orchids, chrysanthemums, camellias, azaleas, acacias, rhododendron, cacti, Liliaceae. Beautifully landscaped gardens. One of the most remarkable gardens in the USA. Access: about ½ mile from junction of US 1 and State 52.

John J. Tyler Arboretum, Lima, Delaware County (1946), 664 acres (1 GH)

SF: Magnolia, peonies, cherry trees, rhododendrons, crabapple trees, Liliaceae, iris, narcissi.

Elan Memorial Park, 116 E Front Street, Berwick, Lime Ridge (1943), 89 acres (1 GH)

SF: Chrysanthemums, Liliaceae, evergreen plants.

Arboretum of the Barnes Foundation, 300 Latch's Lane, Merion Station (1923), 11 acres (1 GH)

Visits by permission of the director. SF: Magnolias, syringas, ilex, Stewartia, roses and conifers.

Mont Alto Arboretum, Pennsylvania State University, College of Agriculture, School of Forestry, Mont Alto Branch, Mont Alto (1903), 40 acres

RVS: Open weekdays.

Ellis School Arboretum, Newton Square (1932), 297 acres

RVS: Open weekdays from 8 a.m. to 4.30 p.m. SF: Flowering trees, evergreen plants.

Morris Arboretum, 9,414 Meadowbrook Avenue, Philadelphia 18 (1932), 173 acres (GH 1,196 sq. yds.)

RVS: May, June. SF: Rhododendron, azaleas, ilex, roses, ivy, phlox, medicinal plants, moor garden, bee garden, etc.

Phipps Conservatory, Schenley Park, Pittsburgh 13 (1893), 2½ acres (21 GH)

RVS: Spring and autumn. SF: Orchids, cacti, tropical and sub-tropical plants.

Reading Public Museum and Art Gallery, Reading (1926), 25 acres

SF: Native and tropical trees and shrubs.

Arthur Hoyt Scott Horticultural Foundation, Swarthmore (1930), 297 acres (1 GH)

SF: Magnolias, cherry trees, crabapple trees, Liliaceae, rhododendron, peonies, narcissi, iris, Hemerocallis, chrysanthemums.

Bowmans Hill State Wild Flower Preserve, Washington Crossing State Park, Washington Crossing (1934), 101 acres

RVS: April to October. SF: Native flowers, trees, shrubs and ferns. Over 800 species of flowers along 12 natural paths. Aquilegia, Canadian lily, American tame poison species, etc. Access: North-east of Philadelphia, State 32.

School Arboretum, Westtown (1906), 50 acres (1 GH)

Visits by prior arrangement. SF: Conifers; Abies, Picea, Pinus, etc.

Tennessee

Arboretum, 'Memphis Campus,' Memphis 12 (1955), 100 acres

SF: Industrial plants (trees).

W. C. Paul Arboretum, 800 South Cherry Road, Memphis 17 (1957), 148 acres

SF: Conifers, evergreen shrubs, magnolias, iris and rose trial gardens, camellias, ilex.

Great Smoky Mountains National Park, North Carolina and Tennessee, Administration Gatlingburg, 795 sq. miles

RVS: April to June, autumn. SF: Large selection of eastern plants. 1,400 species and varieties of herbaceous plants, 130 species of deciduous trees. April to early May: Cornus florida, 25 species of violet, several species of Trillium, phlox, fringed Phacelia, 25—30 species of wild orchids. Mid-June: azaleas, rhododendron. Autumn: splendour of autumn colouring of deciduous trees.

'The Tennessee Botanical Gardens Fine Arts Centre,' Inc. Cheekwood, Nashville 5 (1960), 55 acres (1 GH)

RVS: April to October from 9 a.m. to 6 p.m., Tuesdays to Saturdays; Sundays from 1 p.m. to 6 p.m. November to March: 10 a.m. to 5 p.m. Closed on Mondays. SF: Box, narcissi.

Texas

Texas A. & M. Arboretum and Trial Grounds, College Station (1930), 25 acres

SF: Evergreen and woody plants.

Botanic Garden, 3,220 Botanic Garden Drive, Fort Worth (1933), 84 acres (3 GH)

SF: Roses, succulents, evergreen plants.

Big Bend National Park, Administration Big Bend N.P. (1944), 1,107 sq. miles

RVS: May, June, Summer. SF: Spring flowers in Chisos Mountains, Green Gulch; Yucca carnosana (giant palm lily) grows nowhere else, flowers luxuriantly every second year. Various cacti in the plains and on the plateaux. Many species of opuntia, two night-flowering plants—Cereus and Acanthocereus, Echinocereus, Lophophorus and Ariocarpus (living stones). One of the most noteworthy regions of the Chihuahua Desert. Accessible by US 99 from Alpine by State 118 or from Marathon by State 227.

Utah

Brigham Young University Botanical Gardens, Provo, 15 acres (1 GH)

SF: North American trees.

Virginia

Virginia Polytechnic Institute Arboretum, Blacksburg (1950), 60 acres (1 GH)

SF: Dwarf shrubs, rare trees, conifers.

The Orland E. White Research Arboretum, Blandy Experimental Farm, University of Virginia, Boyce (1938), 140 acres (GH 610 sq. yds.)

RVS: April, May, September, October. Visits by prior arrangement. SF: Conifers, Oleaceae, Buxaceae, American roses, Zephyranthes, Hymenocallis, iris. Access by US 50, 10 miles east of Winchester.

Blue Ridge Parkway, a national park with altitudes of 2,000 ft. to 6,000 ft. (1935)

RVS: Early summer, summer and autumn. Main flowering season mid-June. SF: Hepaticum, Trillium, violets, azaleas, aquilegias, golden rod, asters, Virginian witch-hazel and beautiful autumn colouring of deciduous trees. 466 miles of road through beautiful country, connecting Shenandoah National Park with the Great Smoky Mountains. The flora along this road resembles that of Shenandoah National Park.

Craggy Gardens, 694 1/3 acres

RVS: Mid-June. SF: Many rhododendron species. About 70 miles north-east of Asheville.

Shenandoah National Park (1935), Administration Luray, 302 1/3 sq. miles

RVS: Early summer, summer and autumn. SF: In a day's visit it is possible to see 900 species of flowering plants and about 800 different varieties. In spring amongst others, hepaticum, Trillium, violets; in early summer: azaleas, aquilegias, Virginian witch-hazel; in autumn: golden rod, asters, beautiful colouring of deciduous trees. Access by US Highway 211, Skyline Drive, about 103 miles from Front Royal towards Rockfish Gap.

Botanic Garden, Mount Vernon

RVS: March to October. SF: Oldest renovated garden of America, 16 miles south of Washington D.C. towards Mount Vernon on the Memorial Road.

Botanic Garden 'Norfolk,' Airport Road, Norfolk 18 (1958), 173 acres (2 GH)

RVS: April (and other months of the year, except December and January). SF: 700 different varieties of camellia, rhododendron, azaleas, Lagerstroemia indica, Hemerocallis.

Colonial Williamsburg

SF: Baroque garden architecture. Access by US 60.

Washington

Wind River Arboretum Carson (1912), 11 acres

SF: Many species of conifers: Pinus, Larix, Picea, Abies, Tsuga, Cedrus, Sequoia, deciduous trees.

Mount Rainier National Park, Washington, Administration Longmire (1899), 378 sq. miles

RVS: Beginning of July to beginning of August. SF: Sub-alpine meadows below the glacier-covered summit (15,336 ft.). Erythronium and Pulsatilla flower immediately after the thaw. Forest flowers in rich abundance. Over 700 species of flowers in the park.

Ohme Gardens, Wenatchee

RVS: April to July. Open from April to November. SF: Alpinum, Phlox subalata, Dianthus and Sedum species.

Capitol Gardens, Olympia, 50 acres

RVS: July, August. SF: Cherries.

Olympic National Park—Olympia Peninsula in North-West corner, administration Port Angeles (1938), 1,323 1/2 sq. miles

RVS: End of July to September. SF: Forest and sub-alpine meadow flowers, aquilegia, aster, Indian Paintbrush (Castilleja), lupins, lilies, etc.

Arboretum of the Washington University, Seattle 5 (1935), 247 acres (2 GH)

SF: Azaleas, rhododendron, camellia, ilex, Acer, Cistus, Sorbus, Quercus, roses, conifers.

Drug Plant Gardens, College of Pharmacy, University of Washington, Seattle, 3 acres (5 GH)

SF: Medicinal plants.

Finch Arboretum, Spokane (1947), 55 acres

SF: Evergreen plants.

West Virginia

Arboretum of West Virginia University, Morgantown (1948), 100 acres

SF: Native flora of West Virginia.

Wisconsin

Botanic Garden 'Alfred L. Boerner,' 5,879 South 92 Street, Hales Corners (1929), 445 acres (1 GH)

SF: Lilies, tulips, narcissi, iris, Hemerocallis, ornamental plants, roses, peonies, dahlias. Trial grounds for annual and perennial flowers.

Arboretum Wisconsin University, Birge Hall, Madison 6 (1932), 1,236 acres (1 GH)

SF: Lilies, viburnum, Malus, syringa, Crataegus, prairie plants.

Oshkosh Arboretum, 1,410 Algoma Boulevard, Oshkosh (1947), 11 acres

RVS: Open Tuesdays, Thursdays and Saturdays from 2—5 p.m. SF: Juniperus, evergreen plants.